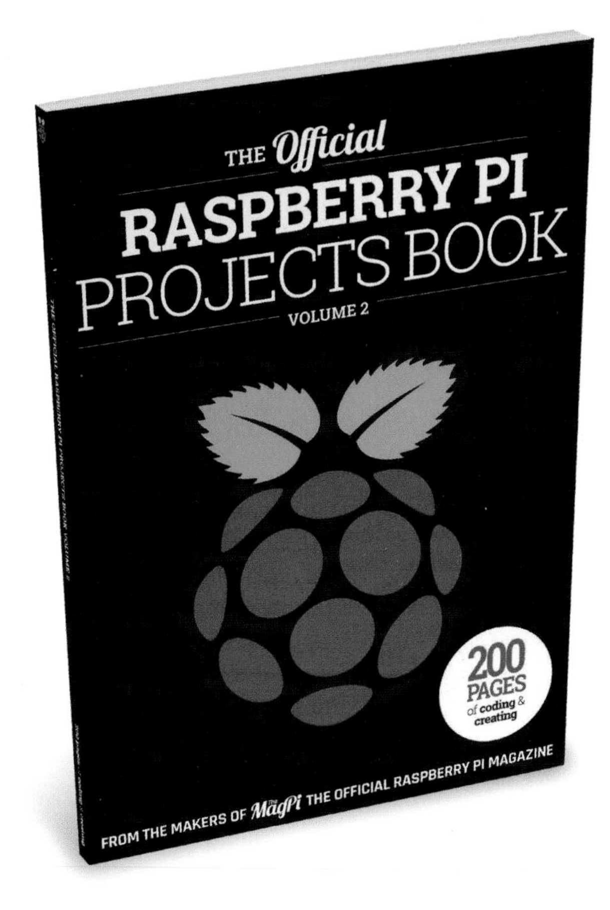

WELCOME

When we introduced our last Official Projects book we were excited that seven million Raspberry Pis had been sold. Since then, the Raspberry Pi has achieved two further milestones: it's reached ten million sales and has become the best-selling British computer of all time. By our calculations that's quite a few new people in the Raspberry Pi community!

If you're one of those new people, then we heartily welcome you to the latest Raspberry Pi Official Projects Book. With 200 pages of excellent guides, inspiring projects, and informative reviews, it should keep you busy learning about all the amazing things you can do with your Raspberry Pi. We even have a Getting Started guide if you're trying to figure out where to begin. For Pi veterans, there are some truly challenging builds to get stuck into as well.

I hope you all enjoy this book!

Rob Zwetsloot

FIND US ONLINE raspberrypi.org/magpi **GET IN TOUCH** magpi@raspberrypi.org

EDITORIAL
Managing Editor: **Russell Barnes**
russell@raspberrypi.org
Production Editor: **Rob Zwetsloot**
Sub Editors: **Laura Clay, Phil King, Lorna Lynch**

DESIGN
Critical Media: **criticalmedia.co.uk**
Head of Design: **Dougal Matthews**
Designers: **Lee Allen, Mike Kay**
Illustrator: **Sam Alder**

PUBLISHING
For advertising & licensing:
russell@raspberrypi.org
Publisher: **Liz Upton**
CEO: **Eben Upton**

DISTRIBUTION
Seymour Distribution Ltd
2 East Poultry Ave
London
EC1A 9PT | **+44 (0)207 429 4000**

MAGAZINE SUBSCRIPTIONS
Select Publisher Services Ltd
PO Box 6337
Bournemouth
BH1 9EH | **+44 (0)1202 586 848**

CONTRIBUTORS
Wesley Archer, Dana Flinn, Tony Goodhew, Brett Haines, Gareth Halfacree, Lucy Hattersley, Richard Hayler & Sons, Phil King, James Singleton, Richard Smedley, & many more Pi-loving people!

This bookazine is printed on paper sourced from sustainable forests and the printer operates an environmental management system which has been assessed as conforming to ISO 14001.

This official product is published by Raspberry Pi (Trading) Ltd., Station Road, Cambridge, CB1 2JH. The publisher, editor and contributors accept no responsibility in respect of any omissions or errors relating to goods, products or services referred to or advertised in the magazine. Except where otherwise noted, content in this magazine is licensed under a Creative Commons Attribution-NonCommercial-ShareAlike 3.0 Unported (CC BY-NC-SA 3.0). ISBN: 978-1-908256-93-5.

Contents

GET STARTED WITH RASPBERRY PI

Our definitive guide on how to set up and become a master of your Raspberry Pi

PAGE 06

Projects

22

46

84

Reviews

167

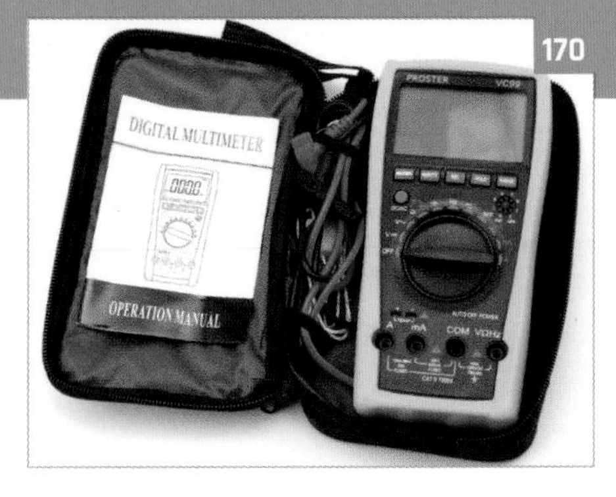

170

Tutorials

120

108

114

142

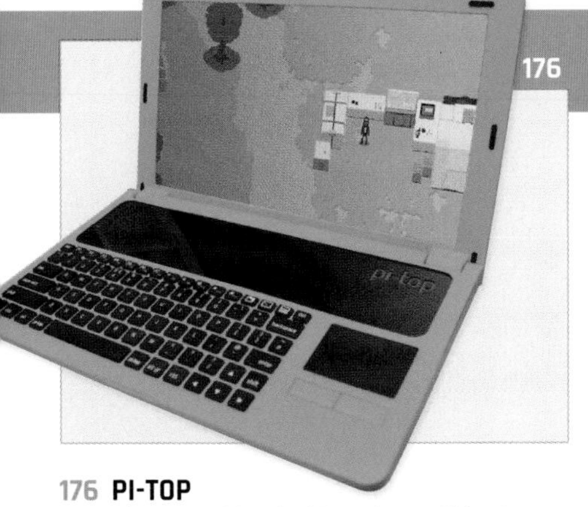
176

186

GETTING STARTED WITH RASPBERRY PI

Creating amazing projects is easy with a Raspberry Pi, but first you need to plug it in and set up Raspbian, the default operating system. This guide will get you up and running in no time

The Raspberry Pi is a wonderful microcomputer that brims with potential. With a Raspberry Pi you can build robots, learn to code, and create all kinds of weird and wonderful projects.

Hackers and enthusiasts have turned Raspberry Pi boards into fully automated weather stations, internet-connected beehives, motorised skateboards, and much more. The only limit is your imagination.

But first, you need to start at the beginning. Upon picking up your Raspberry Pi for the first time, you're faced with a small green board of chips and sockets and may have no idea what to do with it. Before you can start building the project of your dreams, you'll need to get the basics sorted: keyboard, mouse, display, and operating system.

Creating projects with a Raspberry Pi is fun once you've mastered the basics. So in this guide, we're going to take you from newbie zero to Raspberry Pi hero. Grab your Raspberry Pi and let's get going.

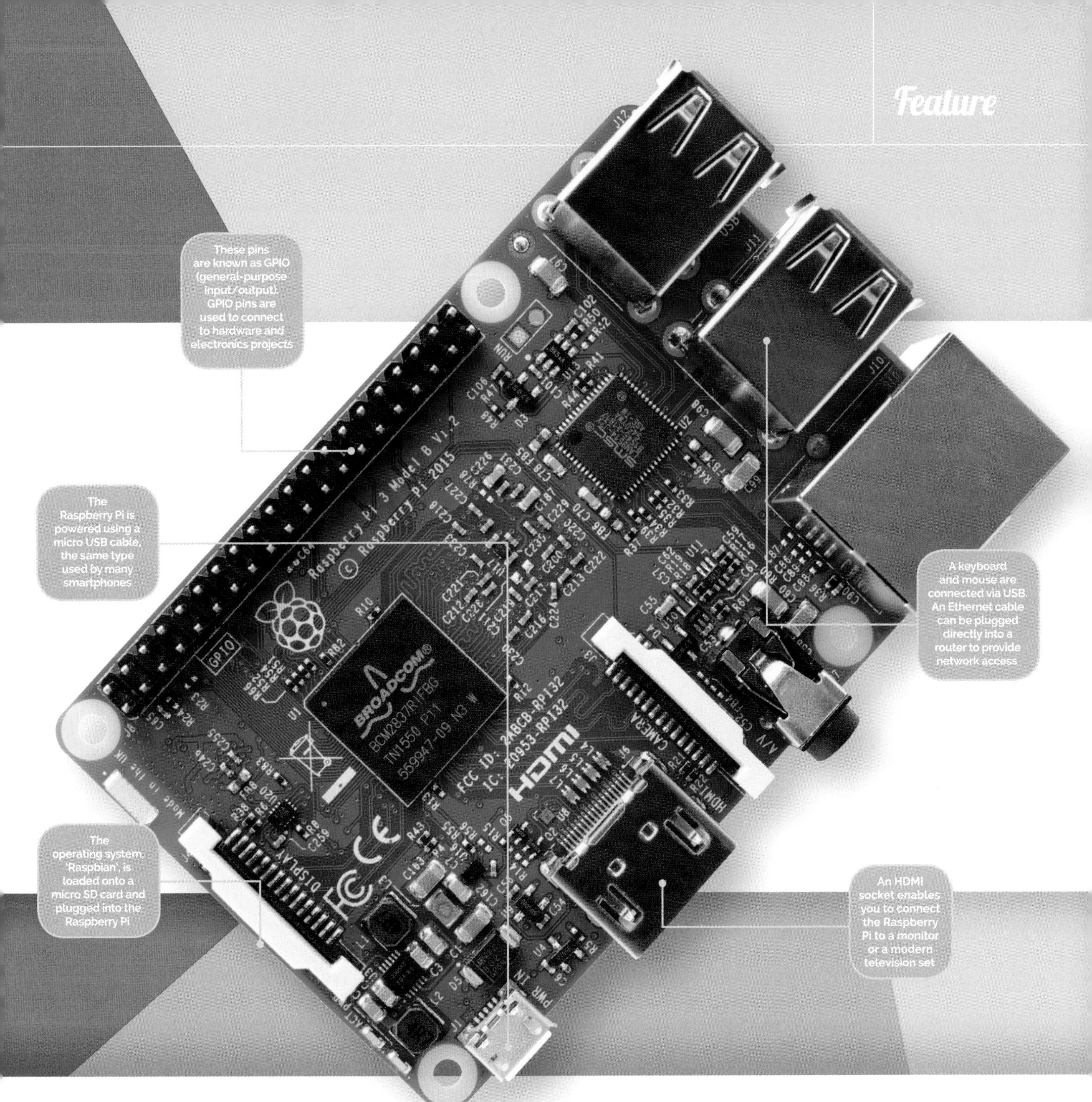
These pins are known as GPIO (general-purpose input/output). GPIO pins are used to connect to hardware and electronics projects
The Raspberry Pi is powered using a micro USB cable, the same type used by many smartphones
The operating system, 'Raspbian', is loaded onto a micro SD card and plugged into the Raspberry Pi
A keyboard and mouse are connected via USB. An Ethernet cable can be plugged directly into a router to provide network access
An HDMI socket enables you to connect the Raspberry Pi to a monitor or a modern television set
Raspberry Pi 3 Model B V1.2
© Raspberry Pi 2015
BROADCOM®
HDMI
CAMERA
DISPLAY
GPIO

RASPBERRY PI 3

The Raspberry Pi 3 is the latest model, and the version recommended for most newcomers

SD card

On the underside of the Raspberry Pi 3 board is the SD card slot. You preload the operating system onto a micro SD card and use it to boot up the Raspberry Pi.

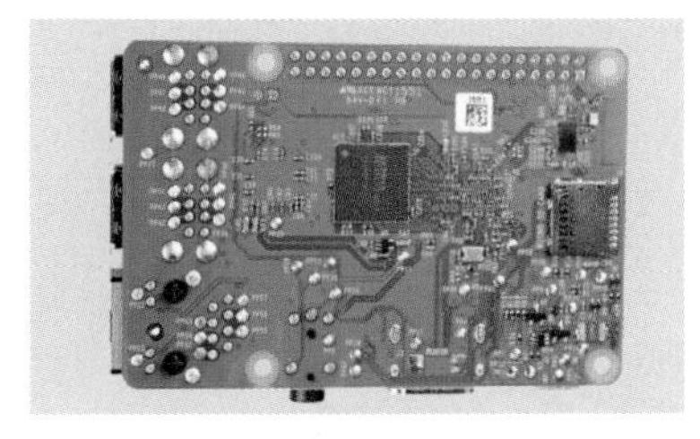

Wireless network

The Pi 3 is the first Raspberry Pi to feature built-in wireless LAN and Bluetooth. This enables you to connect to a wireless router and get online without using a WiFi dongle.

1.2GHz ARM CPU

Featuring the latest 1.2GHz quad-core ARM CPU (central processing unit), the Raspberry Pi 3 is faster than many smartphones, and powerful enough to be used as a desktop computer.

RASPBERRY PI ZERO

Ultra-low-cost, super-tiny, and incredibly powerful, the Pi Zero is the tiniest Raspberry Pi computer

The Pi Zero is an ultra-low-cost and incredibly small microcomputer packed onto a single board. It's roughly a third the size of the Raspberry Pi 3, and has a teenie price tag ($5, or around £4).

For all that, the Pi Zero is packed with enough power to handle demanding computer projects.

Despite its diminutive stature, the Pi Zero is no toy. The Pi Zero is a fully fledged microcomputer with a 1GHz ARM CPU and 512MB RAM. It packs enough technology to run the full version of Raspbian, just the same as the Raspberry Pi 3.

The smaller board is more minimalist than other Raspberry Pi units, which makes it more challenging to set up. But it's a rewarding device that's ideal for creating Internet of Things, wearable, and embedded projects.

To keep the size down, the Pi Zero features a smaller-than-normal mini HDMI socket. You'll almost certainly need a mini HDMI-to-HDMI adapter or cable to connect the Raspberry Pi to a television or monitor.

Alternatively, hackers can hook up an RCA cable directly to the video headers on the board. RCA cables are the red, white, and yellow plugs that you find on older televisions. This feature makes the Pi Zero a great choice for retro gaming enthusiasts.

PI ZERO

Powerful processor

The Pi Zero packs a sizzling 1GHz single-core ARM 11 CPU with 512MB RAM. Despite its diminutive size, it's 40 percent faster than the original Raspberry Pi model.

Tiny form factor

The Pi Zero offers a full computer experience, complete with the Raspbian operating system, and is only a third the size of the original Raspberry Pi.

GPIO to go

The full GPIO header sits along the side of the Pi Zero board. These holes enable makers to attach hardware to the Pi Zero, and you can experiment with electronics projects.

Devices like keyboards and mice are connected to the USB On-the-Go port using a micro USB-to-USB adapter
The mini HDMI socket is rarer than the regular HDMI version found on other Raspberry Pi boards. You'll need a mini HDMI-to-HDMI cable or adapter to connect to a monitor
The Pi Zero is powered using a micro USB cable connected to a high-quality adapter (as you'd find on many smartphones)
GPIO
MICRO SD CARD
HDMI
USB
PWR IN
RUN
TV
CAMERA

The Pi Zero board uses the same micro USB power input as other Raspberry Pi devices, and you can use an official adapter or salvage a high-quality power supply from a mobile phone (2A output is recommended).

Ports are minimal on the Pi Zero, and it sports a single USB port that's smaller than a regular one

Ports are minimal on the Pi Zero, and it sports a single USB port that's smaller than a regular one. You'll need a micro USB-to-USB adapter to connect your keyboard. You may also want a USB hub to connect a mouse and other devices like a USB camera.

A recent version update, Pi Zero v1.3, has a built-in camera connector. Like the other Raspberry Pi devices, you can connect a Raspberry Pi Camera Module or NoIR Camera Module directly to the Pi Zero. This enables you to turn the Pi Zero into a super low-cost camera for taking photos and recording videos.

Thanks to the low power draw of the Pi Zero, this is ideal for time-lapse photography. You just set it up and let it get on with it.

Hooking a Pi Zero up to the internet requires either a USB-to-Ethernet adapter or, more commonly, a WiFi dongle.

Amazingly, the Pi Zero even has the full 40-pin GPIO header of the other Raspberry Pi models, but you don't get the pins pre-built onto the board. Instead, you need to solder two 20-pin male headers to the GPIO holes.

Setting up a Pi Zero is slightly more tricky than a Raspberry Pi 3, but it's also a lot of fun. The end result is a super-cheap, super-powerful computer that runs a full operating system.

A Raspberry Pi camera can be connected directly to the latest version of the Pi Zero

EQUIPMENT YOU'LL NEED

All the kit you need to get a Raspberry Pi up and running for the first time

You don't require much to get your Raspberry Pi started: a micro SD card from an old camera, a smartphone charger, a recycled HDMI cable, and a keyboard and mouse are all you need.

Most items can be sourced from computer hardware around the house, or begged and borrowed from friends and family. If you're looking for the ultimate in low-cost computing; the Raspberry Pi is it.

You should be able to source, salvage, and scavenge most equipment you need to get a Raspberry Pi up and running. To get the most out of your Raspberry Pi in the long term, though, you should use high-quality components.

A good micro SD card from a named brand will be faster and more reliable. Not all USB power adapters are born equal, either. A reliable branded adapter will provide a steady stream of power, even when you attach multiple devices.

The Raspberry Pi board isn't shy, and it'll work just fine naked, but a good case keeps the board safer and makes it easier to store. There's a huge range of cases available, and many offer unique features such as waterproofing, stackability, or wall mounting.

The official Raspberry Pi case is a slick piece of kit that's perfect for any Pi user. Made of five parts that click together, it enables you to quickly open the case and access the board and GPIO pins.

Any equipment you can't recycle can be picked up from the Raspberry Pi Shop (**magpi.cc/2bnamFF**) or from distributors like Element14 (**element14.com**), Allied Electronics (**alliedelec.com**), and RS Components (**magpi.cc/2bnapBl**).

MICRO SD CARD

The micro SD card acts as the hard drive for your Raspberry Pi. You install the Raspbian operating system onto the card, then all your documents, files, and projects are saved to it as you work.

Raspberry PI fan Jeff Geerling did a community favour by purchasing over a dozen different micro SD cards and benchmarking each one. The results were pretty dramatic, with some cards running up to four times as fast as others. Samsung Evo+ and SanDisk Extreme are two popular brands worth looking out for, and both are fairly cheap. You can read more at **magpi.cc/2bncFs3**

The parts of the official Raspberry Pi case can be individually unclipped, offering fast access to the GPIO pins on the board inside
The case was designed by Kinneir Dufort (magpi.cc/2bnbXLu). It's an award-winning design team that has done a great job
The official case provides easy access to all of the ports on the Raspberry Pi, and the micro SD card can be removed without dismantling the case

HDMI cable

An HDMI cable is the easiest way to connect your Raspberry Pi to a computer monitor or television. You don't need an expensive one, and most people recycle one from an old games console or DVD player.

USB power

A good 2A or 2.5A power supply provides you with enough power to run a Raspberry Pi with all kinds of peripherals connected. You can buy an official Universal Power Supply (**magpi.cc/2a14pye**).

Keyboard

Any standard USB keyboard can be used to enter commands to your Raspberry Pi. You can use a Bluetooth keyboard with the Raspberry Pi 3, or any other Pi with a Bluetooth dongle attached. A wired keyboard is easier to use when setting up your Raspberry Pi.

Mouse

Any standard mouse will work with the Raspberry Pi, although ones with two buttons (non-Apple mice) work better. Like keyboards, a Bluetooth mouse will work once it's paired, but a wired mouse works as soon as you plug it in.

INSTALLING RASPBIAN

Discover how to use NOOBS to quickly set up the Raspbian operating system on your Raspberry Pi

Before you start using your Raspberry Pi, it needs to have an operating system (OS). This is the software used to start the hardware, and open and close programs.

Many computers use a specific operating system tied to the hardware. You'll probably be used to Windows on a PC and OS X on a Mac computer.

Most Raspberry Pi owners use an open-source operating system called Raspbian, which is based on Linux. The current version is based on a version of Linux called Debian Jessie, hence the name Raspbian (sometimes you'll hear it called 'Raspbian Jessie').

Linux is like Windows and Mac OS X, but more fun because it's open-source, so anybody can view the source code and improve it.

You can install a range of different OSes on a Raspberry Pi, some based on other versions of Linux, others based on Windows, and even completely unique environments like RISC OS.

Raspbian is the official OS and the one most beginners should start with. It's the simplest to install, easiest to use, and most projects and tutorials use Raspbian as their base.

Start with NOOBS

There are two approaches to installing Raspbian and other operating systems. Beginners should start with NOOBS (New Out Of Box Software). More advanced users may copy an image file containing a whole operating system directly to the SD card.

First, you must format your micro SD card to use the Windows FAT 32 format. The easiest way to do this on a Mac or Windows PC is to use a program called SD Card Formatter (**magpi.cc/2bncvkm**).

Connect your micro SD card to a Mac or Windows PC, typically using a micro SD-to-SD card adapter or a USB card reader, and use SD Card Formatter to erase the card.

Next, download the NOOBS ZIP file from **magpi.cc/2bnf5XF**. Extract the contents of the file and open the NOOBS folder. Copy the contents across to the root of the SD card. See the 'Setting up NOOBS' steps for more information.

AVAILABLE OSES

Raspbian

The official operating system is the easiest to use, and the one beginners should start with. It works a lot like other popular operating systems.

Windows 10 IoT Core

Not the full version of Windows, sadly, but Windows 10 IoT Core enables programmers to run Internet of Things and embedded projects.

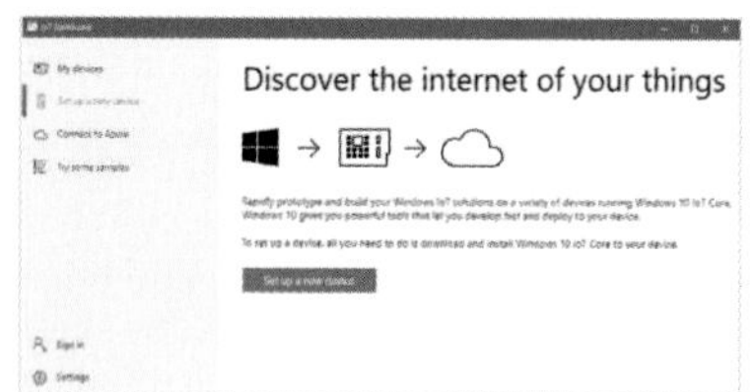

Ubuntu MATE

Ubuntu is one of the world's most popular Linux operating systems, and Ubuntu MATE is a lightweight version that runs just fine on the Raspberry Pi.

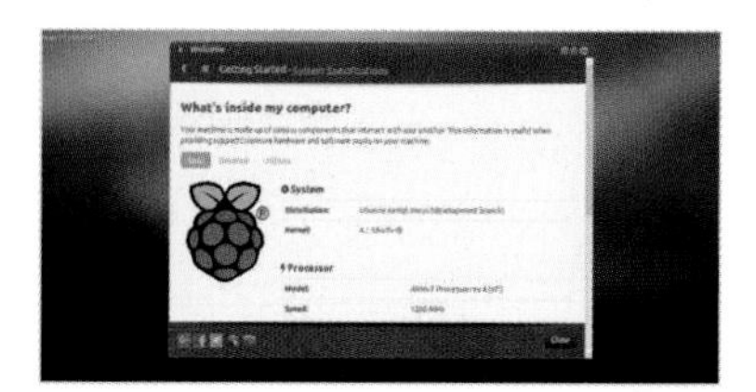

NOOBS automates the process of installing Raspbian. Select the Raspbian option and click on Install to run it

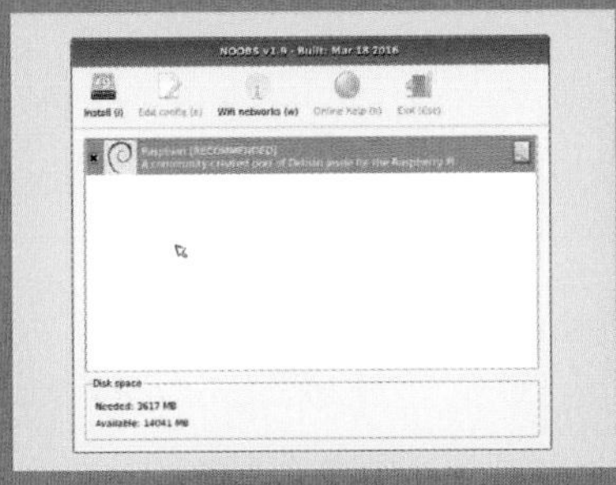

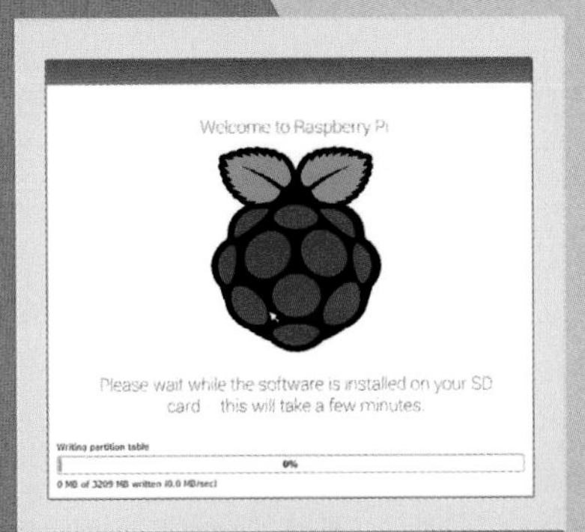

NOOBS automatically copies all the files needed to run Raspbian onto your SD card

With the NOOBS files copied across, remove the micro SD card from your computer and slot it into your Raspberry Pi. Now connect the keyboard, mouse, and HDMI cable. Finally, attach the USB power to boot up the Raspberry Pi.

The Raspberry Pi will boot, displaying the NOOBS installer. By default it only has one option, 'Raspbian [RECOMMENDED]'. Place a tick next to Raspbian and click Install. Click Yes in the Confirm alert to begin installing Raspbian.

Now you just need to wait while the Raspbian file system is extracted. When it's finished, you'll see the Raspbian desktop and the message 'OS(es) Installed Successfully'. Click OK to start using your Raspberry Pi.

Installing image files

Installing an operating system from an image file is a slightly more complex procedure, but one that more advanced (and Pi Zero) users should learn. Image files are copied differently in Windows, compared to Linux and Mac computers.

In both systems, you format the micro SD card to FAT 32 as usual, then you download the operating system as an image file, a large file ending in '.img'. This file is then copied bit by bit as an exact replica to the micro SD card.

On a Windows PC, you will copy the image file using an app called Win32DiskImager (**magpi.cc/2bndEsr**). On Mac and Linux machines, most users copy the file using a command called 'dd' in the terminal.

Full instructions for copying image files for Windows, Mac, and Linux can be found on the Raspberry Pi website (**magpi.cc/1V5Oj8E**).

A good alternative for Mac owners is a program called Apple Pi Baker (**magpi.cc/2bcD53z**). This program enables you to pick the image file and the SD card, and then handles the copying automatically.

Learning how to copy image files is essential if you want to use operating systems other than Raspbian. Beginners should stick with NOOBS to install Raspbian to start with. It's much easier and is the best operating system for beginners.

OSMC

OSMC (Open Source Media Centre) is an easy way to transform your Raspberry Pi into a video and audio player.

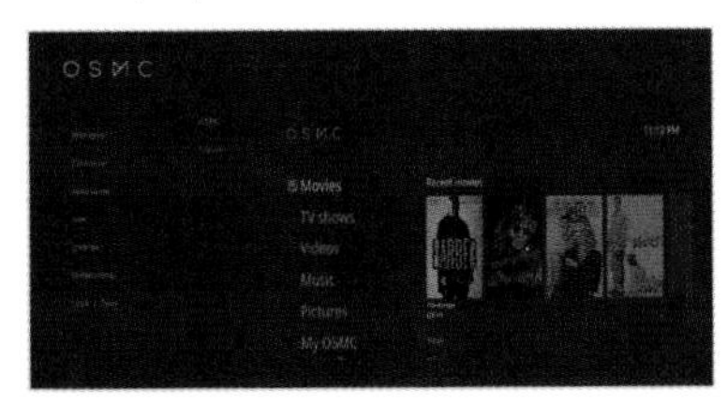

RISC OS

RISC OS is an operating system originally designed by Acorn Computers for ARM-based systems. It's very light and completely different.

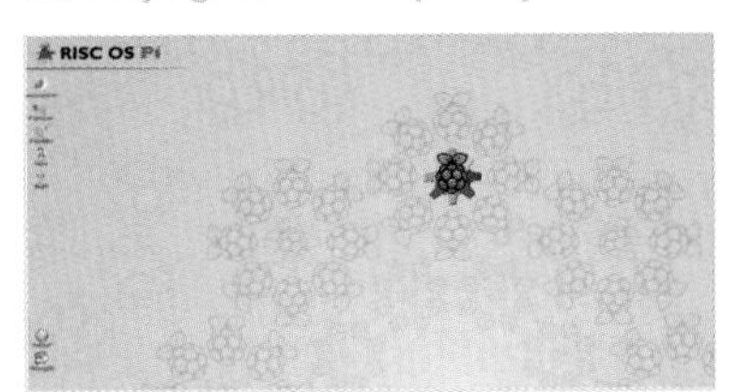

SETTING UP NOOBS

Download NOOBS

In a browser, visit **magpi.cc/2bnf5XF**. Click Download ZIP to get all the files. Open your downloads folder and locate the NOOBS file: currently it's 'NOOBS_v1_9_2'. Right-click on a Windows PC and choose Extract All, then Extract. Just double-click the file on a Mac to extract it.

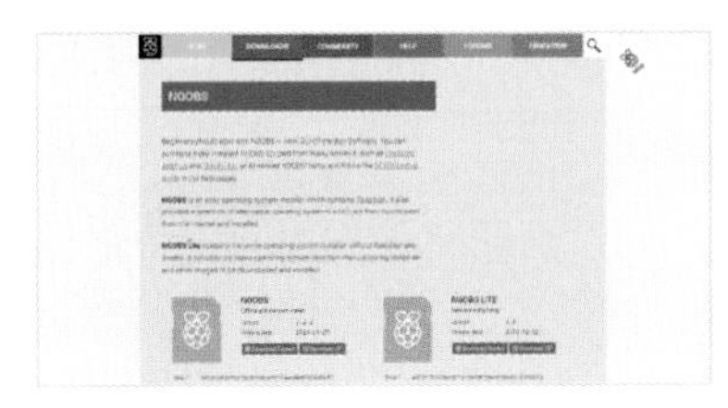

Format SD card

Open SD Card Formatter and you'll see the card in the Drive letter. Change the Volume Label to BOOT so you can identify it later. Now click Option and change Format Type to Full (Erase). Ensure Format Size Adjustment is set to Off and click OK. Click Format, then OK. Click Exit to close SD Card Formatter when it's finished.

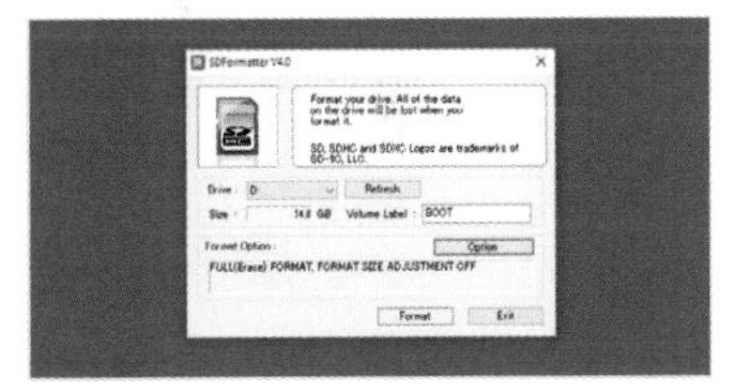

Copy NOOBS files

Open the freshly extracted folder so you can view all the files. It should have folders called **defaults**, **os**, and **overlays**, and files including **bootcode.bin** and **recovery**. Select all of the files and drag them onto the BOOT icon in the sidebar. This copies all of the files inside the NOOBS folder to the root of the SD card. It's important to copy the files inside NOOBS, and not the NOOBS folder itself.

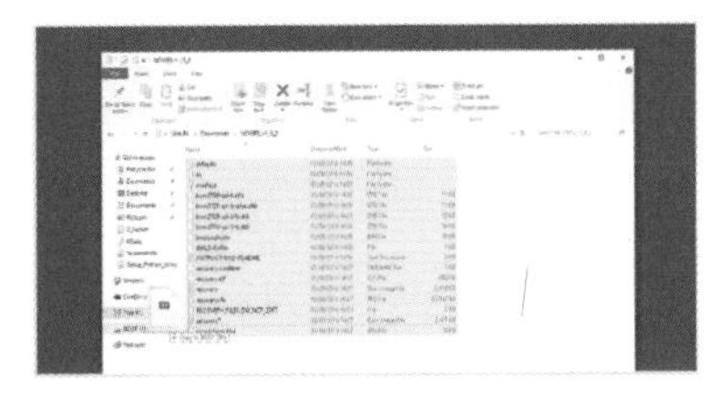

USING RASPBIAN

Getting to grips with the Raspberry Pi's official operating system

A Raspberry Pi can run many operating systems (OSes), but Raspbian is the official OS and the one most newcomers will start with.

Raspbian is a Linux operating system based on the popular Debian distribution. Fully customised for the Raspberry Pi hardware, it's usually a trouble-free experience using a Raspberry Pi with Raspbian.

One aspect of Linux that will be new to Windows and Mac users is being able to choose from different graphical interfaces. Raspbian includes one called LXDE, which stands for 'Lightweight X11 Desktop Environment'.

This heavily modified version of LXDE enables you to use a Raspberry Pi as you would another computer. You have a Menu button, which offers access to most of the programs and apps installed. Programs open in windows, which you can switch between, minimise, maximise, and close using buttons.

Many users might be wondering why this is anything special. Well, computers didn't always have windows; instead, most users used a command-line interface and entered text commands to start programs.

Terminal velocity

In Raspbian, you'll probably spend some time working under the hood of the desktop in a command-line environment. Next to the Menu button is the terminal, a program that enables you to enter Linux text commands. Learning how Linux works, and how to create programs that run from the command line, is part of the joy of owning a Raspberry Pi. It's a return to classic computing where you need to learn how things actually work.

Raspbian is a great environment for learning to code. Along with easy access to the command line, you get all kinds of programming environments built in: everything from MIT's Scratch to Python and Java. You even get a full working version of Mathematica, a cool maths environment that normally costs £190 to buy, with access to real-world data.

It's possible to buy SD cards pre-formatted with the Raspbian software. This saves you from having to install the operating system

Office worker

It isn't just about programming, though. You can use your Raspberry Pi as a desktop computer, and the operating system comes with LibreOffice built in. This is a full office suite of programs, similar to Microsoft Office. Its programs include Writer (word processing), Calc (spreadsheets),

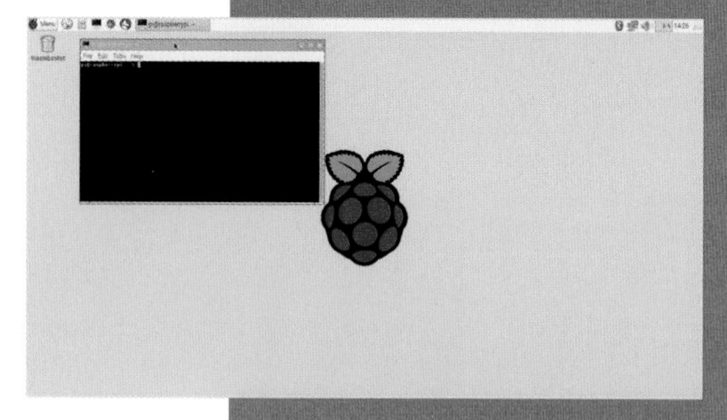
You'll learn how to use the terminal and control your Raspberry Pi computer using text commands

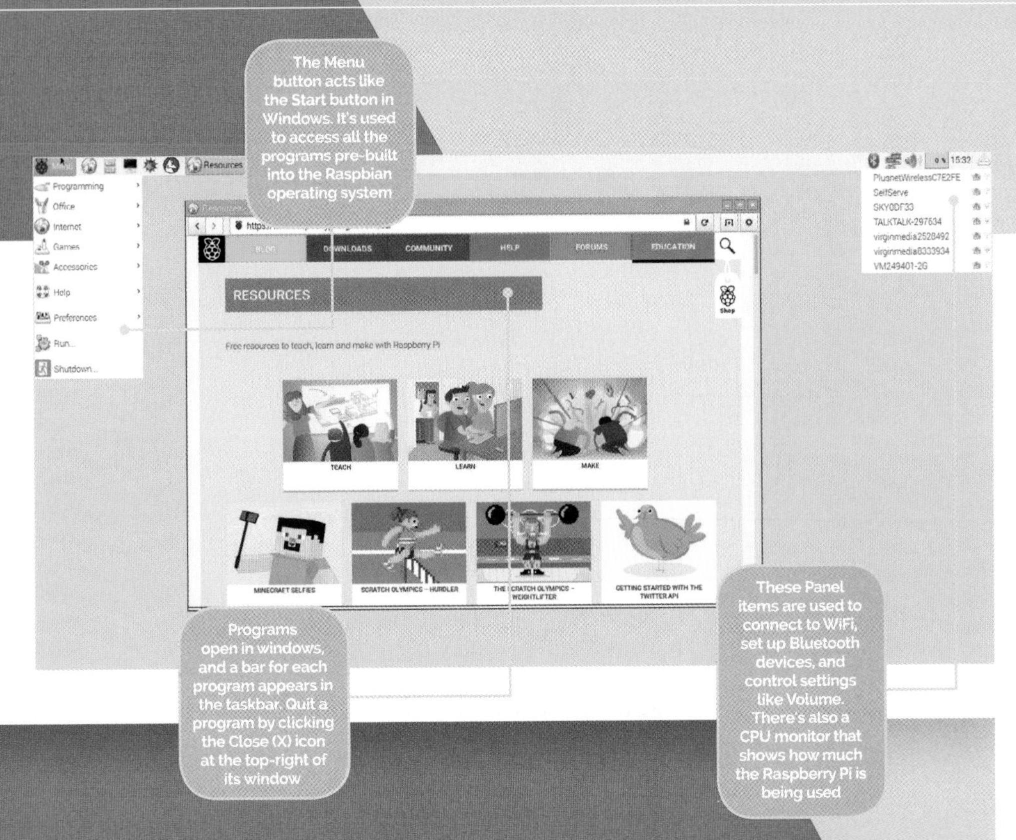

Impress (presentations), Draw (vector graphics and flowcharts), Base (databases), and Math (formula editing).

Raspbian connects to the internet, and has a built-in web browser called 'Epiphany'. You also get an email client called 'Claws Mail'. Both can be accessed under Menu > Internet.

The Menu button acts like the Start button in Windows. It's used to access all the programs pre-built into the Raspbian operating system
Programs open in windows, and a bar for each program appears in the taskbar. Quit a program by clicking the Close (X) icon at the top-right of its window
These Panel items are used to connect to WiFi, set up Bluetooth devices, and control settings like Volume. There's also a CPU monitor that shows how much the Raspberry Pi is being used
RESOURCES
TEACH
LEARN
MAKE

The Raspberry Pi connects to the internet using Ethernet (a cable that runs from your Raspberry Pi to a modem/router) or WiFi. It's easy to connect to a WiFi network, and we'll look at setting up both WiFi and Bluetooth next.

Settings and software

You can adjust the settings for your Raspberry Pi in two ways: using the desktop interface or a terminal program called Raspi Config.

Choose Menu > Preferences to find a collection of different system settings. Add / Remove Software can be used to find and remove packages from the Raspbian system.

Appearance Settings, Audio Device Settings, Main Menu Editor and Mouse & Keyboard Settings all adjust appearance and interaction with Raspbian. Most of the options are self-explanatory.

The Raspberry Pi Configuration choice provides more in-depth options. Here you can change your password (**raspberry** by default) and the hostname of the Pi on the network (**raspberrypi** by default). You can choose to boot to the desktop or the command-line interface (CLI), and enable and disable various hardware interface options.

Raspi Config offers even more detailed options. Open a terminal window and then enter `sudo raspi-config`. A blue screen with options in a grey box appears. Use the up and down arrow keys to move between options; press the right and left arrow keys to move into an option (and back to the main menu). More information on these options can be found at **magpi.cc/2bnfuJF**.

The important thing about Raspbian is not to worry about experimenting with different options and settings. Feel free to explore the menus, command line, and configuration settings. You can always reset your micro SD card with NOOBS and start again.

USING THE RASPBIAN INTERFACE

Programming tools

Raspbian comes with a selection of coding tools, found under Menu > Programming. Scratch makes it easy to learn programming concepts, and popular languages like Python and Java are ready to use right out of the box.

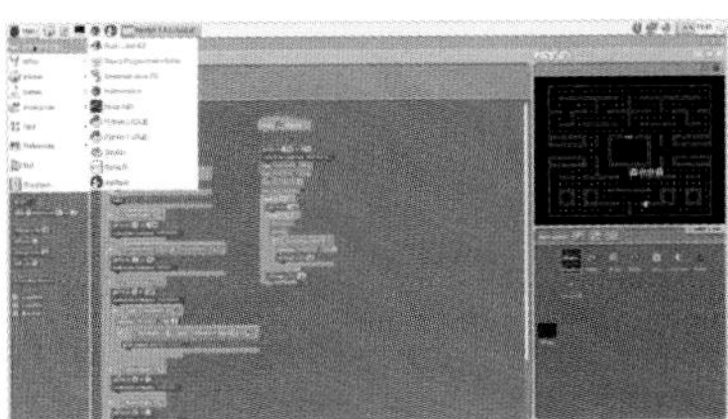

Web software

A web browser called Epiphany is built into Raspbian, along with an email program called Claws Mail. There are links to Raspberry Pi Resources and *The MagPi* under Menu > Internet.

Office suite

Raspbian features powerful LibreOffice programs like Writer and Impress. These are the equivalent of Microsoft Office apps and enable you to create documents on your Raspberry Pi.

SETTING UP THE INTERNET

Get online wirelessly and quickly, with this guide to setting up wireless LAN on your Raspberry Pi

The Raspberry Pi is best when connected to the internet. You can use it to browse the web, play online videos, and send and receive emails. More importantly, you can get the latest updates and install the software packages you need for any project.

To do this, you'll need to get online. With the Raspberry Pi 3 this is easier than ever, because it now has a wireless antenna built into the board.

Other models of Raspberry Pi, including the Pi Zero, require a WiFi dongle connected to a spare USB port.

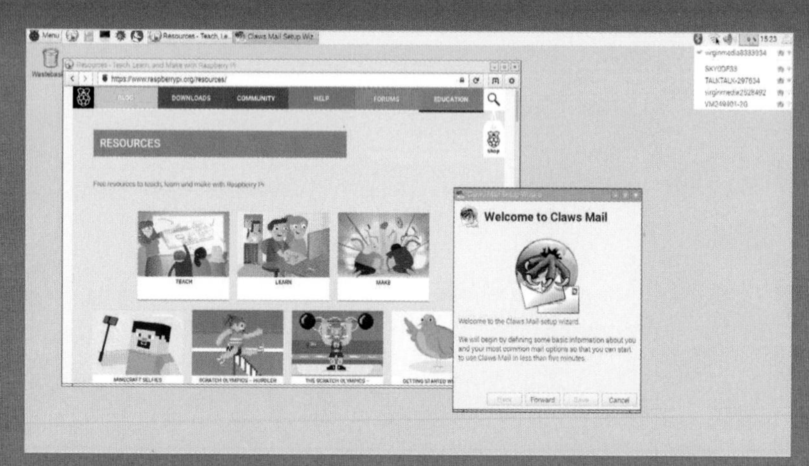

A wireless internet connection enables you to get help online and set up apps like Claws Mail

With wireless added to your Raspberry Pi, it's easy to get online. Boot into the Raspbian desktop and look for the WiFi Networks icon in the Panel (on the top-right of the display).

Click WiFi Networks and you'll see a list of all the local wireless networks. Choose your network and (if you have one) enter your password, also called the 'Pre Shared Key'. The Raspberry Pi connects to the wireless network, enabling you to get online. In this respect it's pretty much like any other computer that connects to WiFi; it will even remember the password for next time.

Once you're online, you can use the Epiphany browser to fetch webpages. Click Web Browser in the Launch Bar.

CONNECTING TO A WIRELESS NETWORK

Check for networks

Click on the Wireless Networks icon in the Panel. Raspbian will display a list of all the wireless networks available in your local area. Click on the one that's yours.

Enter your password

Enter your WiFi password in the Pre Shared Key field and click on OK. The network symbol will switch to a wireless symbol and you'll be connected.

Test your connection

Test your internet connection by opening a webpage. Click on Web Browser in the Launch Bar and enter **www.raspberrypi.org** in the URL field. Press **RETURN** to load the page.

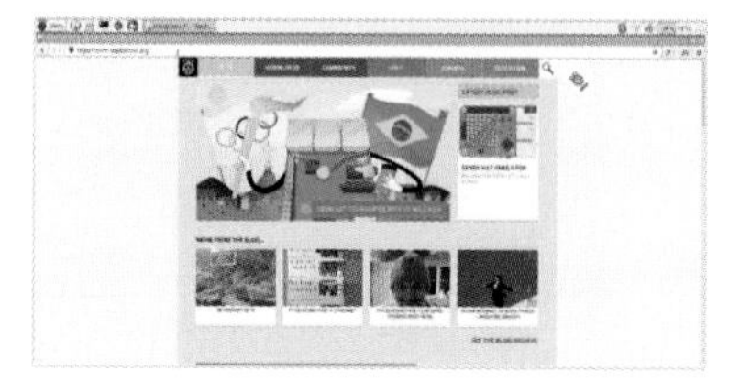

SETTING UP BLUETOOTH

Connect wirelessly to nearby devices with Bluetooth technology

Devices connected by Bluetooth work wirelessly with your Raspberry Pi

Bluetooth is another piece of technology that has been added to the Raspberry Pi 3 board. With Bluetooth you can connect wireless devices, such as mice and keyboards, directly to your Raspberry Pi.

As with wireless LAN, if you own an older Raspberry Pi model or a Pi Zero, you'll need to attach a USB dongle to use Bluetooth devices.

With Bluetooth hardware on your Raspberry Pi board, it's easy to connect to a device wirelessly, a process known as 'pairing'.

You can pair wireless gaming controllers, like a PlayStation joypad, or Android smartphones. Many Raspberry Pi projects make use of Bluetooth, enabling the Raspberry Pi to communicate with nearby electronic components and devices.

The easiest way to test out Bluetooth is to set up a wireless mouse or keyboard; both are fairly easy devices to come by.

In some ways, the process is similar to connecting to a WiFi network, but the Bluetooth device you want to connect to must be set to pairing mode first. This is also known as making the device 'discoverable'. Putting a device into pairing mode varies by device; holding down the power button until an LED flashes is fairly commonplace, but check with the instructions for your device.

You then use the Bluetooth icon in the Raspbian desktop Panel to connect to the device: choose Bluetooth > Add Device.

It's possible to put your Raspberry Pi into pairing mode by choosing **Bluetooth > Make Discoverable** from the Panel. Then you can connect to your Raspberry Pi from other Bluetooth devices like mobile phones.

SETTING UP A BLUETOOTH DEVICE

Pairing mode

Start by putting your Bluetooth device in Pairing / Discoverable mode. We're using an Apple wireless keyboard. Hold down the power button until the LED flashes. Click Bluetooth in the Panel and choose Add Device.

Add new device

The Add New Device window opens and will scan for nearby Bluetooth devices. Some will have names, others just identifying numbers (check on the device). Choose a device from the list and click Pair.

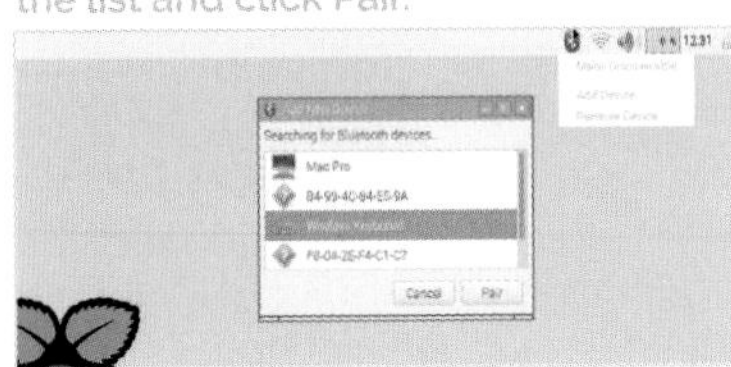

Enter code

The Pi now attempts to pair with the Bluetooth device. You'll be asked to enter a code on the keyboard; press the buttons and **RETURN**. You can now start using the Bluetooth device with your Raspberry Pi.

GETTING TO KNOW GPIO

Discover the joy of electronics by hooking up components, wires, and hardware to the pins on a Raspberry Pi board

One of the most powerful and fun features of the Raspberry Pi is the row of pins at the top. Known as 'GPIO' (General-Purpose Input/Output), these pins enable you to hook up the Raspberry Pi to additional hardware and electronics.

There are lots of hardware attachments for the Raspberry Pi that connect directly to the GPIO pins. Many are known as HATs (Hardware Attached on Top). These connect directly to the GPIO and sit on top of the Raspberry Pi. More importantly, HATs are designed to work as soon as you connect them to the Raspberry Pi, so hardware branded as a HAT is easier to set up.

The real joy of GPIO isn't using pre-made hardware, but building your own electronics projects. You can connect the GPIO pins to all kinds of electronic circuitry and control it using the Raspberry Pi. With the right cables, you can hook the GPIO pins up to switches, buttons, sensors, buzzers, and all manner of electronic gizmos and widgets. These are used to learn all about electronics hardware and circuit building.

While it's possible to wire parts directly to the GPIO pins, most tinkerers place electronic components in a breadboard and connect this to the Raspberry Pi.

> "You can connect the GPIO pins to all kinds of electronic circuitry and control it"

BREADBOARDS AND BREAKOUTS

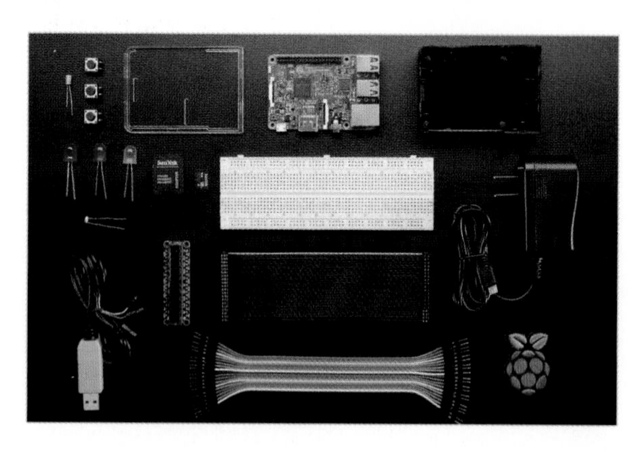

Electronic components are plugged into the holes on the breadboard, and components in adjacent holes are linked. In this way, you can build up a test circuit without having to actually solder components together.

If you follow the instructions, connecting directly to the GPIO pins on a Raspberry Pi is safe, but randomly plugging in wires and power sources to the Raspberry Pi may cause bad things to happen, especially plugging in devices that use a lot of power (like motors).

Because of this, many electronics enthusiasts use a device known as a 'breakout cable' between the Raspberry Pi and breadboard. The breakout cable plugs into the GPIO pins, and into the breadboard.

There are also devices like the Explorer HAT that combine a breakout with a breadboard and enable you to create prototype circuits.

3.3V	5V
2	5V
3	GND
4	14
GND	15
17	18
27	GND
22	23
3.3V	24
10	GND
9	25
11	8
GND	7
5	GND
6	12
13	GND
19	16
26	20
GND	21

There are 40 GPIO pins, each with a specific function. Use this image as a handy guide whenever you're programming electronics

Unlike the type used for cutting bread, an electronic breadboard is a plastic slab with lots of holes in it.

Wiring a breadboard (or circuit) directly to the GPIO pins is generally safe, as long as you avoid circuits with external power sources. Most tinkerers invest in a breakout cable to go with the breadboard (see 'Breadboards and breakouts').

With your circuit set up, you then control the GPIO pins in a programming environment like Python or Scratch. GPIO pins are set to input or output mode. GPIO outputs are easy because the pin is switched on or off (known as HIGH or LOW in computing terms). When the GPIO pin is HIGH, voltage flows through the GPIO pin, lighting up an LED or buzzing a buzzer. Set the pin to LOW and the LED goes out, or the buzzer goes quiet.

GPIO input is a bit more tricky. In this case, the GPIO pin is set to HIGH or LOW and responds to a change from a circuit. A button (or other electronic component) can change the circuit from LOW to HIGH, or HIGH to LOW, with the Raspberry Pi coded to respond accordingly. This is often referred to as 'pull up' or 'pull down'. Don't worry: if this all sounds complicated, you can get started by using GPIO Zero to make programming much easier.

Never underestimate the pure fun you can get from a little computer, a bunch of pins, and a handful of electronic components. Discovering how to use GPIO is a great way to spend your time.

GPIO ZERO ESSENTIALS

Learning to use the GPIO pins is the route to having real fun with a Raspberry Pi. It's a big subject, with lots of tricks and tinkering to discover. Our *GPIO Zero Essentials* book teaches you the basics (and beyond) of using the GPIO port with the GPIO Zero Python library. See **magpi.cc/GPIOZero-book** for more information.

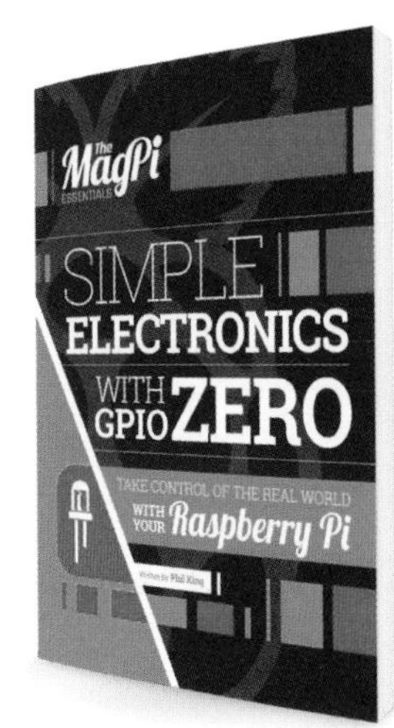

PROJECTS SHOWCASE

Inspiring projects from around the world, courtesy of the incredible hackers and makers in the Raspberry Pi community

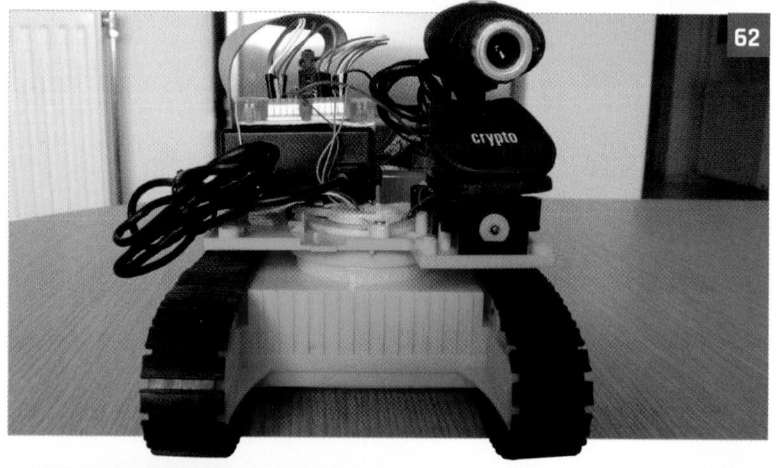

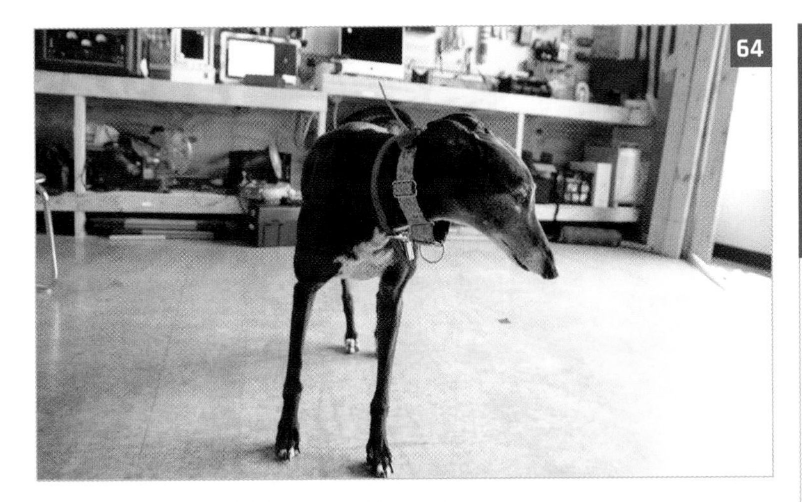

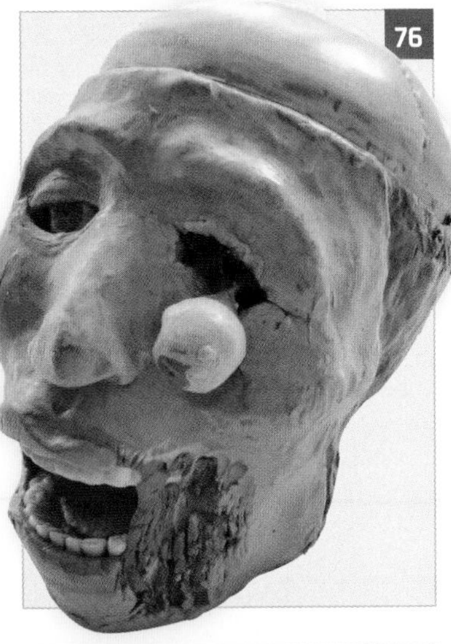

Projects

01 MOTIVATIONAL BATHROOM SCALE

DOT SILVERMAN

Dot Silverman is currently a junior research scientist in Autodesk's Bio/Nano Research Team. When not in the lab, she enjoys long runs, African dance, and crochet.
magpi.cc/1RekKjz

A digital bathroom scale is hacked to measure your weight

10 AMAZING NEW YEAR'S PROJECTS

It's the start of a new year, and (hopefully) the start of a new you. Start 2016 as you mean to go on with these amazing projects...

We all like making New Year's resolutions. Sticking to them is another matter, and there's only so many times you can promise to give up cake and fail after three days.

So, rather than resolving not to do something fun, we thought it would be a great idea to find the greatest Raspberry Pi-powered tech projects with a healthy, feel-good vibe. The makers of these projects have done us proud. What we have here are some of the world's coolest projects to see you into the new year.

These tech projects will help you live a little healthier, be a better citizen, and save some money to boot. Not bad, eh? More importantly, you can do all this while having fun.

Living a little healthier is a great place to start, so our first project is Dot Silverman's Motivational Bathroom Scale. "You type your goal weight into the scales using the keypad," explains Dot, "and the device compares your weight to your goal weight.

"If you're on target, it'll give you a flattering compliment. Otherwise, it'll sass you to get back to the gym. Remember that you're beautiful, no matter what the scale might tell you."

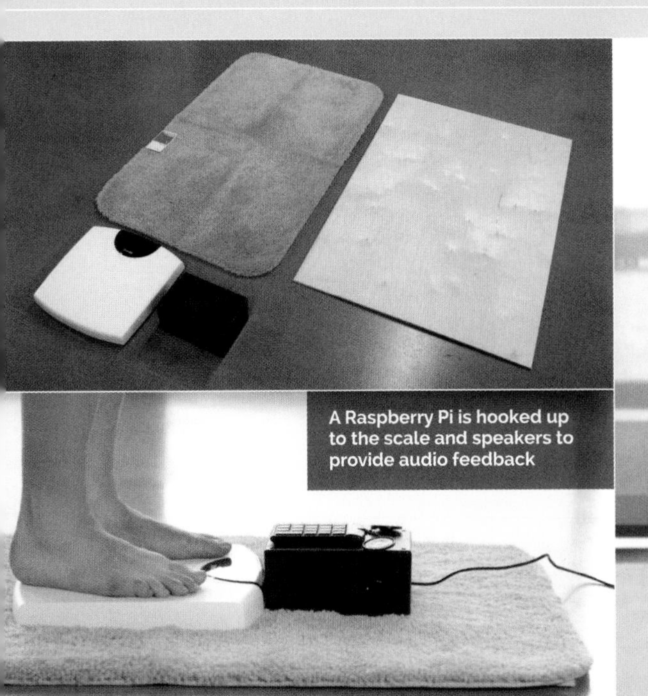

A Raspberry Pi is hooked up to the scale and speakers to provide audio feedback

Enter your goal weight using the keypad, so the Raspberry Pi knows whether to give you grief

02 E-WHEELCHAIR

PHIL CASE

Phil Case is an English maker who was disabled after injuring his C spine in an accident.
magpi.cc/1lU6z6f

The E-Wheelchair incorporates a Cooking Hacks E-Health v2 Sensor to monitor vital body parameters (**cooking-hacks.com**). The E-Health v2 and sensor attachments enable the Raspberry Pi to monitor body levels, such as blood glucose.

> What we have here are some of the world's coolest projects to see you into the new year

If you want to get a little more serious about monitoring health, Cooking Hacks' E-Health v2 sensor is worth investigating. It enables you to connect nine sensors to the Pi to measure blood pressure, oxygen levels, airflow, body temperature, and glucose levels, along with electrocardiogram and electromyography results.

One Raspberry Pi project maker making use of the E-Health sensor is Preston-based Phil Case, whose life goal is to build an affordable smart wheelchair. Phil's 'E-wheelchair' is mind-controlled, using Neurosky MindWave Mobile and Mindflex EEG products to measure the user's brain activity. The E-Health system is used to monitor electrocardiogram levels and blood sugars, and he plans to implement a body position sensor.

Phil is raising money towards the development of his smart wheelchair project, and a GoFundMe page can be found for those looking to be more charitible in 2016 (**gofundme.com/hfymdo**).

03 TECHFUGEES

MIKE BUTCHER

Mike is the founder of TechHub and editor at large at TechCrunch. He initially proposed the concept of Techfugees.
techfugees.com

Techfugees is a community response to the European refugee crisis. It runs conferences and hackathons, and uses a global network of collaborators to address the crisis in technological ways.

TECH FOR CHANGE

The power of geeks to organise for a good cause was highlighted this year thanks to Techfugees (**techfugees.com**), a UK tech community response to the European refugee crisis. The initiative brings together hackers in the UK to crowdsource ideas. So far, Techfugees has organised two conferences and a hackathon, and raised £5,000 to provide free WiFi to the Calais refugee camp. So how about for the New Year you invest some time in providing tech skills to charities?

04 RASPBERRY PI PIGGY BANK

ALEX STRANDBERG

Alex Strandberg is a student at Cornell University College of Engineering.
youtu.be/XanRVZgY6ow

The Raspberry Pi Piggy Bank uses a coin-sorting mechanism to place coins in the correct slots. It counts, sorts and stores coins using a Lego mechanism that rotates for each coin. A fingerprint sensor is used to provide access to the bank.

> So how about for the New Year you invest some time in providing tech skills to charities?

MONEY MACHINE

If your New Year's resolution is to save more money, then take a look at Alex Strandberg's amazing Raspberry Pi Piggy Bank. "After a coin is inserted, it's placed into a stack with the same type of coin," explains Alex. "The LCD screen displays the total amount of money in the bank. If I want to access the coin from inside, I hold my finger on the sensor to unlock the bank."

Another Lego Mindstorms-based project to investigate is the fabulous BrickPi Bookreader, built by Dexter Industries founder John Cole. This robot manually flips pages, photographs each page, and then reads it out loud. "We wanted to build a digitizer that could read books out loud," John tells us. "We were fascinated by the Google Books project and thought 'why couldn't we build this at home?'"

You'll need a Dexter Industries BrickPi device and Lego Mindstorms equipment. The BrickPi turns a Raspberry Pi into the brains for Lego Mindstorms robots. It controls two Lego EV3 motors: one pushes the pages up, and another acts as an arm and flips it over. The Pi Camera Module snaps an image of the page, and OCR software turns it

05 PIBRICK READER

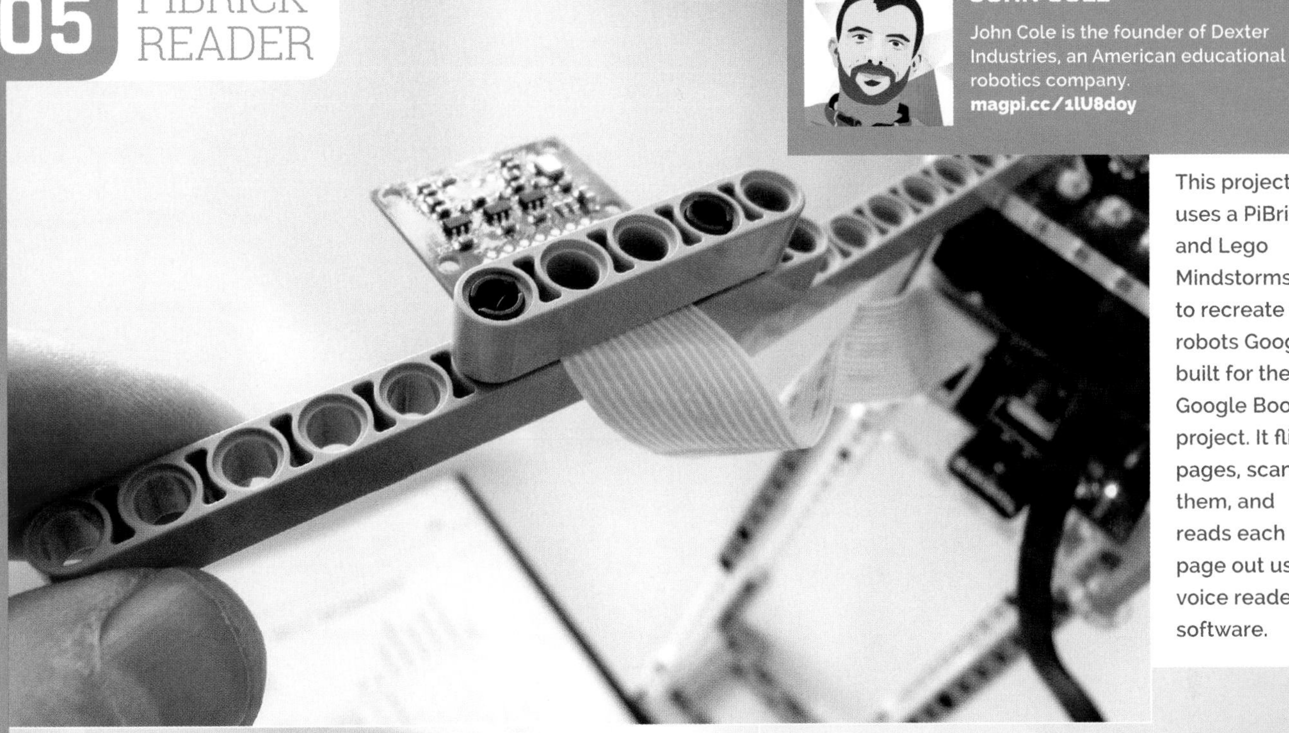

JOHN COLE

John Cole is the founder of Dexter Industries, an American educational robotics company.
magpi.cc/1lU8doy

This project uses a PiBrick and Lego Mindstorms kit to recreate the robots Google built for the Google Books project. It flips pages, scans them, and reads each page out using voice reader software.

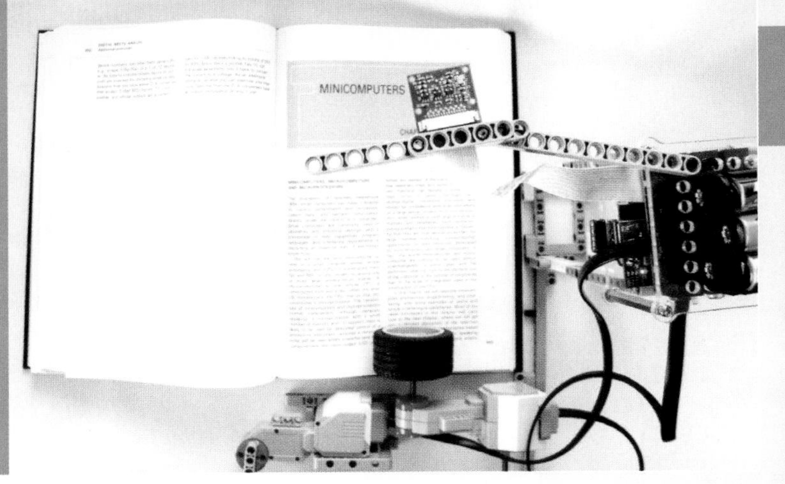

into text. "Just for fun, we used some free text-to-speech software so the Raspberry Pi reads the book out loud," says John.

NATURE CALLING

If your New Year's resolution is to get closer to nature, then one project you should look at is Sam Webster's Tweety Pi Bird Box (**magpi.cc/1lU7cN9**). To be fair, there are lots of Raspberry Pi bird box projects out in the wild. We really like Sam's, though, because it takes things a bit further than most. Sam has fitted his bird box with a PIR sensor, and hooked it up to Twitter. Whenever a bird flits into the box, it automatically starts sharing updates to **@tweetypibirdbox**.

We're big fans of eco projects here at *The MagPi*, and learning how to use solar power in your Pi projects is a noble aim for the upcoming year. Solar panels can be picked up for around £20, and can be used to provide direct power or charge up an attached battery. Veteran maker Koff has a great tutorial over on Instructables (**magpi.cc/1lU7fZh**).

06 TWEETY PI BIRD BOX

SAM WEBSTER

Dr Samuel Webster is an anatomy and embryology lecturer at Swansea University.
magpi.cc/1lU7cN9

The Tweety Pi Bird Box uses a PIR sensor to detect movement, and the Pi Camera Module takes photos. A Python script then tweets each image from @tweetypibirdbox. It's a fun project that lets you watch the birds in your garden.

07 SOLAR POWERED RASPBERRY PI

KOFF

Koff is an international man of mystery, but he's been making stuff since the 1980s and has some great projects on his YouTube and Instructables pages.
magpi.cc/1lU7fZh

Running a Raspberry Pi from solar power is a great project. You get to learn how solar power works, and you can create devices that run outdoors under their own steam.

08 RASPBERRY PI WALL-MOUNTED GOOGLE CALENDAR

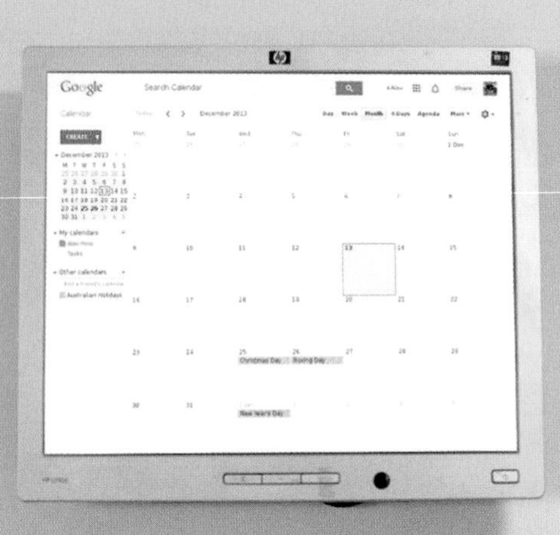

ALEX PINE

Alex Pine is an IT service engineer from Adelaide, South Australia. His projects have been viewed over 800,000 times.
magpi.cc/1Y94RtZ

This popular project turns an old HDMI monitor into a wall-mounted display that shows information from Google Calendar. The Raspberry Pi is placed on the rear of the monitor, and it is bracket-mounted to the wall.

> "Email is a modern curse, but practising inbox zero can bring a lot of relief"

GET ORGANISED

If one of your New Year's resolutions is to be a bit more organised (ours usually is), then we have three great projects for you to take a look at. The first is a fantastic wall-mounted Google Calendar by Alex Pine (**magpi.cc/1Y94RtZ**). You can use it to create a shared calendar for yourself and your family, so everyone can see exactly what's going on.

Our second productivity project is Michael Mitchell's Inbox Zero Taunter (**magpi.cc/1Y953cF**). Email is a modern curse, but practising inbox zero can bring a lot of relief from mail overload. The bright light of a Raspberry Pi LED reminds you that you've got email in your inbox that needs to be dealt with. It's a super-simple project - just one LED and around ten lines of code - but once configured, it'll hassle you into clearing out an email account.

Finally, if you're in serious need of organisational help, then why not turn your Raspberry Pi into a voice-activated digital assistant? We love the Raspberri Personal Assistant by Jan Wante. He's turned a 1950s Bakelite Televox intercom into a voice-controlled digital assistant (think Siri inside an old American radio). Inside is a Raspberry Pi with a USB audio sound card, running Steven Hickson's Voice Command software (**magpi.cc/1Y95Pqc**).

You will undoubtedly learn something new from building any of these projects, and learning something new is the best New Year's resolution you can make in any case. Whatever project you choose to build in 2016, make sure you have fun.

09 INBOX ZERO TAUNTER

MICHAEL MITCHELL

Michael Mitchell lives in Tallahassee, Florida and runs the MitchTech website. He creates projects for Raspberry Pi, Arduino, Android, and Ubuntu.
magpi.cc/1Y953cF

The Inbox Zero Taunter is a simple project that uses an LED connected to your Raspberry Pi. A Python script is used to detect emails in your Gmail inbox, and light up the LED.

10 RASPBERRI PERSONAL ASSISTANT

JAN WANTE

Jan Wante is a maker from the Netherlands. He's a member of the J^3 Associates, who run a project-making lab.
j3associates.be

The Raspberri Personal Assistant project transforms a 1950s Bakelite speaker into a voice-activated personal assistant. Like Siri, it can be programmed to answer requests about the weather and news, or to take messages.

A combination of a 3.5" LCD screen and convex glass creates an authentic look for the Pip-Boy
The Raspberry Pi is kept on the belt of a costume, as it won't fit properly into the case
The main parts fit into a 3D-printed case that clips over your arm

JESSE ROE

An IT worker for an MSP company, Jesse has very little experience with making in this way, but is very good at researching.
imgur.com/a/LFaPP

RASPBERRY PIP-BOY 3000A

Survive the radioactive wastelands or a cloudy day in town with a custom-made, wrist-worn computer

The Pip-Boy from the *Fallout* video games is quite an iconic piece of kit these days. The fictional wrist computer's functionality may be less amazing now than it was when the series debuted in the 1990s, but the retro-futuristic look has kept it in certain corners of pop culture. Now, thanks to the reignition of interest in the *Fallout* franchise, the rise of makers, and the exploding popularity of cosplaying, every so often a new, home-made version of the Pip-Boy will turn up online and go a bit viral. Even with the impending release of a special-edition version of *Fallout 4* with an official Pip-Boy, people are still making their own versions, like Jesse Roe.

"The project was an attempt to make a fully functional Pip-Boy 3000A. Not something to stick a phone in, but an actual working device," Jesse tells us, referencing the official Pip-Boy which will require a smartphone.

Having never found a perfect use for his Raspberry Pi, Jesse decided to use it for this project he was making for a friend. Using a 3D-printed case that he modified himself, the build wasn't simple.

"I worked on this probably about 70 hours total, with a lot of that being just research," Jesse explains about his build process. "There was a lot of stuff out there on making a Pip-Boy, where to get the cast from, materials, etc. The main piece to get was the Pip-Boy cast itself, which I ordered from Nakamura Shop on Shapeways.

"Once it was in, we sanded it down and used model paint for the base with a darker green.

Quick Facts

- Jesse completed the project between October and Christmas 2014
- There are still a few buttons to add, but it's functionally complete
- *Fallout 3* and *New Vegas* are his favourite *Fallout* games
- Jesse now wants to make a robot tank army with Pis
- The cast for the case was from Nakamura Shop, and the RasPipBoy UI by Neal Corbett

USE A CUSTOM PIP-BOY

>STEP-01
Set it up

You will need to get into a full Vault-dwelling outfit with a belt to house the Raspberry Pi, so that you can plug the Pip-Boy screen into it, and the Pi into some power.

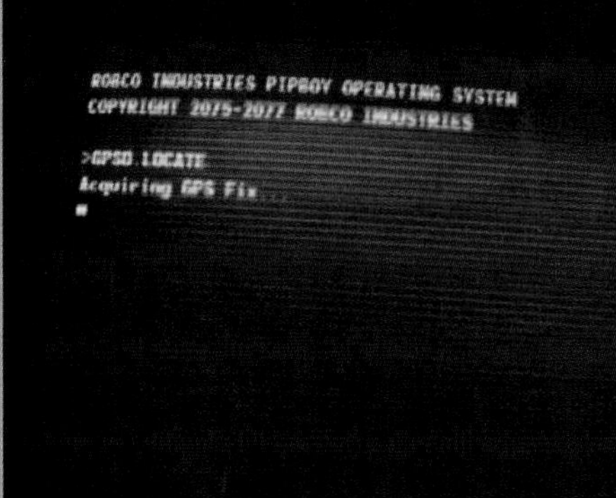

>STEP-02
Boot it up

You can enjoy the custom bootup messages, perfect for when you're cosplaying and making your way to a convention floor to show off your fully functioning Pip-Boy.

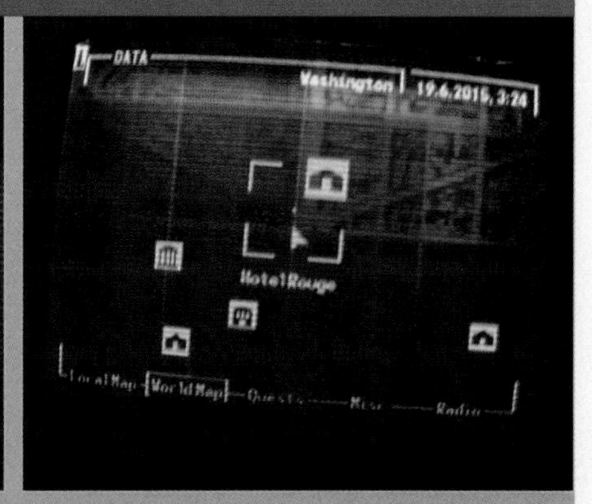

>STEP-03
Show it off

The custom interface, available from **bitbucket.org/selectnone/raspipboy**, has many functions you can show to people who are interested: GPS, VATS simulator, and a Wi-Fi strength monitor.

We detailed it up with scratches and other abrasions to look like a used model. I knew the suit as a whole needed to be separated. Too many people are so close to having a working Pip-Boy and get stuck when they say they can't fit everything in there! I took a mechanics jumpsuit and put the 101 logo on the back as well as other details… I used an old army surplus belt with lots of compartments for a part of the suit as well, and put a hole in the suit so all the wiring could go from the belt, up the back, and to the Pip-Boy.

"Next was getting the Pip-Boy to boot into the slightly tweaked 'OS' on startup, which was fairly simple. I ended up editing the code to have a different startup message for the 'BIOS' and whatnot, to make it more complete, but I didn't mess with the software too much.

> "I worked on this probably about 70 hours total, with a lot of that being just research"

The hardest and almost final part of the build was the screen. I ended up using a 3.5″ TFT from Adafruit. The way the top bezel comes down and how you have to mount the screen means laying it down on something that covers all, for lips behind the bezel. Then after that, I had to lay a piece of glass on top of the screen and glue it very lightly (but not too lightly) around the screen. Any mistake and you have to get a new screen because either you're going to glue it down off-centre or you'll put too much on the screen."

Since Jesse hadn't done much programming before, the modifications and setting up were a little tricky for him, but as you can see, in the end he managed to complete the project and walk around with a sweet Raspberry Pi-powered wrist computer.

Above Dials are to come, but the interface perfectly captures *Fallout 3*'s Pip-Boy

Left A handy army belt allowed Jesse to hide the electronics in the suit

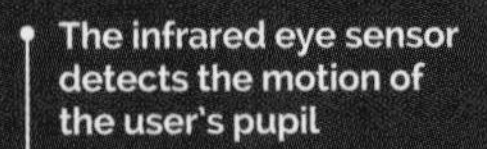

The infrared eye sensor detects the motion of the user's pupil

MYRIJAM STOETZER

Myrijam Stoetzer is a 14-year-old maker from Duisburg, Germany. She has been competing in Jugend forscht, the German science competition for young people.
magpi.cc/2dTGODs

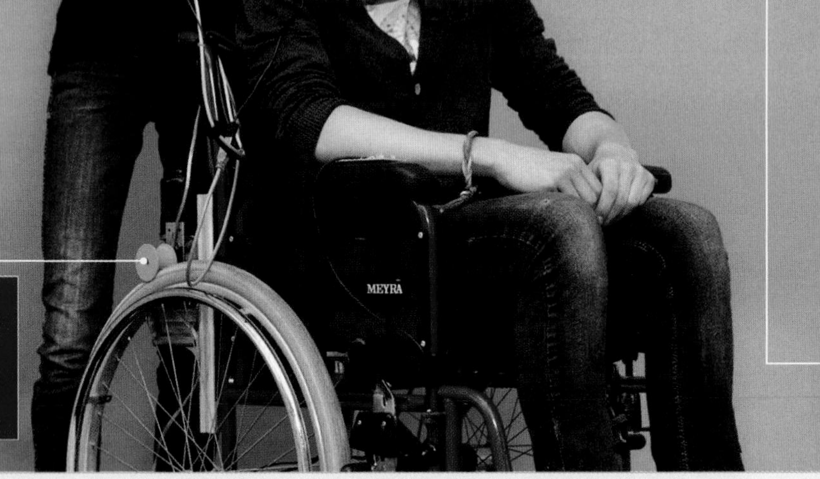

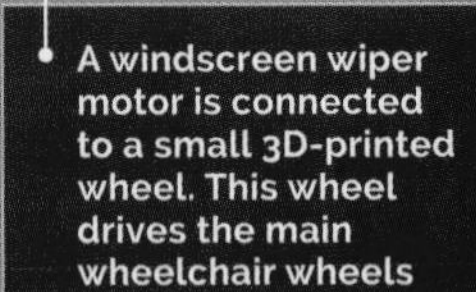

Directions are spoken out loud and are confirmed using the pad

EYE-CONTROLLED WHEELCHAIR

Myrijam Stoetzer and **Paul Foltin** built an incredible eye-controlled wheelchair from 3D-printed parts, motors from a windscreen wiper, and a hacked webcam. **Lucy Hattersley** finds out all about it...

Quick Facts

- The entire project took about 10-12 months to complete
- The files have been released under the CC BY NC licence
- Originally, an Odroid was used instead of a Raspberry Pi
- A robot was used to test the software
- The system can be used with any non-powered wheelchair

Myrijam Stoetzer and Paul Foltin, from Duisberg, Germany, have built this fantastic eye-controlled wheelchair. We caught up with Myrijam to talk about it.

"We did it because eye-tracking was so interesting," says Myrijam, "and then it occurred to us that we might steer something.

"While looking at different ways to build an eye tracker, we stumbled upon the Eyewriter project (**eyewriter.org**) from graffiti artist Tony Quan."

Tony suffers from ALS (amyotrophic lateral sclerosis) and can only move his eyes. "Tony was isolated for seven years before his friends helped him to paint and draw again using an eye tracker," Myrijam tells us. "We wanted to help people like him be able to move again, because it is so horrible to imagine you couldn't move any more."

Tracking eyes

The eye tracker is a webcam modified to use infrared light and mounted on the frame of safety glasses. "We replaced the infrared blocking filter with a piece of analogue film that blocks nearly everything but infrared light," explains Myrijam, "[then] we soldered in two infrared SMD LEDs in exchange for the white LEDs. This way, the eye will be illuminated by IR light, and the pupil reflects it back."

The camera is mounted inside a custom 3D-printed case and attached to the safety glasses frame.

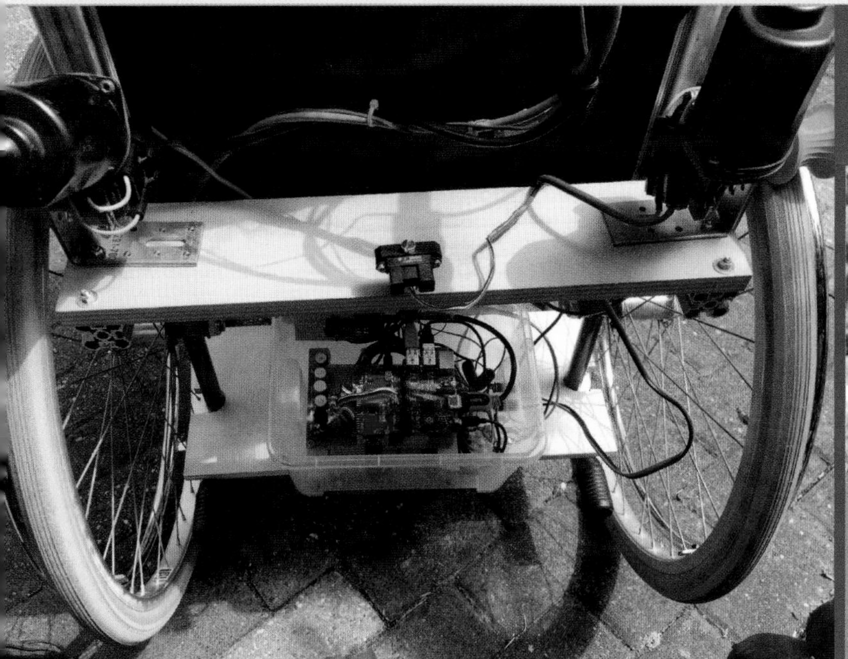

Above A windscreen wiper motor is connected to a small 3D-printed wheel. This small wheel drives the main wheelchair wheels

"The camera films the eye, and the software extracts the position of the pupil and checks if it is within the range of four areas corresponding to the four movements," says Myrijam.

In the current version, the command is read out to the user via speech synthesis, and it has to be confirmed. Then the motors are switched on, depending on the direction. When the wheelchair is moving, infrared rangefinders check for obstacles in the path.

coordinates of the pupil that has been filtered out so far: this was the biggest breakthrough."

The wheels are powered by windscreen wiper motors rescued from the scrapyard. "We wanted to keep it possible so everybody can simply rebuild it on their own," Myrijam tells us. These motors are connected to the wheelchair wheels using a small 3D-printed wheel contoured to fit around the tyre.

> "Our biggest achievement was getting the tracker to find the coordinates of the pupil"

Raspberry Pi-powered

The Raspberry Pi is used to capture images from the webcam, and OpenCV (**opencv.org**) is used for image manipulation. "The software captures images from the webcam with a frame rate of 10-12 fps," says Myrijam. The image is converted to greyscale, before being blurred and converted to black and white. "OpenCV offers a great filter that calculates the centre of gravity of a given shape," she explains. "We use this function to get the

It was a challenging project: "It was very difficult to work on the code because this is our first time of leaving Lego Mindstorms behind," says Myrijam. "Our biggest achievement was getting the tracker to find the coordinates of the pupil. After that, we knew it was possible. I learned to do 3D design, 3D printing, Linux, Python, and image processing. It was amazing to see that you can integrate computer vision into your projects and combine that with physical computing."

EYE TRACKING WHEELCHAIR

>STEP-01

Infrared camera

The eye tracker consists of a webcam modified to use infrared (IR) light. The IR blocking filter is removed, and a film is used to block everything but IR light. IR LEDs replace the standard LEDs. A 3D-printed case is used to mount the device on safety glasses.

>STEP-02

Pupil detection

The Raspberry Pi 2 snaps images of the user's eye from the IR camera at a rate of 10-12fps. A series of filters are applied to each image, increasing the contrast and making the pupil more easily identifiable. OpenCV software is used to map the coordinates of the pupil.

>STEP-03

Motor control

The wheelchair is controlled by motors salvaged from a windscreen wiper unit. These are connected directly to the wheel on the wheelchair using a custom 3D-printed profile (designed to match the wheels of the chair).

YORK HACKSPACE

Hardware hackers in the heart of York making collaborative projects and digital arts installations, and bringing maker skills to the wider community.
magpi.cc/2dTHsRB

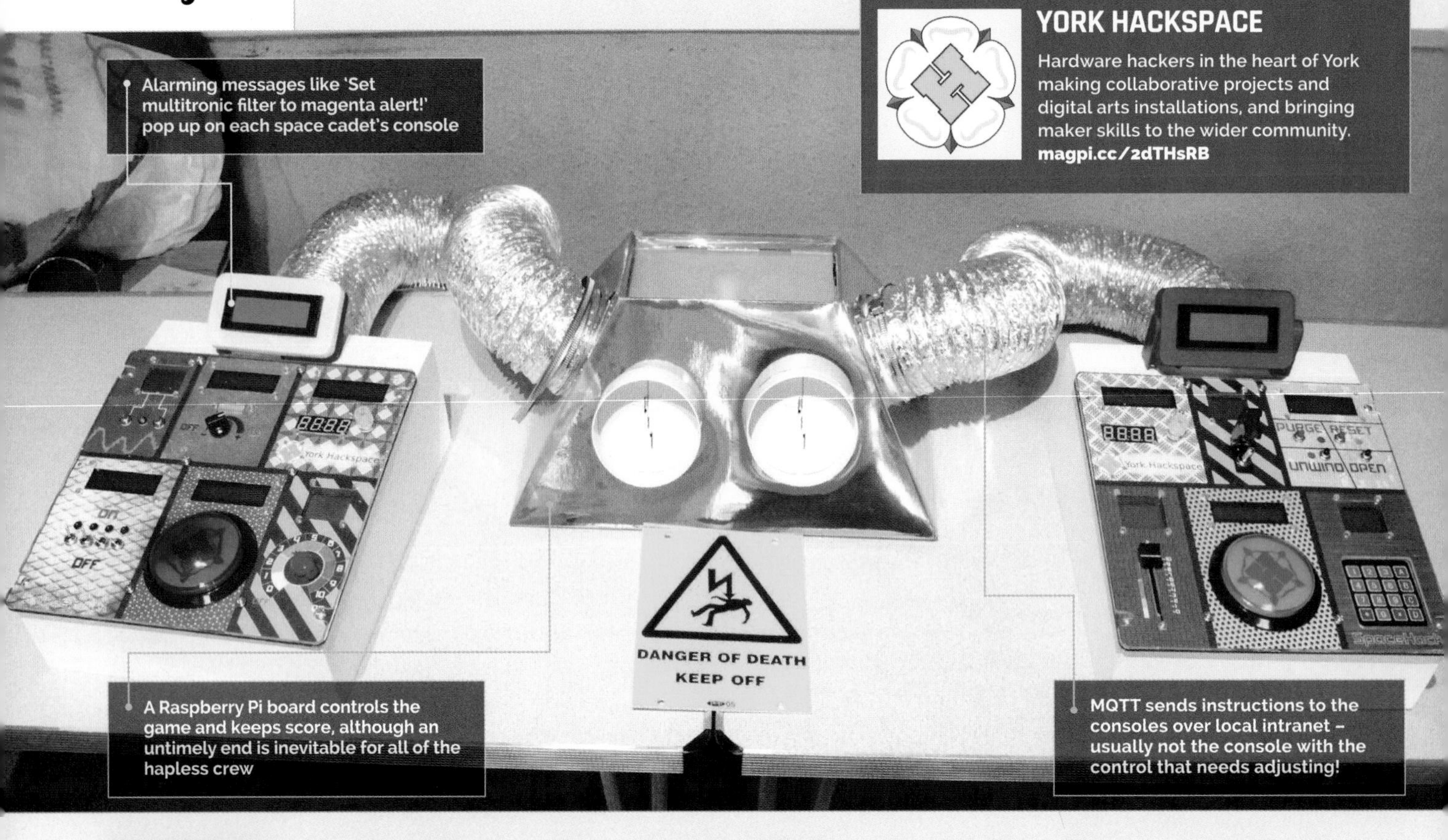

Alarming messages like 'Set multitronic filter to magenta alert!' pop up on each space cadet's console

A Raspberry Pi board controls the game and keeps score, although an untimely end is inevitable for all of the hapless crew

MQTT sends instructions to the consoles over local intranet – usually not the console with the control that needs adjusting!

SPACEHACK

Join the unfortunate trainee crew on the Starship Guppy, as things begin to go badly wrong, and chaotic fun ensues

Quick Facts

- Console One still features its original spaghetti wiring
- SpaceHack has featured at around 15 maker events
- For Towel Day it became the Infinite Improbability Drive
- The laser cutter used lives in Rob Whitfield's bedroom!
- SpaceHack uses the same communications protocol as Facebook Messenger

What other fast-paced, Pi-based console game lets you shout "Set multitronic filter to magenta alert!" to the general puzzlement of passers-by? York Hackspace have been drawing a lot of attention at maker events over the past year or so, fulfilling their aim of creating something memorable for visitors to their stand.

It was Bob Stone who suggested a physical version of Henry Smith's *Spaceteam*, a 'cooperative shouting game for phones and tablets', but given the definitive Hackspace twist with its retro-futuristic spaceship looks, and homebrew hardware and software, "it would sort of advertise itself within the room, as yelling nonsense with a sense of urgency and panic tends to draw attention in crowds."

Right SpaceHack's retro-futuristic look seemed a natural fit in the MakeFest setting of Manchester's Museum of Science and Industry

Disaster simulator

"Welcome aboard the USS Guppy, recently refurbished to the very highest standards of modern space-worthiness by some new lowest-bidding contractors we found on the net. We're proud that this venerable old boat, a veteran of many a heroic space battle, has once again been declared officially 'Good enough for Government work.' "

The hints are all there before you start your "routine pass out by an

MAKING OF THE CONSOLE GAME

>STEP-01
The console case

Heavy-duty woodwork supports a laser-cut ply top, retro-futuristic control graphics designed in Inkscape, and a fairly thick acrylic top to withstand some heavy use by baffled space cadets.

>STEP-02
Inside the console

The BeagleBone Black is a fairly dumb console, picking up its instructions from the controller, displaying instructions sent over MQTT on the LCD, and reporting control values.

>STEP-03
Pi controller

A single B+ Pi board powers the whole game, generating text, as well as sound effects, and hosting the game's MQTT broker. A network switch connects the Pi to the consoles, via spacey-looking ducting.

asteroid belt orbiting an unstable Red Giant star near the edge of the Forbidden Zone, to investigate some unusual radiation signatures."

SpaceHack's control panels have been reconfigured, and as things begin to go wrong on the space mission, emergency instructions issued by the ship's computer – showing on the console's LCD – don't seem to apply to that console's switches, dials, and buttons. The only way to avert disaster is to shout out the instructions so that fellow space cadets at one of the other three consoles can search for the right switch to flip, dial to turn, or button to push.

In a Jam

How long can disaster be staved off? There's no shortage of volunteers to find out, whenever the York team brings SpaceHack to an event. If you follow the maker events online, you'll have seen the favourable comments. Spotting a couple of familiar faces playing SpaceHack at the MOSI MakeFest, we asked them what they'd thought of the experience.

"I thought playing it was great fun and highly engaging. The intentionally confusing instructions add to the madcap antics and to me were reminiscent of TV's *The Generation Game* challenges, where contestants struggled with seemingly simple activities," Raspberry Jam's Alan O'Donohoe told us. Claire Garside invited the York team to Leeds Raspberry Jam, and was enthusiastic about SpaceHack's ability to excite people about STEM in a fun way: "Whether taking the challenge myself, or observing the wide range of contestants it entices, SpaceHack always initiates an enthusiasm and excitement for everyone through gaming with Pi. And I do mean everyone!"

> Welcome aboard the recently refurbished USS Guppy, once again declared officially 'Good enough for Government work'

If you'd like the chance to shout "Plug in the centrifugal F-screen!", then look out for SpaceHack at Derby Maker Faire on 26 October – and if you want to build your own, full details are up at **magpi.cc/2dTHzwu** for the hardware (including laser cutting and 3D printing), console software, and Raspberry Pi controller software. "Increase the omnicrontensor shell! Set multitronic filter to magenta alert!"

Below Families are naturally drawn to what's best described as 'a game of collaborative shouting'

MARIO LUKAS

Mario Lukas is a hardware hacker, computer scientist, and technology tinkerer from Aachen, Germany.
mariolukas.de

FABSCAN PI

Mario Lukas builds 3D scanners from the Raspberry Pi and off-the-shelf components. He tells **Lucy Hattersley** how it's done

Quick Facts

- All the parts cost less than $100 in total
- Commercial scanners cost around $3,000
- The FabScan software creates PLY and STL files
- The mesh files can be used to 3D-print objects
- Mario is experimenting with dual and green lasers

Few things in modern life are more fun than 3D-scanning an object, then using a 3D printer to create a copy. But 3D scanners are still very expensive to buy. FabScan is an open-source, DIY 3D laser scanner being developed by René Bohne and Mario Lukas.

Initially, FabScan was connected to an external computer, but Mario and René have recently created a Raspberry Pi version that houses all the components required inside a single box. This Raspberry Pi-powered edition means you can build a complete 3D scanner for under $100 (£65).

The FabScan project has a long history. It started out as a Bachelor's thesis by Francis Engelman at RWTH University in Aachen (Germany) in 2011. In 2014, development was taken over by Mario and René.

"The FabScan without the Raspberry Pi is an open-source, do-it-yourself 3D laser scanner," says Mario. "After a few months I realised that people had problems [getting] the FabScan software working on all the different operating systems and hardware setups.

"The FabScan uses a laser cut plywood case," continues Mario. There is a stepper motor connected to a turntable in the middle." Inside the case is a 5mW red laser and Logitech Lc270 webcam. The laser and a webcam are mounted in the front of the case. An Arduino with a FabScan shield controls the stepper motor and laser.

You place an object on the turntable so the laser runs across its surface. As the turntable rotates, the webcam monitors the movement of the laser and creates a point cloud of data. The data is turned into a 3D mesh, and this file can be exported and used in 3D software.

"Since I introduced the Raspberry Pi to the FabScan project, the webcam [has

The Raspberry Pi is housed inside the box and runs a web interface. You connect to the latter remotely to begin the scanning process

The wooden case contains a motorized turntable that rotates the object being scanned. It is currently controlled by an Arduino, although a custom Pi HAT is being developed

A 5mW red laser is fixed in the corner of the FabScan. It projects a line directly across the turntable. A Pi Camera Module is used to monitor the laser as the object is rotated

HOW DOES IT WORK?

>STEP-01
Box construction

The FabScan box is laser-cut from wooden parts. A stepper motor, controlled by Arduino, is used to control the wooden turntable. The laser is mounted in the corner and emits a line diagonally across the turntable.

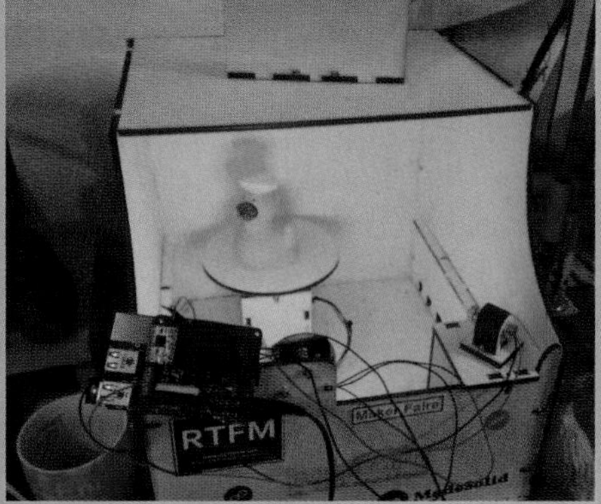

>STEP-02
The Raspberry Pi

The Raspberry Pi runs the scanning software, and a Raspberry Pi Camera Module is used instead of a webcam. Using a Pi enables the FabScan to become a self-contained 3D scanner.

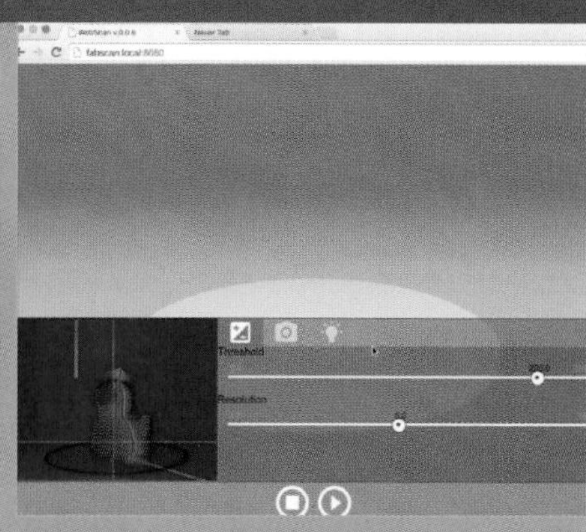

>STEP-03
Scanning the duck

An object (in this case a rubber duck) is placed on the turntable. The web software is used to connect to the Pi-powered FabScan. As the duck rotates, the camera monitors the laser and uses it to create the scan.

been] replaced by the Pi Camera Module," Mario tells us. "We are developing a FabScan Pi HAT to replace the Arduino and the FabScan Shield as well."

You can build a FabScan case yourself using sheets of wood, and a complete bill of materials can be found at **magpi.cc/2dTI8WT**. Alternatively, a FabScan Cube Kit v2 + Electronics bundle can also be ordered from German-based distributor Watterott (**magpi.cc/2dTIjSi**) for €105 (£77).

> Introducing the Raspberry Pi to the FabScan project was a good approach to improve the usability

"Anybody who wants to build a FabScan Pi should order the parts and build it," insists Mario. "We are trying to keep the things as simple as possible, and introducing the Raspberry Pi to the FabScan project was a good approach to improve the usability.

"Most of the work was to write new software for the FabScan," continues Mario. "The software provides a JavaScript-based web-enabled user interface for scanning. The user can call the local FabScan in a browser and the user interface will show up.

"During the software developing process, I scanned a lot of different rubber ducks, other plastic animals, figures made of gypsum (plaster of Paris), and stuff lying around in my workroom.

"After a scan, you will get a one-to-one sized three-dimensional model of the scanned object," explains Mario. "The current FabScan Pi software can export the model in [the] STL file format that is mostly used by 3D printers."

Pushing forward with the FabScan project is a challenge, but Mario and René remain unperturbed. "At the moment, the FabScan project is spread all over the web," explains Mario. "In the upcoming weeks, I will try to create a website where all corresponding threads run together.

"Currently I am working on some DEB packages for Raspbian to keep the installation process as simple as possible," reveals Mario. "The next step is releasing a Raspbian image with a pre-installed version of the FabScan Pi software. I also have a huge to-do list with new features mentioned by the FabScan community."

Above The Raspberry Pi 2 has enough power for a FabScan to work without being attached to another computer

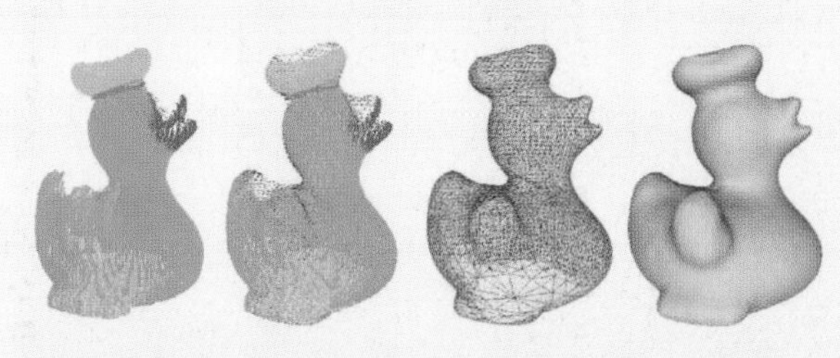

Above The FabScan software is used to create a 3D mesh from the point cloud data detected from the scan

Place your hand over the Pi and, in turn, the ultrasonic sensor to start making noise

All the sound output is done by this old PC speaker, which requires no extra power

Apparently it can lag a bit on this original Model B after some time, but it will work a lot better on a Pi 2

LINUS FORSLID

A Swedish student currently studying Computer Game Design at Stockholm University, Linus has an interest in electronics projects.

youtu.be/-q-D6V8eFZo

ULTRASONIC THEREMIN

An inventive use of the Raspberry Pi that makes use of the kind of components you might have lying around the workshop

Quick Facts

- Linus had been using his Raspberry Pi as a HTPC
- This was his first electronics project of this type
- It only took him an evening to make and two hours to fine-tune
- It's held together with electrical tape, which is not recommended
- Linus hopes to add light guides for better accuracy

Thinking outside the box is what we like here at *The MagPi*. The Raspberry Pi is so versatile and so open that you can do so much with it that perhaps other people wouldn't have dreamt of before. So here's a good question: with a Raspberry Pi, some speakers, and an ultrasonic distance sensor used for robotics, what would you make? Linus Forslid decided to build a type of theremin.

"A theremin is a device that measures distances to objects nearby and turns that into sound, so that when you move your hands around it, you can generate music," Linus explains. It's not exactly like a normal theremin, though. "Unlike a classic theremin, my project uses an ultrasound sensor rather than measuring electrical fields with antennas, and currently my project only has a single sensor, so you can only control the tone it produces. Eventually, I plan to add another so that the beat can also be manually controlled."

Theremins were used to create the eerie, creepy music for classic sci-fi films. Due to this and its unusual method of operation, the theremin has become intriguing to many musicians and techies, including Linus:

"I've always wanted a theremin, from the first day I heard of it. It's just such a cool thing. As it turns out, though, an actual theremin is not cheap or easy to build, but this project was easily doable and I had almost all of the components at home already, so the cost was minimal as well. I decided to use a PC speaker instead of the Pi's own audio jack and an external speaker, mostly because I could, in addition to it not requiring an additional power source."

It's all hooked up to the GPIO ports rather than using any USB speakers or sensors

> I've always wanted a theremin, from the first day I heard of it. It's just such a cool thing

The hardware is one thing, but actually translating it to sound, surely that takes a bit more work on the code to get it operational?

"Not really, I think." Linus adapted some pre-existing code for the project. "The script that controls the theremin is coded in C using wiringPi, and it took maybe an hour to get it working. I've spent a couple of hours beyond that just tweaking the numbers to try out different sounds and find one I like. I wouldn't say it was complex, even if the tuning took a while."

The whole process is deceptively simple then, even though it's hardly your typical Pi-based project. There are a few caveats, however, and Linus's Pi-powered theremin could do with a few improvements, as he explains:

"It's surprisingly hard to operate well, as you need a very steady hand and good aim to get the exact tone you are after... I plan to add another sensor to control the beat of the sound. Right now, it is set entirely by the script, which means it's basically static. By allowing the user to control the beat, my hope is that it will actually be useful as a musical instrument."

CREATE MUSIC

>STEP-01
Wave your hand

The ultrasonic sensor measures the distance to the closest surface in its range quite precisely. Your hand acts as this surface, and moving it up and down creates a difference in measured distance.

>STEP-02
Translate the data

The distance measured is translated to a number, which is supplied to the script. The range is between zero and 120 centimetres, so there's a wide range of sounds the system can make.

>STEP-03
Make a sound

The value is converted into an output signal via the script, which is then played through the speaker. It changes in almost real-time, so moving your hand around changes the tune dramatically.

Six Raspberry Pi boards are housed together inside the enclosure
An Ethernet router is used to connect the devices together
One of the Raspberry Pi units is the master; it controls the other Pi boards
D-Link

SUNG-TAEK KIM

Sung-Taek Kim is a big-data engineer, enthusiastic about solving problems in funny and unique ways. He is currently focused on building a great developer experience.
magpi.cc/2dTJHUR

PI SPARK BIG DATA CLUSTER

One data scientist shows us how to string six Raspberry Pis together to build a supercomputer and experiment with big data

Quick Facts

- Pis aside, the parts only cost around $60
- 106 screws are needed for the enclosure
- A cluster of Raspberry Pis is also known as a 'Bramble'
- GHCQ has the largest Pi Bramble: 66 boards
- China's Tianhe-2 is the biggest supercomputer: 3,120,000 cores

The Raspberry Pi is great for learning computer science, but there's one area that's big news but requires big computers, and that's 'big data'.

Big data software typically runs on clusters of networked computers, working together to perform the heavy lifting required. This clustered nature makes learning big data tricky, because you need several computers wired together to practise. Sung-Taek Kim, a software engineer from Korea, decided that the Raspberry Pi would be perfectly suited to the task. "Raspberry Pi is a great education platform to learn how big data software works," he tells us. "It is [comparatively] slow and low-powered, [so] that you would have hands-on experiences when your data manipulation methods execute as planned."

In fact, the light performance of the Raspberry Pi becomes an advantage when learning big data techniques. "Once you miss a small detail," explains Sung-Taek, "you feel the operation processes slow down."

"Sending data across [a] network takes time," he adds. "All the CPUs in your cluster compete for resources such as memory or disk [space], and a node or two could suddenly refuse to work, just like [in] a Google-class data centre cluster." He explains that the relative slowness of a Pi cluster is actually an advantage, enabling you to prepare for such events.

Sung-Taek's cluster is based around six Raspberry Pi 2 boards wired together with Ethernet cables via a D-Link 8-port Gigabit Desktop Switch.

"Theoretically, you would only need one Raspberry Pi," says Sung-Taek, "since Spark exploits the [nature] of a master-slave scheme. Prepare a Raspberry Pi as a slave and your laptop as a master. Connect two Raspberry Pi devices and you have a Spark cluster."

Sung-Taek suggests using between three to eight Raspberry Pi boards for the project. "Once you have more than ten Raspberry Pis," he says, "it's a headache to find a proper power source, to arrange the network and power cord."

The hardest part seems to be building the enclosure. Sung-Taek hosts schematics on GitHub (**magpi.cc/2dTIn4z**), but accuracy is vital. Even a half millimetre offset in the cutting template could render one of the acrylic tiers useless, he warns.

as well." Java is another must, and the listed software packages include NumPY, Scipy, and Scikit-Learn. On top of that, you'll be learning the MapReduce programming model, which is where you'll encounter Hadoop and Spark.

They are all skills worth learning, though: big data is at the forefront of computer science and is an interesting area to study and work in. "The Raspberry Pi cluster lets you prepare [for] events that could take place in a production environment," says Sung-Taek. "Further, the cluster lets you easily find where to apply optimisation work, since its hardware resource is limited indeed."

> "Once you have more than ten Raspberry Pis, it's a headache to find a proper power source"

Aside from the Raspberry Pi units, the project isn't expensive. The power supply, network switch, cables, screws, and enclosure only came to around $60. A complete list of materials is available via a *Make:* article (**bit.ly/1J2jpDf**) written by Sung-Taek.

The software requirements are quite intense. "Python is a must," he says, "In order to fully exploit what a Spark cluster provides, it would be a good idea to learn Scala

"You might want to plan carefully and start with a small number of nodes," he advises. "Pay attention to details in each step, and make sure your plan is checked with specifications. Once you've successfully built [a cluster], make a bigger one. One of the best strategies to avoid costly mistakes is to follow and observe what others have done."

Below Six Raspberry Pi devices are used to build the supercomputer

BUILDING A PI SPARK CLUSTER

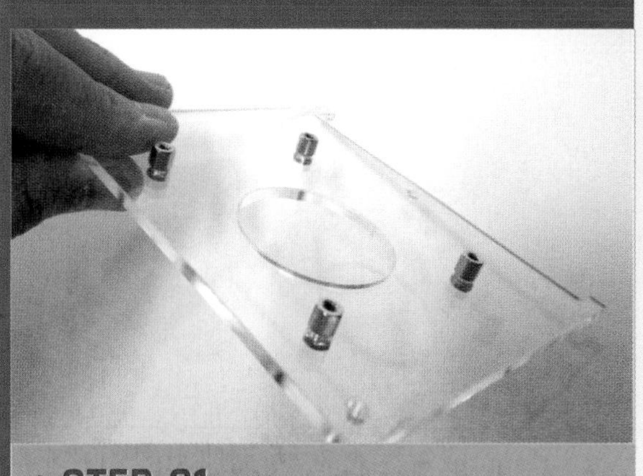

>STEP-01
Building the case

The schematics for the boards can be found on Sung-Taek's website. You can use wood, synthetic, or acrylic panel to cut out the shapes, so long as each is no thicker than 3mm and strong enough to hold a USB charger.

>STEP-02
Cluster assembly

The Raspberry Pis are attached to the boards using M2.5 screws. Then use 5mm pillar screws and hex nuts to screw the boards together.

>STEP-03
Hooking it up

The six-port router is held in the middle of the boards. Each Raspberry Pi connects to the router via Ethernet. Notice that the case leaves enough space for a power socket for each Raspberry Pi.

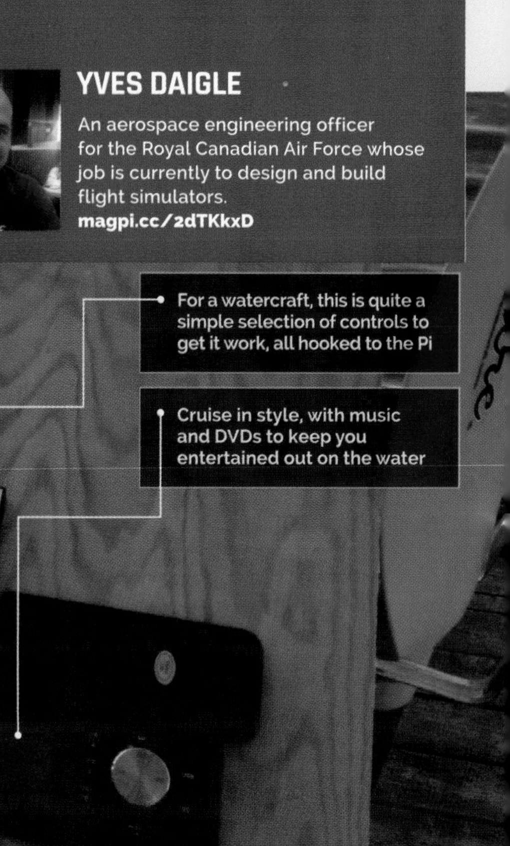

YVES DAIGLE

An aerospace engineering officer for the Royal Canadian Air Force whose job is currently to design and build flight simulators.
magpi.cc/2dTKkxD

For a watercraft, this is quite a simple selection of controls to get it work, all hooked to the Pi

Cruise in style, with music and DVDs to keep you entertained out on the water

The most important part about such a craft is that it floats. And it does

RAFTBERRY

Escape a desert island with your volleyball BFF in style, or just pootle around a lake with some pals, with this Raspberry Pi-powered raft

Quick Facts

- The raftBerry had been planned for about two years
- Yves hasn't programmed since university
- The raftBerry has all the required boating safety equipment
- Yves wants to add crazy lighting and 'look to steer' systems
- For the military, Yves has used 22 Raspberry Pis

Picnics are fun. You fish a cooler bag from the back of a cupboard along with some half-forgotten freezer blocks from the ice tray and fit in as many sandwiches, sausage rolls, and cans of soda as you can. After grabbing some family or friends, you find a nice spot and eat outside. Wonderful, aside from the inevitable invasion by ants, but still great. What if you could take ants out of the equation, though? You could if you were somehow able to have a picnic out in the middle of a lake. Meet Yves Daigle and his raftBerry project...

"The idea is to create a fully autonomous electrically propelled floating dock, controlled by a Raspberry Pi, to drive us around our lake," Yves tells us. As you can see from the resulting picture of Yves and some friends enjoying a meal on the floating dock, the idea has come to fruition.

As an aerospace engineer serving in the Canadian Air Force, Yves is used to creating complex equipment, so it's no surprise that this side-project is not exactly simple as well:

"The control system has two available modes that can be selected via a switch on the console: manual or autonomous. The dock uses two static motors for propulsion that can also steer the dock via differential thrust.

"The Pi reads inputs via the GPIO from the arcade joystick, emergency shutdown button, and mode select switch. Each motor is independently controlled by five automotive relays, three of which are used to set the speed, and the remaining two are used in an H-bridge configuration to set the motors in forward or reverse. The GPIO output pins control a small eight-channel relay board, which in turn controls these ten automotive relays. The whole system, from motors to control panel, is designed to be removed from the dock after every trip, using a hand truck."

The whole thing took him a month to finish after he started to properly work on it and also includes a DVD player, a table, seating, and a camping stove. Less of a picnic, then, and more a floating campsite.

A floating picnic for everyone, thanks to a little hacking

It looks like a phone cabinet, but everything within each subsection is quite simple

"Manual mode works flawlessly," Yves explains. "The relays do get quite hot and full speed appears to not be as powerful as it was with the original control head. I suspect the relays are nearing max load and are causing some voltage drops. I plan to acquire larger relays. The motors may be a little underpowered."

Automatic mode doesn't quite work right now, but Yves is working on it. As well as using Raspberry Pis at home and on watercraft, he's been using them in his job: "We have 22 of them performing various tasks at the moment. I've found that Pis are several orders of magnitude more cost-effective than commercial alternatives. Saving taxpayer dollars is something I take quite seriously."

If you want to see some of the build, along with the raftBerry in action, you can check out the video of it on YouTube: **youtu.be/FZvU3U1wZWo**

AUTOMATICALLY DRIVING MR DAIGLE

>STEP-01

Plan a route

Auto mode should work by allowing you to first create a custom map in Google Maps, then exporting the map to a .kml file the raftBerry can use.

>STEP-02

Start to navigate

The raftBerry uses GPS data to compare your location to the first waypoint, and produces a method to move to the waypoint. This is updated once per second.

>STEP-03

Enjoy the ride

The raftBerry waits until you're within ten metres of the waypoint before calculating the route to the next one. Keep an eye out for anything in your path, though!

MATT REED

Matt Reed lives in Nashville, Tennessee, and is a creative technologist at RedPepper.
mcreed.com

The Raspberry Pi is housed vertically inside the Mason jar

The LED lights flash in time with BitTorrent sync activity to produce the red glowing effect when the Pi is preserving files

The lid is connected to the wooden base, and holes are drilled in it for the LEDs and cables

MASON JAR PRESERVE

Matt Reed backs up his family photos in a Mason jar. He tells Lucy Hattersley how to preserve digital memories in style

Quick Facts

- The Mason jar was invented in 1858 by tinsmith John L Mason
- You can buy Mason Jars in the UK from Kilner – **kilnerjar.co.uk**
- Don't overclock the Raspberry Pi, as it could overheat
- The only storage limitation is what you attach to the Raspberry Pi
- Matt used Node.js to get the LEDs to work in time with BitTorrent

Matt Reed, a professional web developer and maker from West Virginia, has created this amazing project. The Raspberry Pi-powered Mason Jar Preserve is the most stylish backup solution we've ever seen.

At this point, *The MagPi*'s non-US readers might be wondering what on earth a Mason jar is. "They are industrial-grade glass jars with a sealable lid that were originally used at home to preserve foods throughout the winter," says Matt. "Mason jars allowed for foods that were harvested in the summer to last all year round. Who doesn't want tasty fried okra in February?

"In my great-grandmother's basement, there were shelves and shelves of various-sized jars filled with everything from pickled beets to you-name-it preserves."

But rather than preserve tasty foodstuffs, Matt's Mason jar preserves Matt's family memories.

Canning a Raspberry Pi

The idea came to Matt at work: "I had a few various-sized Mason jars sitting around. One day I just grabbed the largest jar and slid the Pi inside. It fit, even with a little room to spare!" Building the Mason Jar Preserve was fairly

PRESERVING YOUR PI

>STEP-01

Building the base

The Raspberry Pi fits inside the Mason jar, but it needs to be held upright. For this, Matt cut a six-inch base. He then sanded it so it had round edges (reminiscent of an Apple TV).

>STEP-02

Put a lid on it

The lid of the Mason jar has a hole drilled in the centre. This is used to secure it with a nut and washer. Then four more holes are drilled to house the LED lights. The power and Ethernet cables are run through another hole.

>STEP-03

Putting it together

The BitTorrent software is installed and set up to back up a folder on other local computers. Finally, the Mason jar is screwed on top of the lid and is lit up by the LEDs.

straightforward: "I used a saw to cut the base into a square, a sander to round it off, and a drill to make the LED, Ethernet, and power holes. A few trips to Home Depot for antique drawer pulls, some rubber feet, brackets and screws, and that was it."

Matt's Mason Jar Preserve connects via Ethernet, but you could use WiFi. "I am still curious how much glass would affect the signal," he tells us. "In the end I chose Ethernet for transfer speed, availability, simplicity, and reliability. Also, because I was low on USB WiFi dongles. Like, zero."

Powered by BitTorrent

Matt used BitTorrent to create the backup software. "It's similar to Dropbox," he says, "but instead of a centralised server in the cloud, you connect two or more of your own devices directly together over the BitTorrent protocol. Just like Dropbox, connected BitTorrent sync machines all sync up a specified folder on their system. So basically, it's free and the storage is only limited to the connected storage."

Unlike BitTorrent file sharing, Matt's system is completely private. "Whenever you create a sync folder, it gets a unique string of letters and numbers," explains Matt. "This key uniquely identifies it over the BitTorrent sync protocol. Keys can provide either read/write access or read-only access to anyone you give it to. You generally want to keep them safe. If I shared that key publicly, then I'd have a public file-sharing seed similar to the BitTorrent everyone knows and loves."

Matt uses his the Mason Jar Preserve to back up family photos and videos. "I really just wanted one more layer of redundant backup of things like the birth of our kids, wedding photos, and various family-related media. It uses the Raspberry Pi's SD card for storage. Therefore, the larger the SD card you put in your Pi, the more you can store."

We think the end result is glorious. When the Mason Jar Preserve is syncing, it animates the LEDs using the Node.js script, BitTorrent Sync API, and the GPIO pins. When it sits idle, they glow red. "I wanted it to look like the jar was filled with red raspberry preserves," says Matt. "It especially looks great at night."

Some furniture fittings from Home Depot were used to embellish the design

The Mason jar looks especially good in low light when its LEDs are illuminated

CHRIS DUERDEN

A mechanical engineer with a fresh law degree, and experience of a lot of electronic projects and systems.
imgur.com/a/8uO6E

If you're sick of bad *Super Mario Bros 3* levels in *Super Mario Maker*, try out the original on this 3.5″ screen with many other games

There are enough buttons to play all major home consoles up to the PlayStation

A mixture of old and new: a GBA volume control and USB input for loading ROMs

SUPER GAMEGIRL

Want a better handheld games console? The answer may be to make one yourself with a Raspberry Pi and a 3D printer

Quick Facts

- This was Chris's first Raspberry Pi project
- The volume wheel is from a Game Boy Advance
- Chris created custom PCBs for this project
- Unfortunately, it doesn't run Nintendo 64 games well
- Chris's favourite game to play on it is *Super Mario Bros 3*

Over the past few issues, we've covered a handful of retro gaming projects of varying types: a refurbished SNES, a 3D-printed NES, a Power Glove running games, and so on. While these are all definitely cool projects, you know what's *really* cool? A portable retro gaming machine! In the past, this spot has typically been taken up by the very hackable Sony PSP, but Chris Duerden made the decision to go down a much more homebrew route by making his machine from scratch using the same Raspberry Pi that powers those other retro gaming projects.

"My project is a Raspberry Pi 2-powered Game Boy-looking thing," Chris tells us. "It runs RetroPie, so it can play games from a lot of different systems. The goal was to have enough buttons to support PlayStation games, have a 3.5″ screen, and enough battery life for seven hours of play while being smaller than the original Game Boy!"

The seven hours requirement is so it can survive a long plane trip, something modern handhelds can't quite handle. "I love retro gaming and wanted something to do while travelling," Chris explains. "I didn't want to have to bring a case full of game cartridges or AA batteries with me everywhere, and wanted it all-in-one and easy to use for anyone that would play it."

The idea came to him after learning about RetroPie, and he began to tinker with the Raspberry Pi. The whole thing is custom-made, and it starts with a Raspberry Pi 2 and a 3D-printed case. The case takes the Game Boy as its base inspiration, adding more face buttons as well as shoulder buttons to accommodate PlayStation (and other console) games. There's a 3.5″ screen, a 6000mAh portable battery, amps, speakers, jacks, LEDs, and various buttons and

The buttons on the rear are very basic, but Chris is unsure how to improve them

> Enough battery life for seven hours of play while being smaller than the original Game Boy!

switches cannibalised from a NES and several Game Boys.

"It was complex to get everything to fit and work together," Chris admits. "I designed the housing in SolidWorks, wrote programs for the Pi in Python, programmed the AVR in C, designed custom circuit boards, lots of breadboard time, some talking to Adafruit to see what their products can and can't do, etc. But it was relatively easy to build."

The result works well enough for Chris, with power on and off switches, games loading from a USB port on the side, and the ability to charge the battery from the bottom of the case with a micro-USB cable.

Right now, Chris is making a second one for his girlfriend and will eventually write up a full rundown on how to make your own, including slightly improved plans for the circuit boards. Soon you'll be able to make long trips much more interesting.

THE MECHANICAL PROCESS

>STEP-01
On standby

The power switch is controlled by an ATtiny chip that stays in sleep mode until the power is switched on, which then wakes it up so it starts to provide power to the screen.

>STEP-02
While it's on

The Raspberry Pi has a piece of code that lets the ATtiny know that it is on, and it boots straight to RetroPie. The power switch begins a shutdown procedure.

>STEP-03
Turning off

When the ATtiny is told the Pi is shutting down, it turns off the screen and grounds the power, turning off the regulator before going back into sleep mode.

MAC MINI PI

Arguably the smallest, cutest classic Mac-inspired project, the Mac Mini Pi is actually much more than a swanky case for your Raspberry Pi...

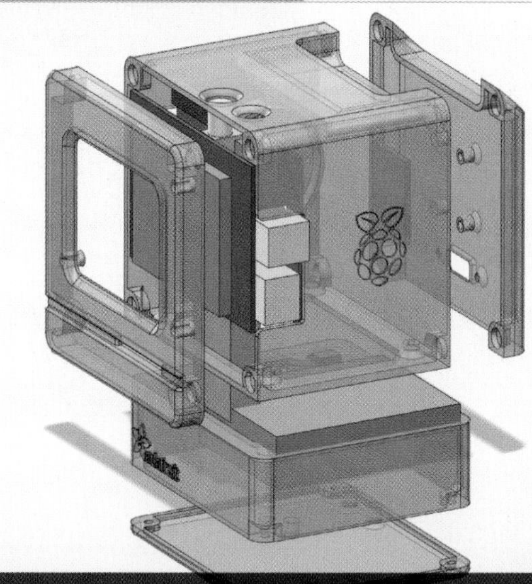

Above The CAD design of the Mac Classic-style chassis itself. You could send the design off to a 3D printing service or pop into your local makerspace to get it printed

Adafruit knows a thing or two about building impressive Raspberry Pi projects, and the Ruiz brothers' Mac Mini Pi – originally inspired by RetroMacCast's John Badger – is certainly no exception. Besides being an unashamedly cute design, this tiny Mac is much more than a fancy case for your Raspberry Pi – it's a fully functioning emulator, so you can relive those Mac OS 7 glory days (or experience them for the first time). The software used for emulation is a flavour of Mini vMac (**magpi.cc/2dq3f0j**) that perfectly emulates early Macs that ran Motorola's 680x0 microprocessor. The software runs happily alongside Raspbian, too.

Adafruit.com's guide includes everything you need to build the project yourself, including detailed instructions and the files you need for the 3D print (you can use a 3D printing service if you lack a printer of your own). Under the hood, the project uses a standard Raspberry Pi Model B, the 320×240 3.2″ PiTFT screen, a 3.7V lithium-ion battery, and a simple audio amp, among other things. Some basic soldering skills are a must and you can expect to spend most of the weekend on the build itself (it's fiddly!).

You can check out this amazing project in its entirety at: **magpi.cc/2dq4e0x**

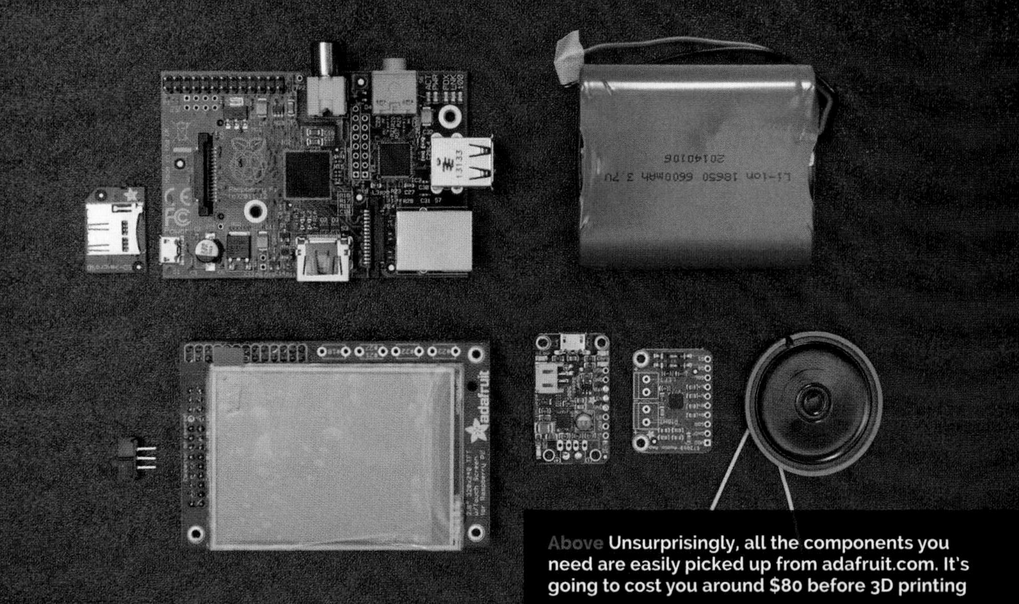

Above Unsurprisingly, all the components you need are easily picked up from adafruit.com. It's going to cost you around $80 before 3D printing

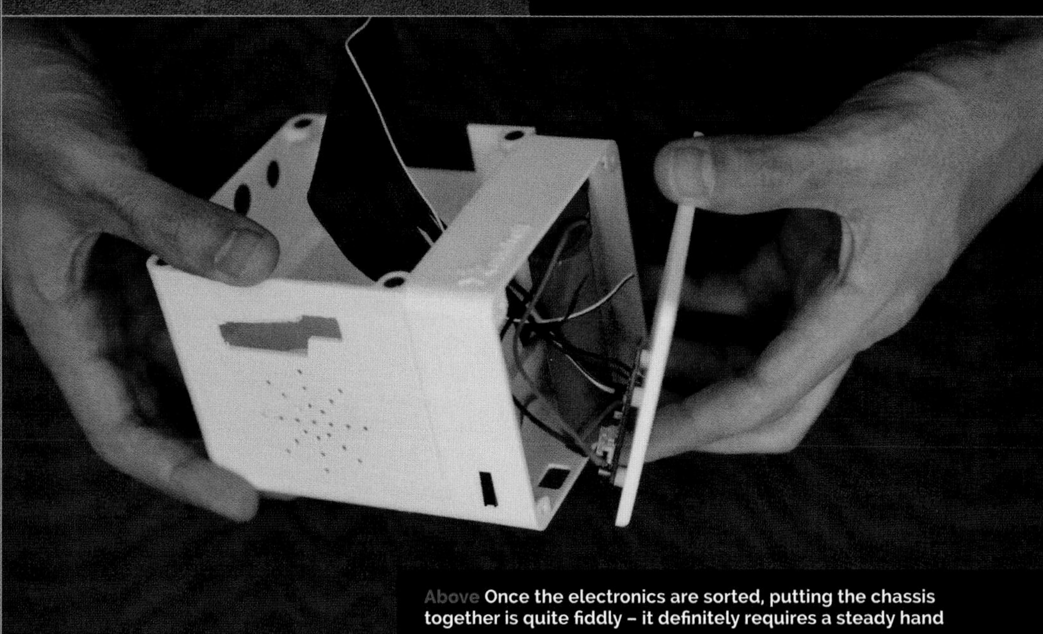

Above Once the electronics are sorted, putting the chassis together is quite fiddly – it definitely requires a steady hand

MARK BUTTLE

Mark is a software engineer from Shropshire with a passion for woodworking and electronics – combining both in this project.
bit.ly/1hZFUmu

PI-POWERED CNC MACHINE

How do you combine a passion for beautiful woodworking with an interest in electronics? **Mark Buttle** did it with a Pi-powered CNC machine...

Quick Facts

- The project started as a challenge from a colleague
- This was Mark's first Pi project
- The controller wires terminate in aircraft connectors
- The power supply comes from an LED lighting set
- A buffer prevents leakage current triggering end-stop relays

Rural Shropshire, one of the coldest and wettest parts of England, is home to many makers and inveterate tinkerers, with plenty of time holed up in the maker shed, allowing genius to ponder and grow. In fact, the county has a history of makers and thinkers, being the place of origin both of Charles Darwin, and of the industrial cradle of Ironbridge.

Mark Buttle is an engineer who loves to work with wood. His home is full of lovingly handmade furniture, as well as quirky items like a fridge-freezer masquerading as a traditional red telephone box (naturally, there are plans for a familiar blue police telephone box, too). But Mark is a software engineer by day, and also interested in electronics, so is happy to mix technology with traditional crafting skills.

Mark had originally bought an Arduino as a birthday present for a colleague and, intrigued by the board's possibilities, had then bought one for himself. The colleague set a challenge, to see who could come up with the most interesting project, and Mark began looking into building a Computer Numerated Control (CNC) machine for woodworking.

It soon became apparent that the Arduino, while ideal for controlling the stepper motors, would need some extra help, and Mark certainly didn't have time to write all of the software himself. Research online turned up both Grbl – the open-source controller code that runs on the Arduino – and the Zapmaker controller software, which is written for the Raspberry Pi.

"I'd wanted a Pi for a while," Mark tells us. "This is the first

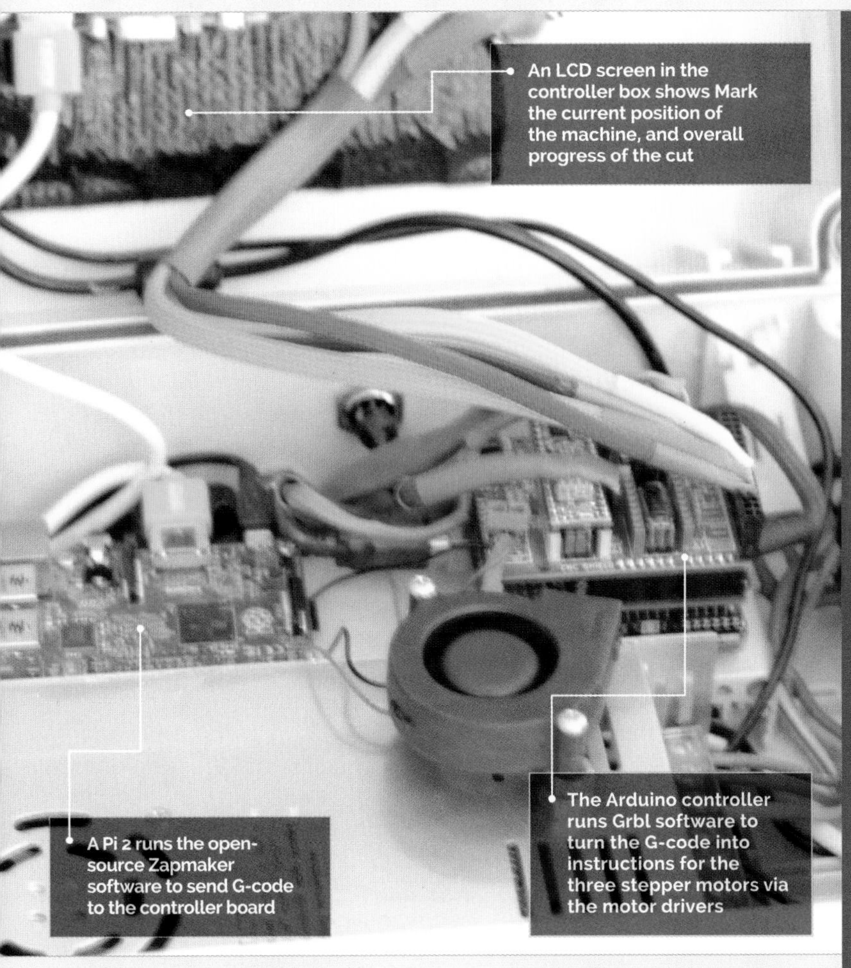
An LCD screen in the controller box shows Mark the current position of the machine, and overall progress of the cut

A Pi 2 runs the open-source Zapmaker software to send G-code to the controller board

The Arduino controller runs Grbl software to turn the G-code into instructions for the three stepper motors via the motor drivers

thing that I've done with it. It brings together my passion for electronics and for woodworking."

The build

"I've made the complete CNC out of marine ply, all handcrafted, and mounted a DeWalt router to do the cutting," Mark reveals, "using the Raspberry Pi 2 as the controller, which runs a bit of software called CNC Zapmaker, which passes the instructions in G-code to an Arduino Uno. This runs a version of Grbl controller, which has a CNC shield connected to it that drives the three X Y Z stepper motors."

"This is just an overview," admits Mark. "The controller and machine took about two months to build: mainly evenings." In that time, Mark also had to build the physical apparatus of the cutting machine – a 1000mm long, 500mm wide, 700mm high framework, with tracks for clamping the wood, trapezoidal bars for the stepper motors to drive across each axis, and a lot of cabling.

With 200 steps per revolution (on the current setting), the motors allow precision control of movement. One revolution moves the cutting tool 2mm, so one step is just 10 micrometres! – with one thou (a thousandth of an inch), the traditional measure of fine tolerances in engineering, equalling circa 25 micrometres, this is extremely precise for woodcutting. Theoretically re-gearing the stepper motors could improve this again, but that fine a level of detail would be lost against the size of the grain of the wood.

The stepper motors – around £12 each from China – have a power of 107oz holding torque; add in Mark's use of trapezoid rods and heavy-duty fixing bars, rather than the threaded rod and drawer rails used in budget CNC home-builds, and we have a strongly engineered machine that's built to last. Yet, including all the electronics as well as the other hardware, the build price was around £400. A decade ago, you'd find similar

RASPBERRY PI CNC IN ACTION

>STEP-01
At the drawing board

The first task is to work through the design in your choice of CAD software, then let it generate the G-code needed. FreeCAD users will need a CAM plug-in or HeeksCNC.

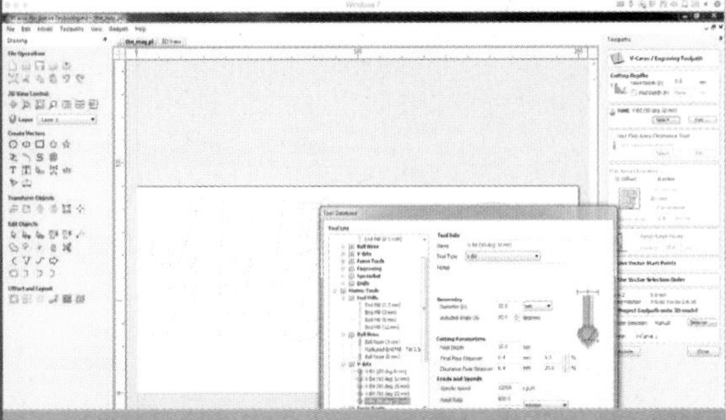

>STEP-02
Grbl

Mark uses AutoCAD, which enables him to select the tool bit used, as well as plan the cutting path. The recently open-sourced Blender CAM is one possible alternative for this.

>STEP-03
MagPi meets timber

The Pi creates the Grbl code used by the Arduino, which handles putting the router in the correct places to turn our 3D design into a sculpted or carved piece of wood.

The frame holds everything together

commercial machines costing well into five figures – these are great times for makers. Indeed some of those obsolescent commercial CNCs are being repurposed with homebrew controllers by those without the time to follow Mark's total DIY route.

In control

In the controller, a touchscreen interfaces to the CNC controller, running on a Pi 2 with Zapmaker software: on screen, the control software's grey, pleasingly industrial panel complements the electrical box used as a casing. The Pi communicates with an Arduino Uno board, which uses Grbl to control the stepper motors. The Grbl handling of the Arduino is quite sophisticated – you can send a one-line command such as 'a circle to here, of this diameter,' and it will work out the cuts for you.

The power supply is a heavy-duty 24V unit from some LED lights. 12V and 5V step-down transformers provide power for the LCD screen, Raspberry Pi, stepper motors, Arduino, and shields. The shield controlling the motors can become very hot, and so a small fan is used to cool it.

Eagle-eyed readers will have spotted the extra board between the Arduino and the controller shield – this is a buffer board installed after the early prototype kept switching off: "Someone said you need a filter between the Arduino and the CNC controller board," says Mark. A filtering board stops current bleeding through from the motors to the relays for the end stops and switching off the device. This has fixed the problem: "I've checked the voltage drop now on the end stops; it stays at a constant 5 volts."

Making the cut

Before use, G-code is needed to give the coordinates for cutting. The logo in the pictures was converted into a black and white image, then into vectors – as well as optimising the cutting path, and the correct cutting head. FreeCAD is used by many CNC makers, but needs some form of CAM plug-in to generate the G-code and the cutting path.

The G-code is just lines of coordinates. The CAD/CAM software has the job of generating it, together with the cutting path that makes the most sense – a CNC machine's version of computing's famous travelling salesman

BUILDING A PI CNC MACHINE

>STEP-01
Stepper motors

Stepper motors – dividing each 2mm revolution of the trapezoidal bars into 200 steps – position a DeWalt router in the X, Y, and Z planes, with an accuracy of 10 micrometres.

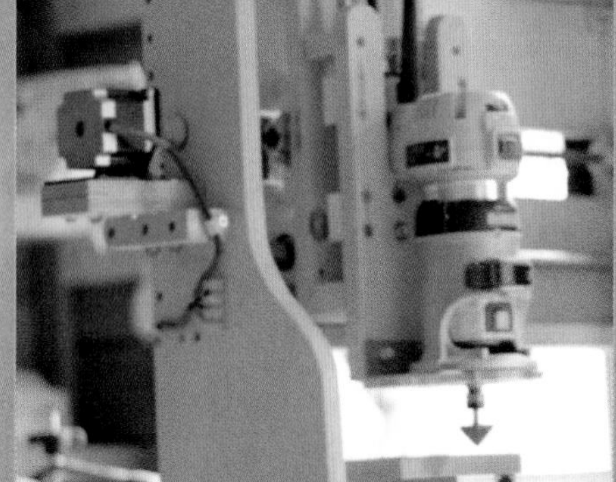

>STEP-02
In the frame

Hand-cut from 18mm (¾") marine ply, the frame rigidly holds the trapezoidal bars, stepper motors, and router, as well as keeping the work in place with clamps in the built-in tracks.

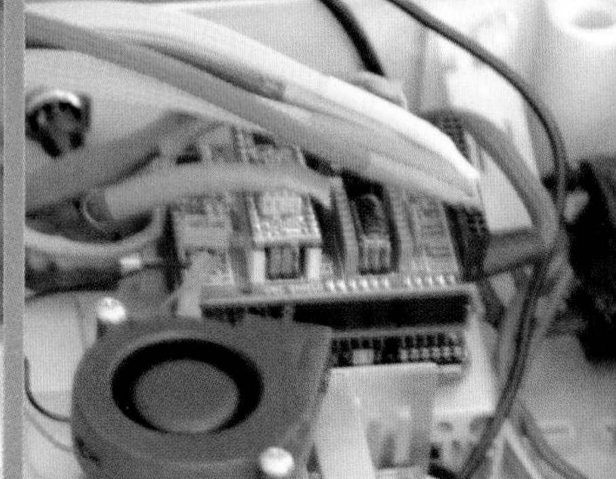

>STEP-03
Arduino

An Arduino Uno runs Grbl software to accept cutting instructions in G-code and turn them into electrical pulses to control the stepper motors and position the router precisely in three planes.

problem to find the optimal route between multiple destinations.

Mark is a long-time user of AutoCAD. While it's an expensive option for anyone buying just for a CNC machine, it readily provides everything you need if you're already a user: "On my Mac, I design any shape or carving and convert the 2D or 3D model into G-code, then Wi-Fi it or USB-stick it to the Raspberry Pi. Using the touchscreen, I start the controller up and off it goes."

There are also tripper switches at the end of each trapezoidal guiding bar, to stop the router should it ever be sent to the end of the bar. These were what was being tripped by the current leak before the buffer board was added to the Arduino.

The controller box has four buttons by the screen: on/off, panic!, restart, and emergency stop. It can cut into a 60mm depth of wood. As an alternative to a complete cut, you can optionally set up the controller to leave tabs in, to make it easier to lift out pieces together from the bench.

> It brings together my passion for electronics and for woodworking

Well, not quite: safety features are an essential part of any CNC machine. After lining up the cutting tool to the wood block, locking the wood in with retaining bolts set into the tracks, and manually correcting the height, the safety must be clicked on the controller. There's also an emergency stop button on the front of the machine's base. Any powered cutting tool must be built with ways to quickly stop it, just in case of something going wrong.

Looking at *The MagPi* logo in the photo (and on Mark's YouTube channel – **bit.ly/1hZFUmu**), you may be able to see the grooves on the side, matching different depths of cut. This was cut in three passes, taking around five minutes, to allow for the quality of the router bit, which cost only £1.20. Given a better bit, the logo could have been cut in one pass, taking less than a minute-and-a-half.

WHAT NEXT?

Mark tells us he did much of the CNC machine's design ad hoc: "I hand-cut the frames, testing out sizes as I went." This is apparently a contrast to his usual way of working. "Normally I like to have everything carefully thought out from the start."

Should he wish to build another, "Now I can do a template for it to cut a new version of itself." Future plans may include alternatives to Zapmaker: "There are other things I'd like it to do with it. I just like to try things my way." There's also the possibility of similar mechanics and controlling apparatus for a different head: powering a 3D printer, possibly, or to rig up to a Blu-ray laser to try as a cutter (suitably shielded, of course).

"I like to build," says Mark, which seems to sum things up quite well for many in the maker movement. Having seen some of Mark's other builds – from oak drawers that convert into a Sony PS3 racing car controller, to the famous telephone box refrigerator – we're sure that whatever follows will be an interesting project, as well as something extremely well engineered.

>STEP-04
On the Pi

Zapmaker's Gbrl controller software was originally optimised for a Pentium III with 256MB of RAM, and readily made the transition to the Pi Model B, hardly troubling the Pi 2 in Mark's CNC controller box.

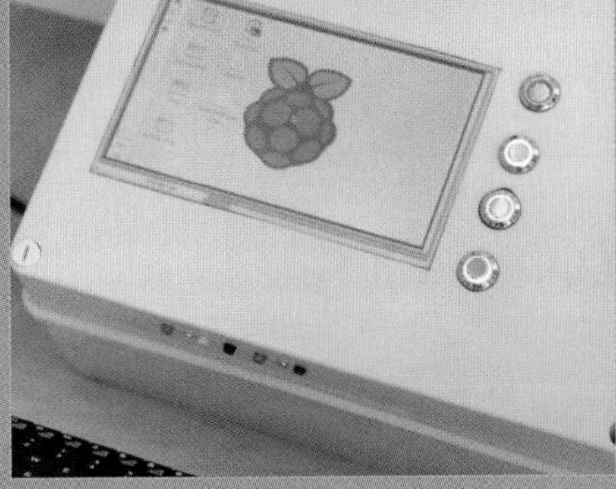

>STEP-05
Raspbian

Zapmaker's CNC software runs on a standard Raspbian install, and the **zapmaker.org** website has full instructions for those new to the wonderful world of Raspberry Pi, as well as Grbl information.

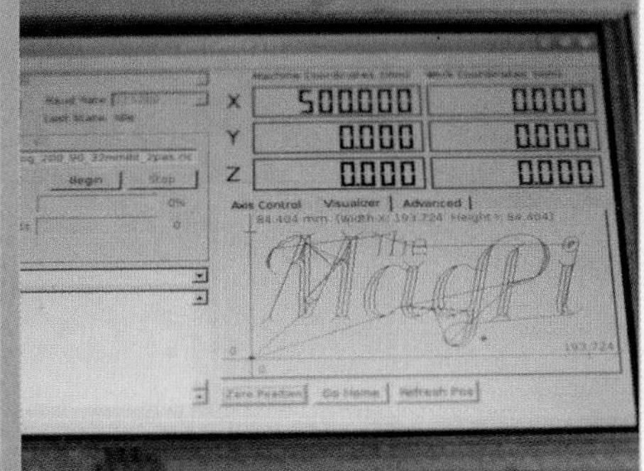

>STEP-06
Grbl controller

Put it all together and the screen shows the cut to be made, waiting for you to hit the Start button after you've secured the block of wood safely in place.

A spectacular sculpture, SeeMore is also a functioning parallel computer comprising 256 Raspberry Pi Model B+s

Each Pi is connected to a servo that moves its arm, and therefore panel, outwards in proportion to its workload

Each plastic panel is etched with the IP address for the Pi mounted upon it

The articulating arms are designed with a double linkage to create a fluid 'waveform' movement

VIRGINIA TECH

SeeMore was created via a collaboration between the School of Art and Department of Computer Science at Virginia Polytechnic Institute and State University, by teams led by Sam Blanchard and Kirk Cameron respectively.
seemoreproject.com

SEEMORE

THE PI-POWERED PARALLEL COMPUTING SCULPTURE

Powered by a cluster of 256 Raspberry Pis, **Virginia Tech**'s stunning kinetic sculpture gives a visual representation of how parallel processing works

Quick Facts

- 580lb (263kg) of high-density plastic was used in the construction of SeeMore
- It comprises 1,280 moving parts and 7,312 pieces of hardware
- 1,320ft (402m) of extruded aluminium was used to create the framework
- SeeMore's construction involved 60 hours of CNC machining and 80 hours of volunteer assembly
- It takes around one and half days to wire it all up, using 1,536ft (468m) of USB cable and 2,200ft (670m) of Ethernet cable

Standing nine and a half feet tall, the SeeMore sculpture-cum-supercomputer suddenly whirrs into life, its green translucent panels sliding fluidly outwards in mesmerising waves across its spiral surface, delivering a physical representation of the computations being performed. Resembling something from a science-fiction movie, SeeMore is powered by a network of 256 Raspberry Pi Model B+s; one is attached to each plastic panel, whose articulating arm swings outwards whenever that particular Pi is actively working on a parallel computing task.

The idea for SeeMore originated in 2013 when Virginia Tech (**vt.edu**) computer science professor Kirk Cameron was working on a 32-node Raspberry Pi cluster in his lab. Seeking a way to help more people understand the concept of parallel computing, he approached his colleague Sam Blanchard, assistant professor of sculpture, to help create an interactive art installation for that purpose. Since Sam's main area of interest lies in robotic creations, he immediately suggested making a kinetic sculpture that responds to what's going on inside the computer. "LCDs are cool," explains Sam, "but you can really get a visceral reaction from people by showing them something that is moving... and has a presence in a space."

Sam tells us that the cylindrical design of SeeMore was partially

BUILDING A KINETIC SCULPTURE

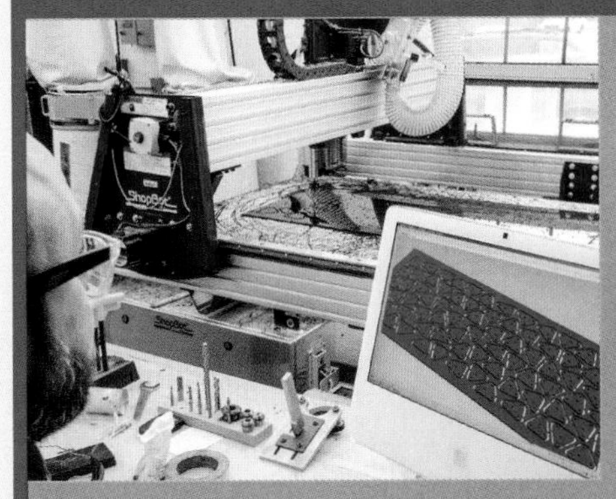

>STEP-01

Custom-made parts

The components for the mechanisms were all custom-designed by Sam using PartWorks CAD, then cut from acrylic sheets using a ShopBot CNC machine. In this photo Sam is making support brackets for the sculpture's metal framework.

>STEP-02

Articulating arms

Assembled from several components, 256 articulating arms were required for the full-scale version of SeeMore. Each features a double linkage that results in a fluid, curved movement of the plastic panel holding the Pi when triggered.

>STEP-03

Bending metal

Since the team couldn't find anyone to bend the T-slot aluminium to create the arcs for SeeMore's framework, they had some special rollers made for a bending machine, as used here by Virginia Tech sculpture student Robert Redfearn.

inspired by the classic Cray-1 supercomputer of the mid to late 1970s, a time when computers were far from being boring black boxes. "They had a physical presence, almost like a sculpture or a piece of furniture," says Sam. Indeed, the Cray-1 even had a bench around it so that people in the office could sit and have their coffee! While SeeMore lacks a seating facility, its footprint is proportional to that of the Cray-1, although it's almost twice as big and also has an hourglass shape to it. In addition, an early design decision was taken to deliberately expose all SeeMore's workings, including the combined 2,736 feet (834m) of wiring, in much the same way as the Cray-1. "One thing I really appreciated about that form was that it had this interior space and an exterior facade and so it was very transparent in the way that you could not just literally see through it but walk around and see [all the wires and workings]," reveals Sam.

> "SeeMore was partially inspired by the classic Cray-1 supercomputer of the mid to late 1970s"

The power of parallel

This transparency of design ties in perfectly with the project's main aim of helping the general public to visualise how parallel computing works and emphasise the important work of high-performance computing researchers. As Kirk points out, we all benefit every day from the advances made in large-scale systems that are essential to the infrastructures of services like Google, Twitter, and Dropbox. "Yet, the general population that relies on these technologies doesn't understand the importance and the elegance innate to what folks like us do. By using aesthetics and visualisation, my idea was to impart the most basic information such as the fact that we use lots of devices collectively and in parallel to solve problems larger than those we can solve with a single system. The algorithms you see on SeeMore represent synchronous and asynchronous communications and collaborations common in parallel codes and systems."

The original panels were replaced with green translucent ones for the 2015 World Maker Faire in New York City

Above Each panel moves out in proportion to its Pi's workload

When SeeMore was exhibited recently at the World Maker Faire in New York City, it was set up with a local open-source database to enable users to search (via a custom touchscreen) for points of interest around a given subway stop. Kirk tells us that multiple steps are required to for such a task. "The first is to break this problem into smaller sub-tasks such as having each Pi search part of a very large database of points of interest. In this example, the Pis in our cluster would be assigned portions of a database to search and all of them would be given the same subway stop as their 'token' to use in the search. This divide-and-conquer approach is a common algorithm used in parallel computing and this example is similar to the algorithm used in Google search and demonstrated on SeeMore."

Scaling it up

Having started out with a modest budget, the project was gradually scaled up via three prototype stages, which used first one Raspberry Pi, then nine, and then 30 (see 'Prototyping process' boxout). Extra funding was subsequently provided by the National Science Foundation and Virginia Tech's own Institute for Creativity, Arts and Technology, which enabled it to be scaled up to the final 256-node version.

SeeMore's mechanisms were all custom-made and designed by Sam, and their design evolved over time. Most notably, the articulating arms that move the panel-mounted Pis were designed specifically to create a more fluid effect. "The movement of the Raspberry Pis is actually a curve... so it doesn't just flap out, it articulates outward," says Sam. "It has a double linkage that some might see as superfluous, or overly complex, but I think that what you get... is this waveform that relates to these ideas of fluidity and that springs from what a lot of parallel computers are built to process: things like weather simulation or fluid dynamics."

BUILD CONTINUED...

>STEP-04
Assembling the frame

The metal framework's circular sections are made up of two arcs for easier assembly. Furman power blocks screwed into the frame supply the electricity via wall-warts with twin USB ports to power each Pi and servo separately.

>STEP-05
Servos galore

256 Hi-Tec HS-7966HB servos are used to move the articulating arms and therefore the attached Raspberry Pi panels. When exhibiting SeeMore at an event, the team have spare components on standby just in case anything should fail.

>STEP-06
Plastic panels

Each plastic panel is etched with that Pi's IP address. Networking them together isn't that great a challenge since all the Ethernet cables run down to the inner base, where they can be connected (in any order) to six 48-port Ethernet switches.

Also, rather than moving straight to its maximum 90-degree outward position when triggered, each panel moves in proportion to the percentage of computing capacity being used by the respective Raspberry Pi. To achieve this, each Pi is linked to its arm's servo via a GPIO pin. While in the prototype designs, the servo also received its power from the Pi, a switch from the original Pi Model B to the B+ for SeeMore's final version necessitated that both be powered separately. Not wanting to overcomplicate the design with battery packs or external power supplies, Sam ended up buying PSUs with two USB ports so separate cables could be run to the Raspberry Pi and its servo.

"The logistics of exhibiting SeeMore at an event involve it being transported in six crates"

On the software side, Kirk tells us that the combination of controlling the servos and running a full OS on the Pis led to complications. "For example, there is a software stack or a series of tools that we typically install on top of the operating system across the whole cluster. In the Pi environment, combining this stack with the servo controls and synchronising the movement of the Pis to running tasks was challenging... there is not a lot of community software support available since this had never been done. Thus, we created a lot of custom software to make this work in a visually compelling way."

Custom components

The arms themselves comprise a number of pieces made from HDPE (high-density polyethylene) plastic, milled out on a ShopBot CNC machine. These had bronze bearings inserted, all using steel shafts cut by the team. "Almost every single piece is custom: some people assume we bought those off the shelf, but I can assure you we spent many hours machining those pieces," laughs Sam. He tells us that this provided students with many hours of milling experience.

The plastic panels are all laser-cut and etched with the IP address of the attached Pi in two places, so they can be seen whether the panel is flat or has moved out. Having started out with blue and clear panels, the team changed them to a translucent green for the New York Maker Faire. "I like the idea of customising the project for where we show it."

The logistics of exhibiting SeeMore at an event involve it being transported in six crates and then assembled at the location. "My students and I show up three days ahead of time," says Sam. Once the framework's rings – which are split into two for shipping, with Pis still attached – are put back together, there's a day and a half of wiring to be done. "It's one guy on the outside and one guy on the inside, and then you're just passing wires to each other. It's actually pretty loose in there and I like to keep it that way: I like how the wires move on their own inside the structure." While routing all the USB power lines correctly is a major challenge, Sam tells us that getting the Pi network connected is less problematic since the cables are connected to six 48-port Ethernet switches in SeeMore's base, so it doesn't matter which ports they're plugged into.

Although the overall assembly process is arduous, the end result is certainly spectacular, attracting a crowd of visitors at the couple of events at which SeeMore has appeared so far. Sadly, Sam tells us there's no suitable space at Virginia Tech to keep SeeMore in assembled form, so it's currently back in its crates, but there are plans to exhibit it again in 2016. Watch this space for more news.

PROTOTYPING PROCESS

Before scaling up to the final full-scale version of SeeMore, three prototypes were created...

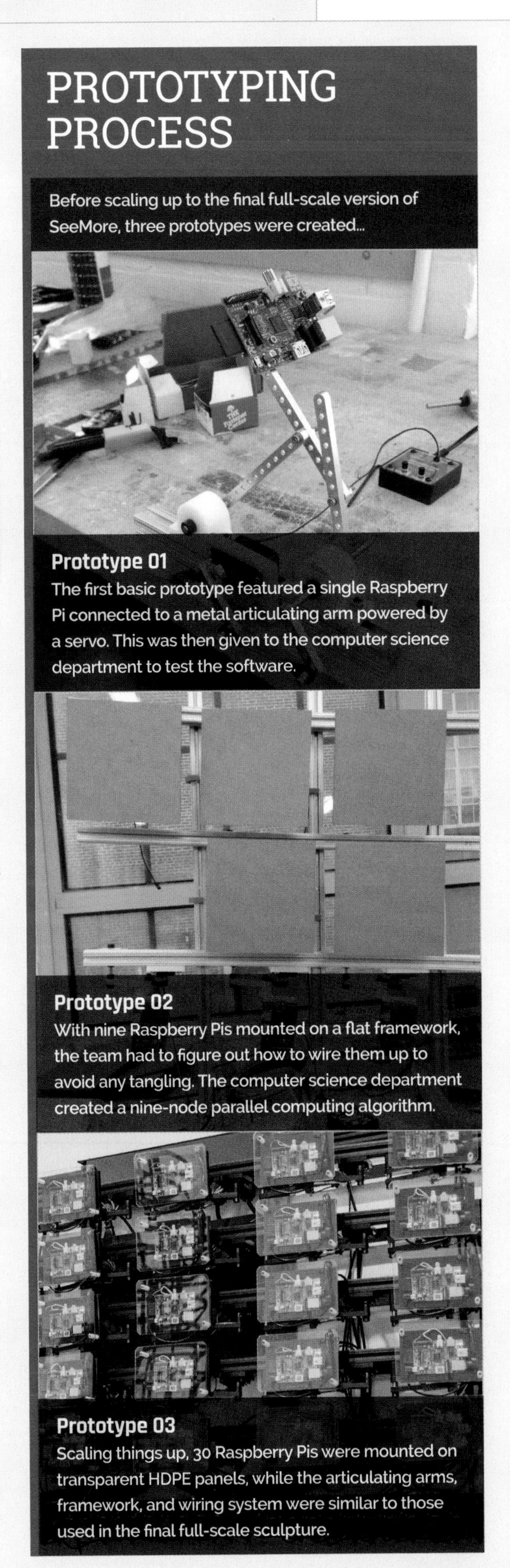

Prototype 01
The first basic prototype featured a single Raspberry Pi connected to a metal articulating arm powered by a servo. This was then given to the computer science department to test the software.

Prototype 02
With nine Raspberry Pis mounted on a flat framework, the team had to figure out how to wire them up to avoid any tangling. The computer science department created a nine-node parallel computing algorithm.

Prototype 03
Scaling things up, 30 Raspberry Pis were mounted on transparent HDPE panels, while the articulating arms, framework, and wiring system were similar to those used in the final full-scale sculpture.

BRADLEY MELTON

A network engineer and aspiring 'professional geek' who loves to use and sing the praises of the Raspberry Pi.
imgur.com/A4kjx7w

MAGIC MIRROR

Mirror mirror on the wall, what's the weather going to be like today? Should I bring an umbrella?

Quick Facts

- The project is made with Google Coder
- It took a week to do the frame, a few days for the code
- This is Bradley's first creative Pi project
- In the past, he has used Pis in his home Cisco networking lab
- The online community helped a lot to get this to work

It's amazing how the *Iron Man* films have inspired people due to the way they portrayed almost-attainable technology. Watching someone look over sunny Malibu while the weather info was displayed right in front of them was a great visual. It's not exactly brand new, unseen technology – cars have been projecting HUDS onto windscreens for a while now – but it has never been popularised in a major blockbuster before. While we don't seem to have quite reached the stage of the incredible glass tech of Tony Stark's bedroom just yet, apparently we're close enough to get mirrors working in the same way, or at least Bradley Melton has managed it with his Magic Mirror.

"It's called a 'Magic Mirror', but a more accurate name would be a 'Smart Mirror'," Bradley tells us. "It's a mirror that displays the information you need to know at a quick glance: the time, the date, the weather, and of course a compliment!"

It's not the first mirror of its type, and Bradley admits that he's taken some cues from a previous project by Michael Teeuw (see more details about it on Michael's blog: **magpi.cc/1PzFbWa**), taking the concept and bringing it down to a more beginner level for himself so he could learn more about web development.

"Plus, because I know what each and every function does and how it

It's an extra-useful mirror as it displays up-to-date weather information taken from the internet

It looks like a mirror, but it's actually a cunning disguise – a monitor, and some two-way glass covered by a frame

Of course, a mirror should also be able to reflect your image and make sure you're looking good

A TECH REFLECTION

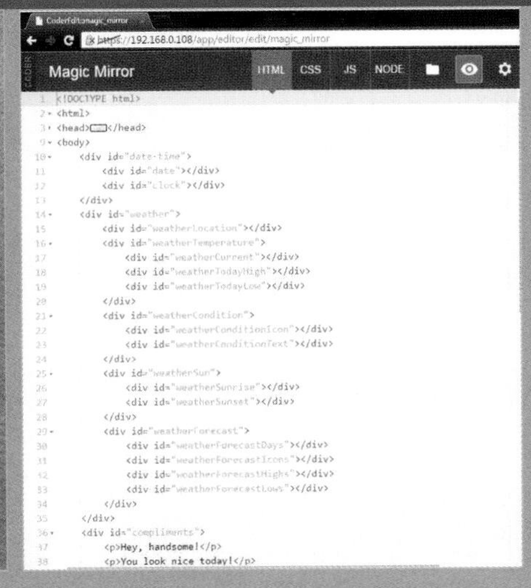

>STEP-01
Turn the mirror on

Turning the display on activates the Raspberry Pi, which is powered via a USB port on the mirror itself. It boots into the Chromium web browser, which is displayed on the screen.

>STEP-02
Getting the data

The weather info is taken from Yahoo, scraped using the simpleWeather.js jQuery plug-in which then displays the weather on the display. Time is displayed as well, along with a compliment.

>STEP-03
Keep me updated

Everything works on a timer, so the weather and time are updated on the browser window that makes up the display every 15 seconds, while the compliment is updated every 30 seconds.

works, it makes it easier to fix bugs as well as make improvements in the future."

Rather than use an actual mirror and project the data upon it, the Magic Mirror uses a widescreen monitor that has been put in a portrait orientation with an acrylic two-way mirror on top. With the right lighting and display tweaks, it can be reflective enough to use as a mirror while also displaying the weather data. The electronics are fairly simple: it's just a Pi with HDMI linking to the mirror, a WiFi dongle to retrieve online data, and a USB cable to the monitor as well, which is how it draws its power. To finish it off, Bradley built a wooden frame to be laid over the bezel so that the whole thing was camouflaged a bit better.

> "Rather than use an actual mirror and project data upon it, the Magic Mirror uses a widescreen monitor"

"It's not very complex," Bradley informs us. " As long as you have a little bit of carpentry or DIY skill to build the frame and have a basic understanding of how to program, you should be able to build this. I have never used JavaScript or CSS before this project, and I only had a little bit of experience with HTML, but this webpage is built almost entirely from JavaScript and CSS."

At the time of writing, the mirror has been running for a few weeks without any problems. It seems like Bradley wants to include some holiday-themed extras to it, starting with some spooky additions for the Halloween just past. We're hoping he will add some jollier ones for the Christmas period.

Above Say 'Bloody Mary' three times into the mirror on Halloween for a voice-activated fright

ADRIAN ATWOOD

Dad, engineer, tinkerer, woodworker, borker, and crazy hobbyist who is always building weird projects.
buildxyz.xyz

Turn the system on with a code and set a timer, giving you full parental control

A standard LCD screen is built into this beautiful cabinet, and displays Kodi or Emulation Station from the Pi

The many USB ports allow for controllers and USB storage drives; however, media is accessible over the network as well

RPIKIDS

Not a spin-off Saturday morning cartoon, RPiKids is a new entertainment system built for **Adrian Atwood**'s children

Quick Facts

- It took 90 hours to build
- This is Adrian's first Pi project
- Scratch is installed to encourage the kids to code
- He's adding wireless PS2 controllers very soon
- Adrian has more cool Pi stuff planned – keep an eye on his blog

We've all seen wacky parental control methods for kids' entertainment. Our favourite is the exercise bike that powers a PlayStation, which may seem cruel but at least means there's a cut-off point for how much they're able to play. The best method is still the simplest: a key code and a timer so that the kids can then do something other than stare at a screen all day, freeing up the TV so you can binge-watch the entirety of *Once Upon a Time*'s third series. With the Raspberry Pi being a far more powerful option for operating an entertainment centre, it was only a matter of time before an intrepid hacker made the ultimate version for their kids. Meet RPiKids, created by Adrian Atwood.

"RPiKids is an all-in-one kids' entertainment centre with integrated parental control features," Adrian explains. "My kids can enjoy 16-bit games, watch movies and more, provided an adult has granted them access by entering a password and setting the timer."

The RPiKids is a mix of hardware; the system itself is powered by a Raspberry Pi, handling Kodi, Emulation Station and the like for the entertainment side. The passcode and timer are handled by an Arduino Uno using a rotary encoder (think bank safe), which can be pushed as a button to confirm selections. It's all built into a wonderful-looking, steampunky case that was handcrafted by Adrian himself from wood with 3D printed detailing.

There are USB access ports on the front for connecting controllers and portable media storage, and the hardware is visible behind a removable clear Perspex panel. While it all looks extremely impressive, Adrian claims it's an overall 'intermediate' level of build.

"I will say the Raspberry Pi configuration was very straightforward and a beginner can mirror my configuration," he tells us. "Coding the firmware for the Arduino parental controls, and having the Arduino and Pi 2 communicate with each other, was a little more complex. The case is no problem if you're into woodworking and auto body repair. I have access

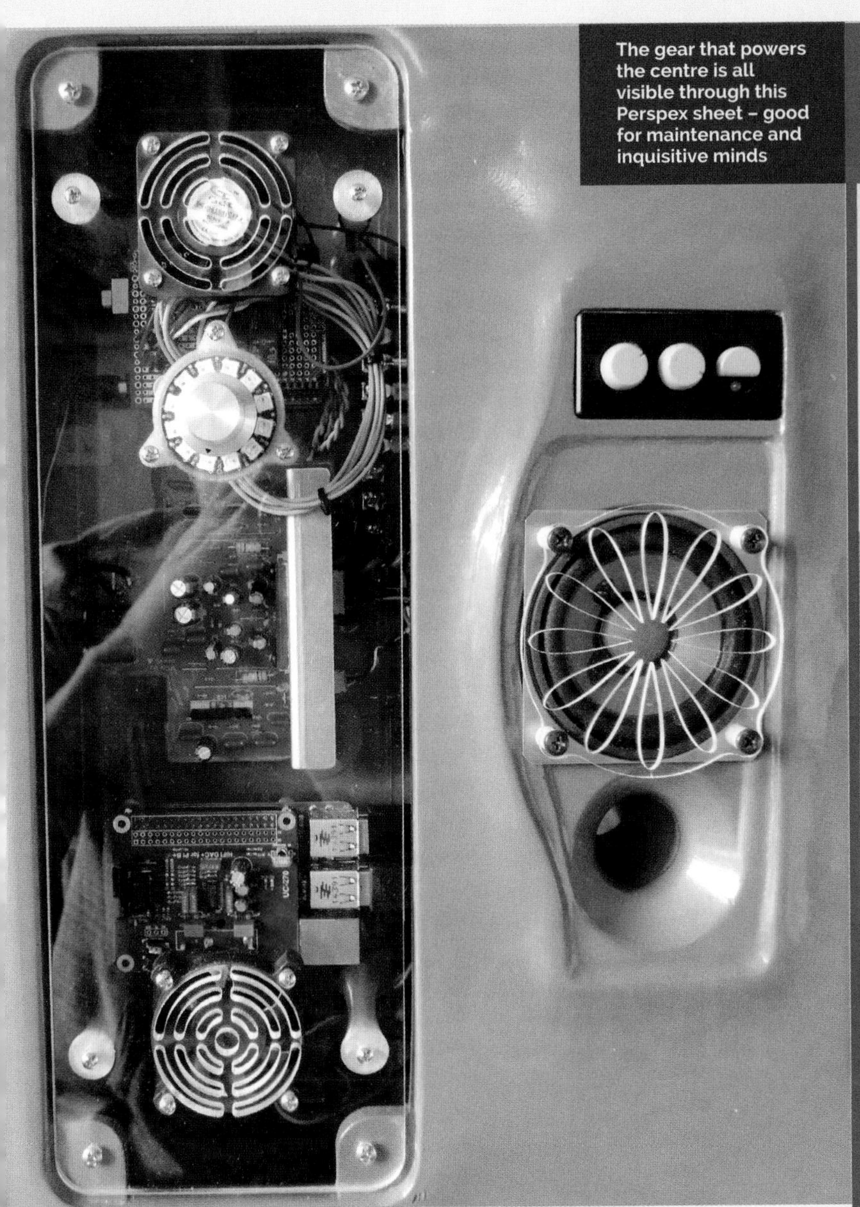

The gear that powers the centre is all visible through this Perspex sheet – good for maintenance and inquisitive minds

> RPiKids is an all-in-one kids' entertainment centre with integrated parental control

to a 3D printer and laser cutter and enjoy CAD modelling, but those parts could be contracted out or replaced."

Although he expected 'all sorts' of glitches, the system has worked extremely well for him and his children, requiring only minor adjustments to the brightness of the ring of NeoPixels used in conjunction with the encoder.

One thing Adrian recommends for anyone trying to replicate the project is an upgrade to the sound output: "The Pi definitely needed a DAC (I²S) sound card because there was a lot of hissing and artifacts with the onboard sound."

The kids have been very much enjoying it. Although it's an entertainment centre, he's also programmed an intentional security vulnerability into the lock mechanism, hoping his kids will learn something about security systems. We wish them the best of luck in figuring out to unlock 'unlimited mode'!

ENTERTAINING THE KIDS

>STEP-01

Dial it up

Using a digital encoder and a NeoPixel LED ring, the user (parent) enters a combination to unlock the system so the children can use it.

>STEP-02

Set a time

When unlocked, the encoder can then be used to set a timer on the system, from ten minutes to forever. Once selected, the Arduino lets the Raspberry Pi turn on.

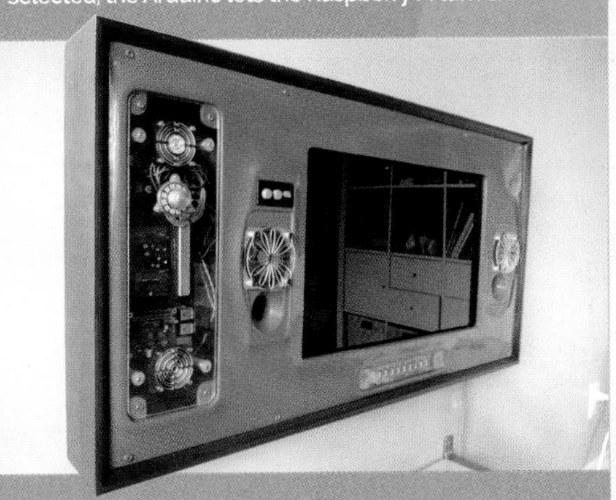

>STEP-03

Shut it down

When time is up (or the off button is pressed), the Arduino part issues a shutdown command to the Pi. The Pi then shuts everything off safely, and the Arduino cuts power shortly afterwards.

RON OSTAFICHUK

Ron is a tech enthusiast who has been playing on computers since the Z80. He is married with three kids and lives in Airdrie, Alberta, Canada.
ostafichuk.com

The Raspberry Pi acts as the brains, and the Dalek is remotely controlled via a web interface

The Dalek's body was built from leftover shed parts covered in glossy black paint

The base is designed to work as a robot lawnmower, and the Dalek body is placed on top for Halloween

RASPIMOWER DALEK

Ron Ostafichuk set out to build a robot lawnmower and ended up with a fully automated Dalek (you know how it is)

Quick Facts

- Ron used just a jigsaw, drill, and utility knife
- The whole project cost around £60 to build
- It uses a worn out battery but runs for three hours
- Ron plans to add ultrasonic and bump sensors to the Dalek
- The Dalek 2.0 will be based on a mobility scooter

Daleks are the most feared race in the universe, so what could be more fun than building your own Raspberry Pi-powered Dalek?

That's what developer Ron Ostafichuk thought. "I've been tinkering with the Raspberry Pi ever since it came out," he tells us, "and I've seen many small robot projects, but decided that a big robot would be much more fun."

The Dalek didn't start out as a Dalek: Ron wanted to build a robotic lawnmower. "I have a huge lawn and I wanted to show my kids that you could build a large robot, using spare parts and scraps."

The wooden base contains two 12V motors recycled from a life spent adjusting the seats on cars. These motors are connected to the big off-road wheels using a V-belt system.

"Once I had the motorised base completed, my kids hopped onto it and proceeded to ride it around the neighbourhood. They loved it, and remarked how great it would be to ride it around for Halloween. Since I am a pretty big *Doctor Who* fan, the idea that came to me was to turn it into a Dalek!"

For power, Ron is using an old 12V deep-cycle camper battery. "[It] was no longer strong enough to use in my camper," says Ron, "[but] it lasted for around three hours of continuous operation this Halloween."

"I am running the standard Raspbian distro on the Pi," says Ron, and the Raspimower Dalek control code is written in C++ (available on Bitbucket – **magpi.cc/1HWNV8j**).

The Dalek is a body that sits on top of the Raspimower base. The frame was built from ¾-inch (19mm) chipboard, and the outside from ¼-inch (6mm) sheeting.

RASPIMOWER DALEK

>STEP-01
Raspimower base
The base of the Raspimower Dalek is a frame to house a 12V battery and motors connected to the wheels via a V-belt system. It's designed to work as a robotic lawnmower and is controlled by a Raspberry Pi.

>STEP-02
Dalek frame
Turning the Raspimower base into a Dalek required a chipboard frame. This was constructed from ¾-inch chipboard and ¼-inch sheeting left over from a shed-building project.

>STEP-03
The Dalek
A used bin, plunger, and aluminium pipe create the rest of the Dalek, and the whole thing is painted in glossy black paint.

"This was all left over from building a shed," reveals Ron. One arm is a toilet plunger and the other is an aluminium pipe wrapped with wire, and the whole thing is painted over with glossy black paint.

> The old computer speakers inside are so loud, they actually vibrate the sides of the Dalek

The Dalek was originally controlled with a wireless keyboard, but Ron has built a web interface to control the Raspimower Dalek. Ron has also bought an old Zappy mobility scooter for $60CND (around £40) and plans to use it to replace the 12V motors. He explains that it's much more powerful and mechanically sound.

"[The Dalek] is nowhere near completed and constantly changing, as I have lots of plans and want to make it autonomous so it will actually 'exterminate' any long blades of grass in my yard," jokes Ron. Speaking of extermination, no Dalek would be complete without its famous voice command. "It has some old computer speakers inside that are very loud; they actually vibrate the sides of the Dalek. It has about 15 sound clips from *Doctor Who*, but 'exterminate' is my favourite one!

"It was a huge hit this Halloween, and as the kids would approach, I would turn on all the lights and rotate the robot towards them while belting out 'exterminate!' or 'destroy!'. Watching the kids react was so much fun; my favourite reaction came from a little girl who turned to her dad and matter-of-factly said, 'Well, I guess we know which house we will never ever go to again!' "

After the Dalek has done its Halloween duty, the base returns to being a robot lawnmower

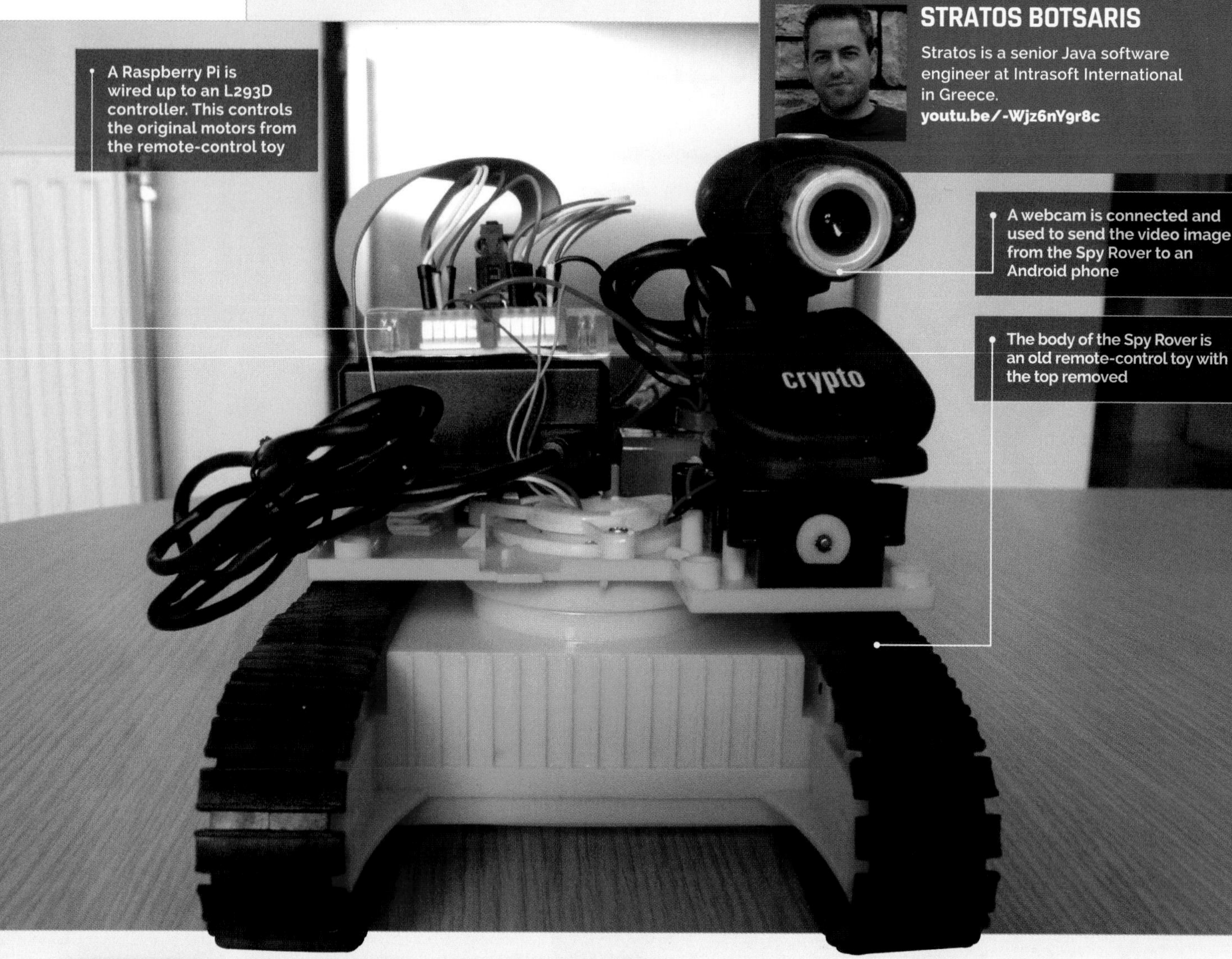

A Raspberry Pi is wired up to an L293D controller. This controls the original motors from the remote-control toy

A webcam is connected and used to send the video image from the Spy Rover to an Android phone

The body of the Spy Rover is an old remote-control toy with the top removed

STRATOS BOTSARIS

Stratos is a senior Java software engineer at Intrasoft International in Greece.

youtu.be/-Wjz6nYgr8c

REMOTE CONTROL SPY ROVER

Fancy turning an old toy into a remote-control spy? **Lucy Hattersley** talks to Stratos Botsaris about his Spy Rover project

Quick Facts

- The Spy Rover works for around 40 minutes
- At around 2mph, it won't break any speed records
- It took around three months to build
- The range is limited by the WiFi connection
- With port forwarding, it can be controlled over the internet

Java engineer Stratos Botsaris hacked a remote-control toy and turned it into a far cooler Pi-powered Spy Robot. If that wasn't exciting enough, he now controls it from his Android phone while it bounces the video display to the screen.

A project like this deserves further investigation, so we caught up with Stratos to ask about the Spy Rover. "I did not want to build just another moving robot," he says. "At the same time, I was experimenting with the video recording capabilities of Raspberry Pi. So that was the moment that I came up with the idea of building a rover that could take real-time video.

"I wanted to use my Android programming skills to develop an application that could display live video to the user."

Rather than build a robot from scratch, Stratos took apart a Big Bargain King Force Excavator. With the top half removed, he slotted in an original Pi Model B hooked up to a breadboard, WiFi dongle, and USB webcam.

An L293D chip controls the motors. "The L293D is a motor driver integrated circuit that can simultaneously control two motors in either direction," says Stratos. "If I want to move the rover forward, I make both motors turn clockwise, and if I wish to get the rover to reverse, I make both motors turn anticlockwise. In case the rover needs to turn right, I stop the right motor and make the left motor turn clockwise, and the same logic applies when the rover needs to turn left."

With the mechanics in place, Stratos turned his attention to the controller. It made sense to use a controller with a screen so that he could see through the webcam. Eventually, he decided to build a controller app for Android and control the Spy Rover directly from a phone.

"I have developed some Android applications in my spare time, so implementing an Android application for this project was not so difficult."

As Stratos discovered, streaming the video would prove a bigger challenge than controlling the Spy Rover. "After a lot of research, I found out that I had to use some libraries, written in C++, inside the Android app to accomplish my task. Fortunately, I found another project that had solved this problem, so by using parts of the source code, I was able to complete the implementation of the Android application."

> "I came up with the idea of cutting a USB cable and joining its power cables to those of the UBEC"

Aside from video streaming, the hardest part of the project was power. "The Raspberry Pi requires a constant power supply of 5V voltage and up to 3A current. After some research, I decided to buy a UBEC (Universal Battery Eliminator Circuit), which provides 5V from an input of 5.5V-20V and is capable of supplying up to 3A. Then I bought a battery box of six AA batteries to provide enough voltage (9V) to the UBEC.

"The next challenge I faced was connecting the UBEC to the Raspberry Pi. I had to find a way to connect the power output wires of the UBEC to the USB connector. Fortunately, I came up with the idea of cutting a USB cable and joining its two internal power cables to the output power cables of the UBEC; this was my real eureka moment."

Stratos aims to make the next project faster. "The plan is to transfer the rover to a plastic toy car with normal wheels."

Above The parts are wired up using a breadboard. This enabled the Raspberry Pi to be tested with the L293D controller and motors

HACK YOUR SPY ROVER

>STEP-01
Dismantle the toy

Rather than build a robot from scratch, Stratos decided to modify a remote-control toy. The Spy Rover started life as a Big Bargain King Force Excavator. This toy comes complete with tracks, as well as motors that can be modified to work with the Raspberry Pi.

>STEP-02
Adding the Raspberry Pi

The top half of the King Force toy is an excavator mechanism, which was removed to provide a base for the Raspberry Pi, WiFi dongle, webcam, and batteries. The L293D controller is slotted into a breadboard and wired to the original motors inside.

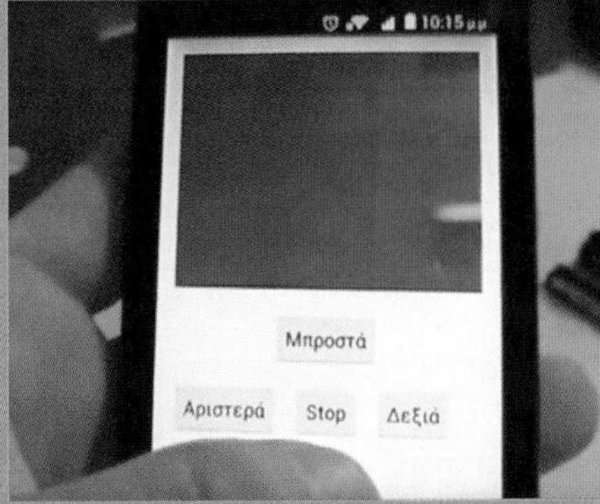

>STEP-03
The Android controller

The toy connects to a local WiFi network, and a custom-built Android app is used to send commands to the Raspberry Pi. Meanwhile, the view from the webcam is bounced back to the Android app. The result is a remote-controlled Spy Rover.

MATT REED

Matt Reed lives in Nashville, Tennessee and is a creative technologist at Redpepper. **mcreed.com**

A beacon is attached to a collar and placed around Bean's neck

Bean is a greyhound that lives with the Redpepper marketing agency in Nashville, Tennessee

Raspberry Pi devices are placed around the office, and the distance between each one and Bean is used to locate her

Quick Facts

- The battery in a beacon can work for up to a year
- Each beacon has a unique ID number
- The signal strength is used to detect Bean's distance
- It uses trilateration, not triangulation, to detect Bean
- Sniffur can detect Bean in a 50-metre range area

SNIFFUR

Matt always knows where **Bean** the dog is, thanks to his beacon-powered Sniffur system – by **Lucy Hattersley**

We love animals here at *The MagPi*, so when we heard about a Raspberry Pi dog-tracker called 'Sniffur', we had to learn more.

Sniffur uses tracking technology called 'beacons'; these are relatively new devices being placed in department stores to track the precise location of customers.

Sniffur flips this idea on its head, by putting the beacon on a moving object and using three Raspberry Pis to detect where it is. The object in question is Bean, an adorable greyhound adopted by Redpepper, a marketing agency in Nashville, Tennessee.

"We're a culture-first company," says Matt Reed, the project's maker. "A lot of us have dogs or pets in some form, so part of us being happy is knowing our pets are happy. It doesn't hurt that our CEO also has two dogs.

"Bean is absolutely the sweetest dog. Very shy, timid, loving. She wanders around into people's offices and just stands next to their desks waiting for rubs, then just wanders on to the next spot."

But all dogs like to go out and play. "When [greyhounds] do, they are very hard to catch because they are so fast," Matt tells us. "They are the second-fastest land animal after the cheetah: top speed 43mph. Greyhounds also have a high prey drive; if they see a squirrel then it's 'bye bye'.

"The need to know where she is at any moment and see if she's close to the front doors is the reason Sniffur was built," continues Matt. "We have done retail experiments using Estimotes (**estimote.com**) and constantly keep a stock of beacons available in our lab for experimentation.

"I grabbed one of the Estimote beacons from the lab and zip-tied it to Bean's collar. Usually, beacons are attached in stationary

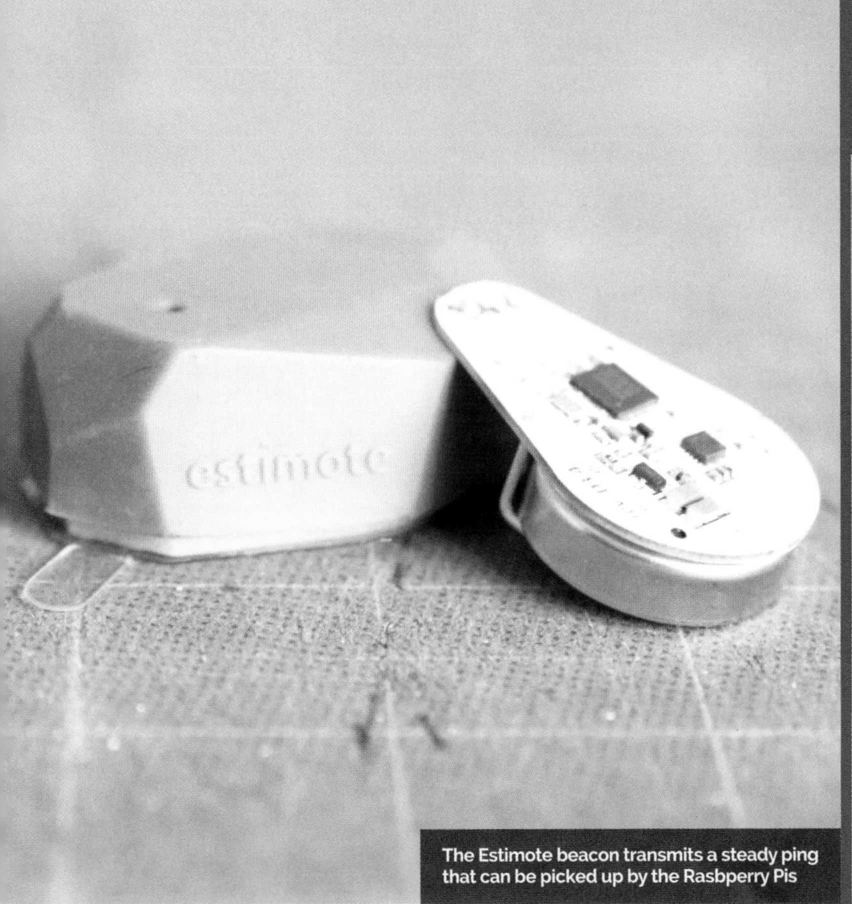

The Estimote beacon transmits a steady ping that can be picked up by the Rasbperry Pis

physical locations, but Bean is now a mobile beacon transmitting a polling signal everywhere she goes.

"I put a Bluetooth USB dongle into three Raspberry Pis and coded them to listen for Bean's Unique Beacon ID," reveals Matt.

One value transmitted by a beacon is RSSI (received signal strength indicator). This is the distance of a beacon from the antenna. "I've referred to it as triangulation because everyone knows what that means," says Matt, "but I've recently learned on Hackaday that 'trilateration' is the correct term, because I'm calculating distance instead of geometry."

Matt built an app for the iPad to display Bean's location. "It's just an HTML, JavaScript and CSS page that connects over the local WiFi network to the three Raspberry Pis," he explains.

"I think this could be a fun project for anyone looking to familiarise themselves with beacons. A cheaper version would be to use one Pi to generate a single radius distance from that antenna. You could also set an antenna by an exit and just throw an alarm, flash lights or lock the door, whenever the roaming beacon comes within range.

"Hmm," ponders Matt, "that is actually not a bad idea. I think Sniffur is fun from a visualisation standpoint, but from a practical standpoint something more proactive might be better."

> 'Trilateration' is the correct term, because I'm calculating distance instead of geometry

BUILDING A SNIFFUR SYSTEM

>STEP-01
Beacon
A Estimote beacon is attached to a collar and placed around the dog's neck. Powered by a single cell battery, it'll give away her position for up to a year.

>STEP-02
Three Raspberry Pis
Three Raspberry Pis are set up, with WiFi and Bluetooth dongles to act as antennas. They measure the distance of Bean to each Raspberry Pi, which is used to determine her position.

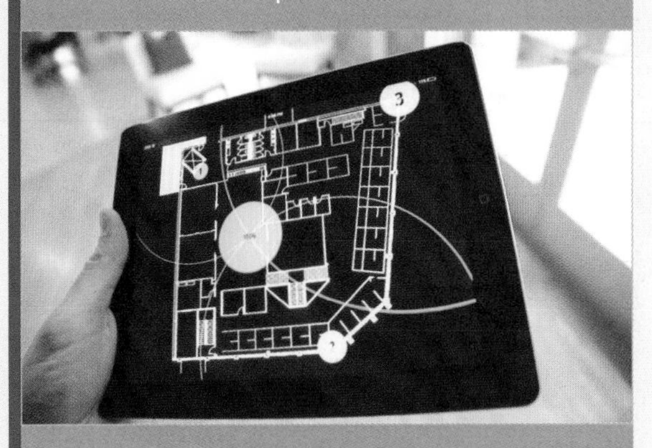

>STEP-03
Tracker app
A webpage (wrapped as an iPad app) connects to the local WiFi network and obtains the values from each Raspberry Pi. These are used to display the position of Bean on a map.

Elevation data fed into Blender ensured an accurate representation of Mount Kilimanjaro, with detailed contours

KURT HUNTER

Combining decades of experience in high tech with a passion for alpine climbing, Kurt co-founded Madison Mountaineering and also developed his own RainOn web-based tracking solution.

rainon.com

magpi.cc/2dUhfSP

Each of the seven LEDs marks the position of a camp or the summit, and lights up when the climber approaches that point

The Raspberry Pi and all the cabling are completely enclosed within the model, which was hollowed out after printing

At the rear of the model are cut-outs for the power and Ethernet ports, connected to the Pi with extension cables

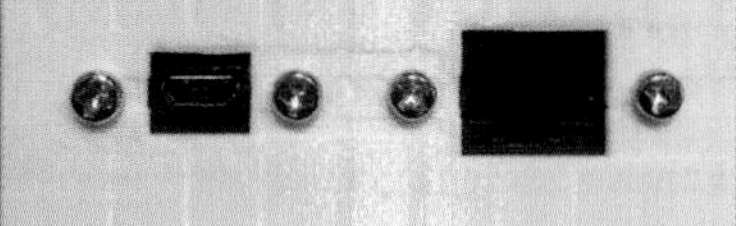

LOCATION-TRACKING MOUNTAIN MODEL

When **Kurt Hunter** wanted to create a smart 3D model to show family and colleagues his progress while climbing Mount Kilimanjaro, he turned to the Raspberry Pi

Quick Facts

- With its summit 5,895m above sea level, Kilimanjaro is Africa's highest peak
- Two models were created: one for Kurt's home and another for his office window
- The scale used is 1:100,000, so 10mm on the model equates to 1km
- Kurt's previous mountain climbs include Aconcagua and Denali
- He also acted as a Mount Everest base camp manager for a major 2014 expedition

An LED lights up on a scale model placed on a kitchen counter in Washington State, USA, to signify that over 9,000 miles away in Tanzania, Kurt Hunter has reached the summit of Mount Kilimanjaro. Climbing Africa's highest peak had been a long-held ambition for Kurt. "Ever since moving to Seattle 20 years ago, I would look up at Mount Rainier and dream of climbing it," he tells us. "After getting myself in shape in 2004, I did indeed climb it and got hooked on climbing. That year I set a goal of climbing Kilimanjaro, but never got around to it until [2015]."

In preparing for the two-week expedition, Kurt set himself another challenge. He wanted to combine his passion for 3D printing and programming in an interesting way, to enable his family and co-workers to follow along with his climb in a fun, visual experience. To this end, he set about creating a Raspberry Pi 2-powered 1:100,000 scale model of Kilimanjaro, complete with LEDs to mark the spots of all his planned camps, along with the summit itself. The location data would be supplied by a personal GPS locator device, via his own RainOn web-based tracking solution.

Model making

Kurt spent a weekend designing the 3D model in the Blender CAD program, using accurate elevation data for Kilimanjaro gleaned from Viewfinder Panoramas (**magpi.cc/1Sd7psw**) – see **magpi.cc/1J0osv3** for a tutorial on the technique – and calculating the physical offsets for the surface holes required for the LEDs. The model needed to be tall enough to contain the Raspberry Pi, mounted on a removable base panel, and include cut-outs for its power and Ethernet connections (via extension cables). The final

150×150mm model was then 3D printed using a PrintrBot Metal Simple, a process that took 26.5 hours to complete.

Once the support scaffolding was removed to hollow out the model, it was time to wire it up. "The biggest labour component was soldering up the individual LEDs and resistors to the GPIO ribbon cable," reveals Kurt. "The LEDs are held in place on the model by friction and silicon sealant." While he didn't encounter any major problems getting it working, since he'd already made a simple prototype with a breadboard, Kurt did discover a difference between the GPIO pin assignments on Windows IoT Core and Raspbian.

> Essentially, the system acquires real-time location data from a personal locator device

Trip tracking

When developing the Pi code for the project, Kurt was keen to evolve the RainOn Adventure Tech (**rainon.com**) web-based tracking system he'd developed for previous adventures as a Microsoft Azure solution. "Essentially, the system acquires real-time location data from a personal locator device, such as DeLorme inReach or SPOT, for a provisioned 'trip' like the Kilimanjaro expedition. It then provides geofence-based waypoint proximity notifications, among other features."

Each trip is a combination of an objective (typically the latitude/longitude of a mountain summit), a route (which can include a list of waypoints), and a start and end date/time. "The system polls the services of the personal locator manufacturer and retrieves the last reported location for each device assigned to an active trip. That retrieved location is tested against the geofence for each of the registered set of waypoints associated with the trip."

The trips and waypoint information are created in advance. "For example, Kilimanjaro using the Machame Route that we climbed has six

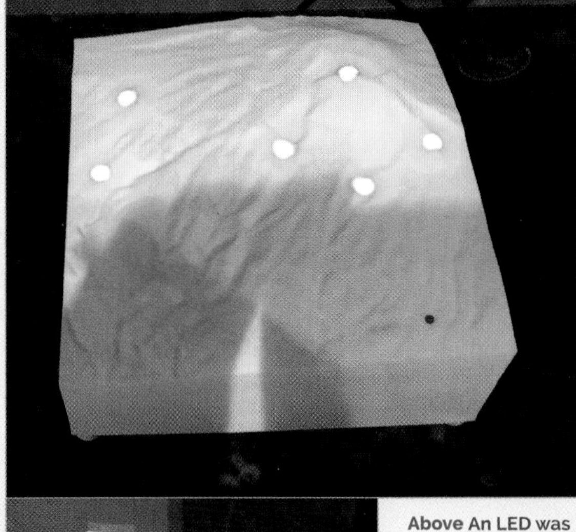

Above An LED was lit as Kurt reached each waypoint

Left A second model was put on display in Kurt's office window

CONSTRUCTING THE 3D MODEL

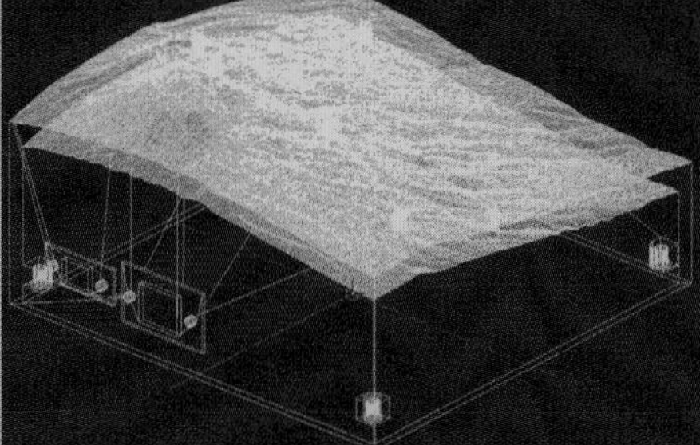

>STEP-01
Elevation data

To ensure the accuracy of the 3D model, Kurt obtained DEM (digital elevation model) data from Viewfinder Panoramas (**magpi.cc/1Sd7psw**) for a 15km square area around Kilimanjaro, including locations of the summit and six camps.

>STEP-02
Model in Blender

The elevation data was then fed into the Blender CAD program. The height of the model was set to provide the minimum vertical clearance required to accommodate a Raspberry Pi 2 and cabling. A square base was also modelled.

>STEP-03
Punching holes

Surface holes for the 3mm LEDs were 'Boolean punched' out of the surface layer. Cut-outs for the power and Ethernet ports, extended from the Pi with cables, were added using 3D model data from DataPro (magpi.cc/1Sd9ynZ / magpi.cc/1Sd9x3L).

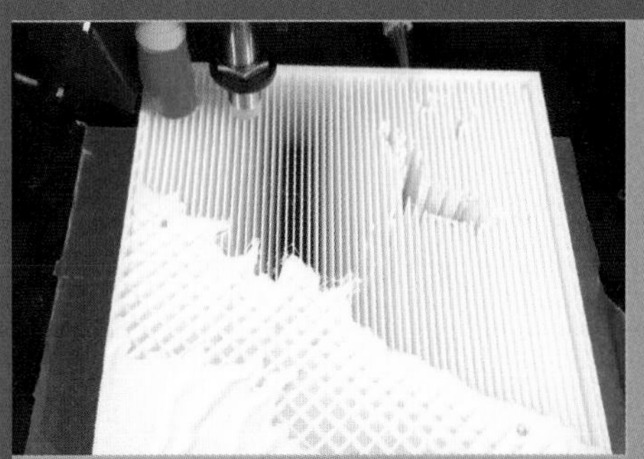

>STEP-04

3D printing

The 3D print of the 150×150mm primary model was completed on a PrintrBot Metal Simple printer, using Microsoft 3D Builder, in just over 26.5 hours. The interior scaffolding was then removed manually to hollow it out.

>STEP-05

Mounting the Pi

To enable easy removal of the Raspberry Pi from the model, it was mounted to the square base via the latter's four bosses, which accommodated McMaster-Carr press-fit threaded inserts to take the M2.5 Pi mounting screws.

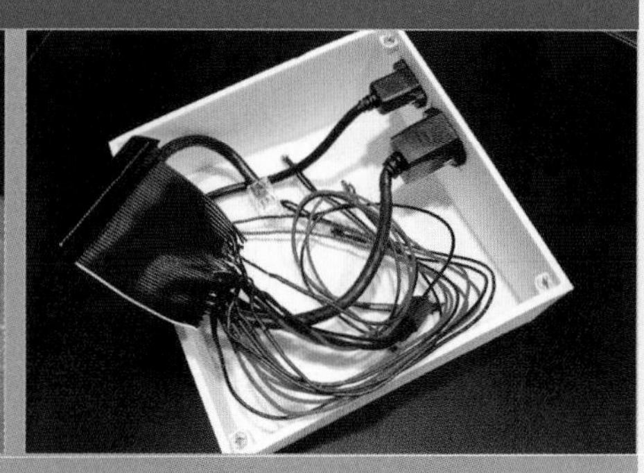

>STEP-06

Wiring up

All LED wiring to the Pi's GPIO pins was via a single 40-pin socket, using a pre-made ribbon cable with one end cut off, and the relevant GPIO pin lines soldered to power and ground hook-up wires for the LEDs, along with resistors.

Above The 3D printed model with scaffolding removed

Below A breadboard prototype was used to test the system

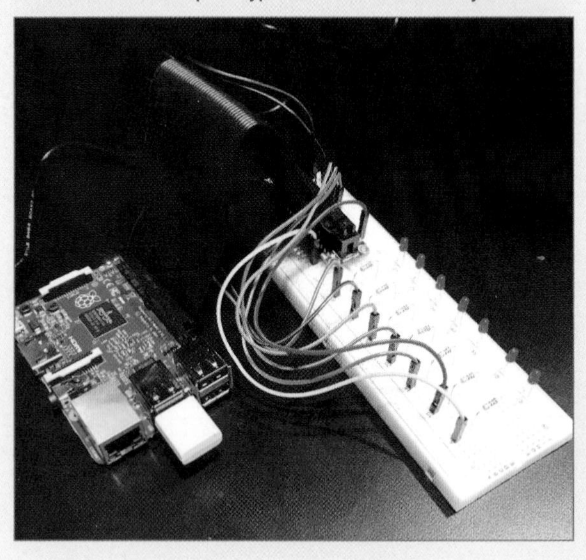

camps (in fixed locations) and the summit, plus the start and end locations, so that trip has nine associated waypoints, seven of which are on my 3D model. All of the data is stored in a SQL Server database which also supports spatial data, so geofence tests and other geospatial calculations are super easy."

> "The system worked in real-time and the waypoint LEDs stay lit after I had reached that location"

Coding the Pi

When it came to programming the Raspberry Pi to process the location data, Kurt ended up using the Windows 10 IoT Core operating system. As a senior partner engagement manager in his day job at Microsoft, Kurt was already well versed in Windows and its Visual Studio developer tools. Even so, he tells us he also developed a Python version of the code under Raspbian, but found the Windows 10 IoT Core / Visual Studio route much easier. "Three things were very attractive about using Windows 10 IoT Core: 1) Visual Studio is awesome (and familiar), 2) I could develop in C#, and 3) the remote debugging/deployment was super easy to set up and use."

Based largely on Microsoft's Blinky example code (**magpi.cc/1ndOkcN**), Kurt's program calls the RainOn Azure service API every ten minutes to obtain JSON location data. If this is within a geofence, set at a 200m radius, for one of the camps or the summit, the corresponding LED is lit.

Testing it out

To check everything was working properly before leaving for Tanzania, Kurt used the Postman test tool to call on his RainOn APIs and simulate data from the personal locator device. "I also use Google Earth quite a bit to find the lat/long of various places and measure distances. So I tested the system by sending simulated locations near the waypoints. When I first developed the geofence/waypoint feature, I did actually use local locations and drive around in my car with the device to test it."

Above Success! Kurt and his fellow climbers reach the summit

Above left Kilimanjaro rises majestically from the African plain

When it came to the actual Kilimanjaro climb, everything worked, although Kurt admits he could have used more error checking and recovery. "The system worked in real-time and the waypoint LEDs stay lit after I had reached that location. However, if the power went out then only future waypoints would light up, as I didn't store the previously reached waypoints in the Pi, nor did I report the history in my web APIs. So, sometime between camp three and four, this happened to the setup I had in my office window, but the one at home worked for the whole climb."

Always another mountain

Kurt admits that a few shortcuts and compromises had to be made in the last-minute rush to get the project completed in time for the Kilimanjaro trip. Given more time, Kurt says he would have liked to use the Pi's HDMI output to provide an animated map view and real-time data and graph displays. He plans to make improvements to the system for future expeditions. "I would very much like to figure out a way to show more discrete climbing progress on the model, rather than a single LED per day. I've thought about a number of ways that I've found to be impractical: light pipe projector from an LCD panel, laser, tight string of tiny LEDs... I'm looking for an idea!"

As for the experience of climbing Kilimanjaro, Kurt tells us it was awesome. "The climb itself takes seven days and you hike through four climatic zones before reaching the summit: rainforest, heather and moorland, alpine desert, and finally arctic above 5,000m - the summit is 5,895m. It's really quite amazing and the local staff make the experience so enjoyable. Every afternoon, when we reached camp, the staff would sing and dance with us... The view from the summit is spectacular as you arrive at sunrise, well above the clouds, and can see for miles and miles."

ACONCAGUA EXPEDITION

Kurt has since created another model for a January 2016 expedition to Mount Aconcagua in the Andes - at 6,961m, it's the highest peak in the Americas, and indeed anywhere outside of Asia. While Kurt didn't take part in this expedition, he has climbed the mountain previously. His 1:100,000 scale model of Aconcagua was constructed in a similar fashion to the Kilimanjaro one, with the Raspberry Pi enclosed within a hollowed-out 3D printed model. Six LEDs mark the positions of the summit and camps. Madison Mountaineering, one of the world's leading mountain guide services, are transmitting their real-time expedition locations using an inReach device – **magpi.cc/1J0o13Y**.

KRIS TEMMERMAN

A freelance developer who creates interactive displays for museums and advertising agencies. He's building a robot in his spare time.
neuroproductions.be

BALANCE BOT

A sociable, balancing robot built with a Raspberry Pi to power it. How tricky is balancing a robot via code, though?

Quick Facts

- The robot has currently taken 20 days to build
- Its reactions to detected people still need work
- The screen displays faces when detecting people
- Arms are planned for the robot
- It uses a Pi camera for the face recognition

There's a reason a lot of robots don't use two wheels or two legs: very simply, it's difficult for them to balance. It's much easier and sturdier to be on three (or more) wheels or four (or more) legs; generally, just having a low centre of gravity is a good thing. For two wheels in particular, you need some way of maintaining balance. Usually, this task is left up to humans; as Kris Temmerman shows us, though, a good bit of coding and construction can accomplish the same thing.

"The idea came after seeing some social robots, like Nao and Pepper," Kris tells us. "Technologically they're great, but I think they are also kind of boring. Too polite, too cute. I wanted to see if I can make a social robot with a little bit more character."

The robot is self-balancing so that it can achieve a similar look to these personal assistant robots, and hopefully look a little less weird than the robot from *Rocky IV* in the

The robot will display an expression on the 7″ screen once a face is detected

As more weight is added up top, more balance is required near the wheels, hence these stabilisers

The whole thing is wireless and will eventually have a higher level of autonomy than it does currently

The expressions are admittedly a little terrifying at the moment, although they do allow the code to be tested

process. It has facial recognition built in so it can detect and react to people properly.

"For me it's a sandbox – a way to try all kinds of hardware and software," Kris explains. Since he wanted to do some intensive computations, in combination with a display and sound, he opted to use a Raspberry Pi 2. "The quad-core [CPU] came in really handy. I have the face recognition running in a separate thread on its own core, so the main process that handles the graphics, sound, and motion can run smooth and uninterrupted. And I still have two cores left over for future improvements."

While Kris says it's certainly not a project for beginners, it's not as hard as it seems. "If you have a reasonable amount of programming experience, it's definitely something you can make. You can find plenty of information about balancing robots online. For the face recognition I use OpenCV, an open-source computer vision library that has the hard parts already solved for you."

Kris made lot of the body and chassis himself with nylon sheets, together with some spare motors and drivers. There's an Arduino layer in the build as well, to aid with the balancing.

> It has facial recognition built in so it can detect and react to people properly

That works well and there are a few online videos you can watch of the little robot racing around on its two wheels (**magpi.cc/1URY7zT**). The robot still has some work left to be done. In particular, Kris is looking at mounting a lidar onto it so that it can have a better sense of its environment, allowing it to move around autonomously.

"This was my first project with a Raspberry Pi, but I really like that it has a full-blown Linux distro... I'm definitely going to use it more in the future."

OPERATE A ROBOT

>STEP-01
Balancing act

Once turned on, the robot starts to balance itself to stay upright. Much like the Boston Dynamics robot, pushing it will cause it to right itself.

>STEP-02
Remote control

The robot is not currently fully autonomous, so to control it you have to use a wireless keyboard connected to the Raspberry Pi. It will maintain balance as you drive it around, though.

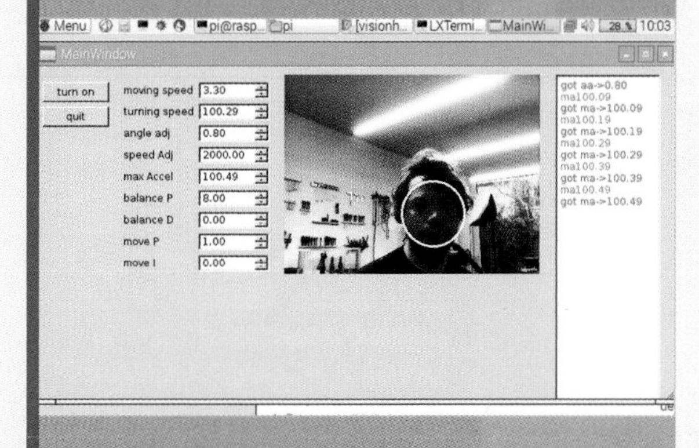

>STEP-03
I see you

The camera can detect faces. If one appears in its line of sight, the robot will look in the direction of the face and react to it with noises.

KRZYSTOF JANKOWSKI

A pixel artist and indie game developer, Krzystof likes to hack around with Raspberry Pis and Arduino gear in his spare time.
krzysztofjankowski.com / p1x.in

As the IR range is mostly heat, the sky will be darker than usual, while other objects are highlighted unusually

Take surreal, IR photos during the daytime for a slightly different look at the world

It works roughly like a normal camera – just point and shoot to take a photo!

EYE-PI CAMERA

Never mind a portable Raspberry Pi camera – how about a portable Pi IR camera for taking stunning and unique shots?

Quick Facts

- It was tested and completed in a morning
- Krzystof likes to make different portable projects using Raspberry Pi
- Krzystof plans to make a smart wall with RSS feeds and stats
- He plans to work with Arch next
- The project uses a B+ and not a Pi 2 or 3

Infrared (IR) cameras are traditionally used in low-light situations. Typically, IR is used in security cameras at night, and you can also implant an IR camera into your birdhouse for a live view of some hatchlings. Using it in daytime for 'normal' photos, though, is something quite unusual. However, it's what Krzystof Jankowski decided he wanted to do using a Raspberry Pi and the Pi NoIR Camera Module.

"I've been a photographer for many years and I've always wanted to take surreal (at least to our eye) infrared photos," Krzystof tells us, "but there was no commercial camera that can do that easily. Also, those cameras for astronomers were always pricey. Using filters was too time-consuming and requires using high ISO.

"When I was ready to buy the [Pi] Camera Module, I chose the NoIR to test how it works. After the few first tests, it turned out it works perfectly fine, but using it with wires, monitor, keyboard, and making photos by command line was absolutely not fun. A camera needs to be small and have a physical button to make photos."

Krzystof made a prototype "using a lot of duct tape" and went for a walk with it. It worked as he'd hoped, so he began work on a more robust and easier-to-use version.

"For me it was very easy as I know Linux, programming, and soldering," he explains. "I think that even for newbies it will still be easy. The whole thing is fairly basic to make yourself: connect camera, solder button and LED on, put wires to proper GPIO ports, and download my script and install a few required packages."

His custom script is what makes it possible, and is downloadable from GitHub (**magpi.cc/1K2PRgi**). It's only 23 lines long, but it has some tweaks to the way photos are taken to get them to look the way they do, and to optimise the speed as well, according to Krzystof:

"There's a small lag like in early digital cameras. For landscape photography it's absolutely acceptable, though. The only

Glare produces amazing effects when delving beyond the range of visible light into IR

downfall is the booting time: as it boots the whole of Raspbian, it takes 30–40 seconds. However, it can work for hours on my power bank without shutting down."

Right now, the camera is a little simple, and upgrades are planned for it eventually. Software-wise, Krzystof wants a software shutdown to prevent data corruption, but he also wants to add a small OLED screen for a live preview and settings. These settings would then be changed with additional switches on the build.

Krzystof has done many little Pi projects himself and doesn't plan to stop here: "I encourage people to experiment with Raspberry Pi – each project is an opportunity to learn something new. And it's always a lot of fun to make something yourself."

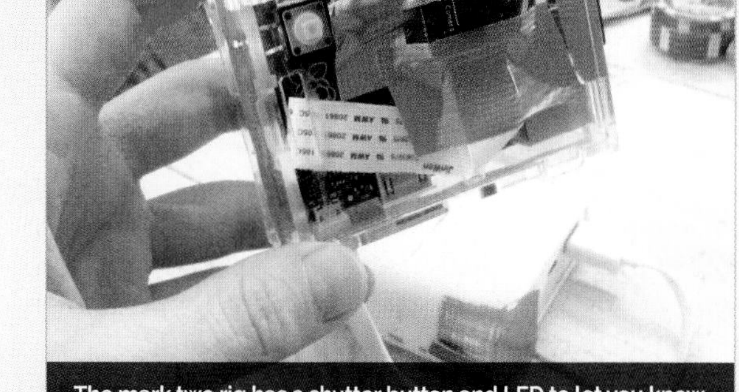

The mark two rig has a shutter button and LED to let you know when it's ready, although a preview screen will be added

TAKE A SURREAL PHOTO

>STEP-01
Boot process

There's no switch just yet, so plugging in the portable battery turns it on. This boots Raspbian on the Pi, and an LED turns on and then off once the camera is ready to go.

>STEP-02
Take a photo

Like with any camera, you just need to press the shutter button. This one activates the Python script to turn the LED on, set the camera up, and take the photo. It then turns the LED off.

>STEP-03
Get the photo

You could grab the photo off the SD card manually. However, it's set up to be retrieved using SFTP over WiFi as well, for quick access.

FREDERICK VANDERBOSCH

Frederick is an electronics hobbyist and software test and integration engineer. One of his recent projects won Element 14's 'Forget Me Not' challenge.
frederickvandenbosch.be

A Raspberry Pi-powered smart display rises out of the desk

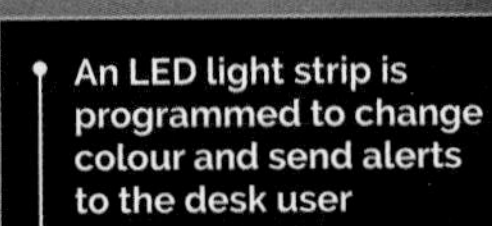

An LED light strip is programmed to change colour and send alerts to the desk user

Touch controls are hidden in the bottom-right of the table. Tapping them toggles desk features on and off

PIDESK

Make any desk job exciting with this futuristic PiDesk: a touch-controlled table with lights, sound, and a computer that rises from the surface

Quick Facts

- The entire build took about 18 weeks
- Frederick divided the project into sub-tasks to stay motivated
- The monitor lift is a drawer mechanism turned sideways
- The time it takes the screen to rise matches the Pi's boot time
- A USB sound card is used to power the built-in speakers

Nobody wants a boring desk, so one hobbyist, Frederick Vanderbosch, decided to build this futuristic workstation. Complete with a touch surface, speakers, and a motorised display that rises out of the table, the PiDesk is one of the cleverest projects we've come across.

"The build was part of a design challenge," says Frederick. The Sci-Fi Your Pi competition was launched by the Raspberry Pi Foundation and Element14 to inspire inventors to build smarter homes.

"PiDesk is an attempt at making a space-saving, futuristic-looking desk," Frederick explains. "It can change from a regular desk to a computer workstation and back at the touch of a finger."

The idea for the project came when he was running out of space in his workplace. "By combining a computer workstation and desk in one, I would be able to get extra space to work when the computer was hidden inside the desk. For the project's futuristic accents, I was inspired by the *Tron* movies, on which I based the light patterns of the desk."

At first glance, it looks like a normal desk. As soon as the user places their hand above a specific area, however, a desktop computer is powered on and starts rising out of the desk. This action is accompanied by visual and audio effects.

"Two Raspberry Pis are involved in the project," says Frederick. One serves as the brains of the desk; the second is a built-in desktop computer. As well as two Raspberry Pi units, the table contains a broad range of components.

The desk itself is from Ikea. "It's one of the cheaper models, which have the advantage of being hollow," reveals Frederick.

"I started by drawing some shapes on the desk to work out

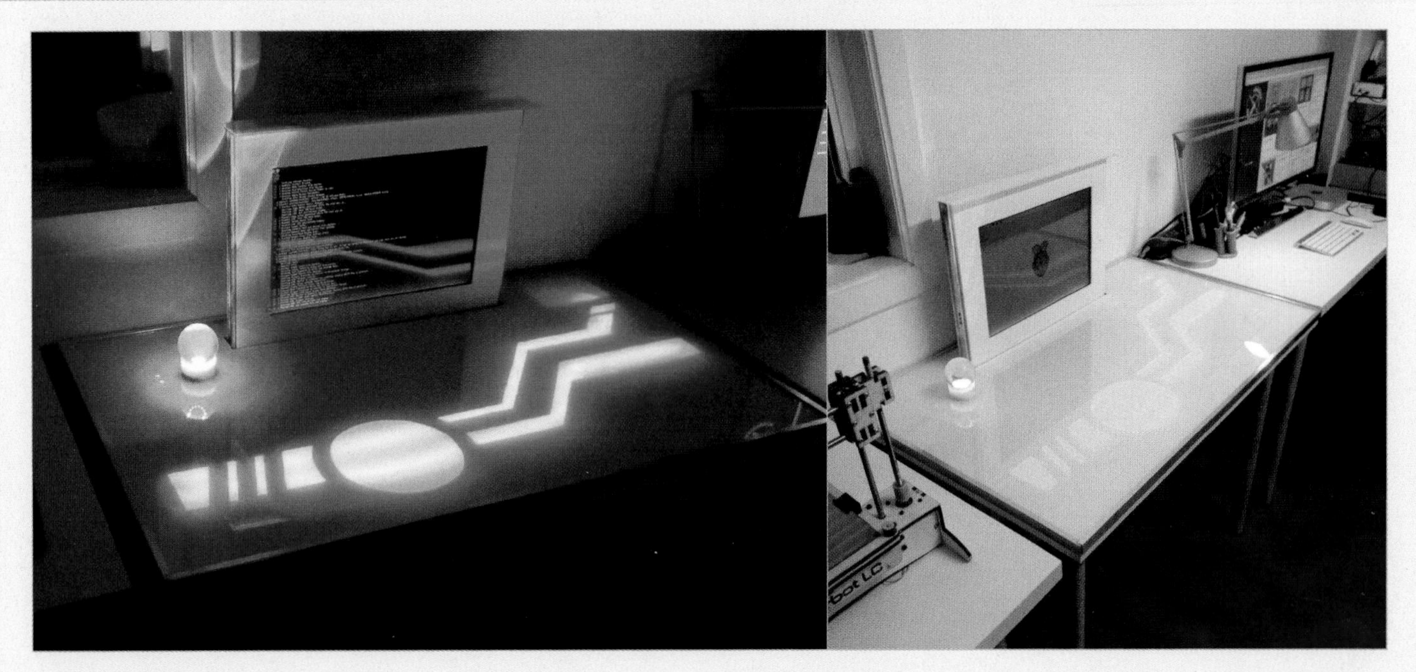

where I would perform the cuts and embed the electronics.

"Then the surface was recreated using two layers. The first layer was paper, which is used to diffuse the light and hide all the cuts and embedded electronics. The second layer is a large sheet of transparent Plexiglass, giving the desk a new and shiny surface."

Touch controls are embedded into the surface using a combination of conductive paint and copper tape. The paint creates touch-sensitive pads, while the tape makes a connection to the Raspberry Pi.

One neat feature you might miss is the built-in wireless charger. This is a "little bonus feature I had in mind," says Frederick. The Magic Lamp turns on when it is placed in the right spot. "The wireless charger is embedded in the desk, and when the lamp is moved on top of it, the lamp is powered." The light consists of the wireless charger receiver, a microcontroller board, and a ring of Adafruit NeoPixels.

If you're thinking of building a similar project, then planning is vital. "Plan ahead and think things through," advises Frederick. "Break down the project into smaller, more manageable projects. There's a lot to learn by building a project like this because so many different components are involved."

Above left The built-in LED strip and Magic Lamp are especially effective in low light

Above The finished product is a usable desk with a display that can be lowered to provide more surface area

BUILDING A PIDESK

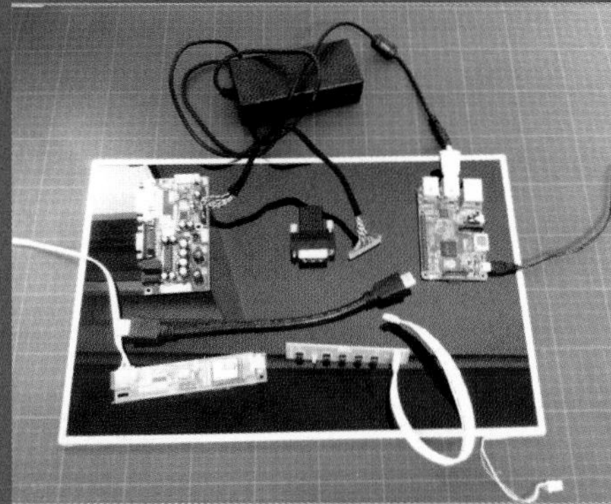

>STEP-01
Double Pi

Inside the PiDesk are two Raspberry Pis. One controls the desk interaction (lights, touch interface, and motorised display); the second acts as a built-in computer for the desk.

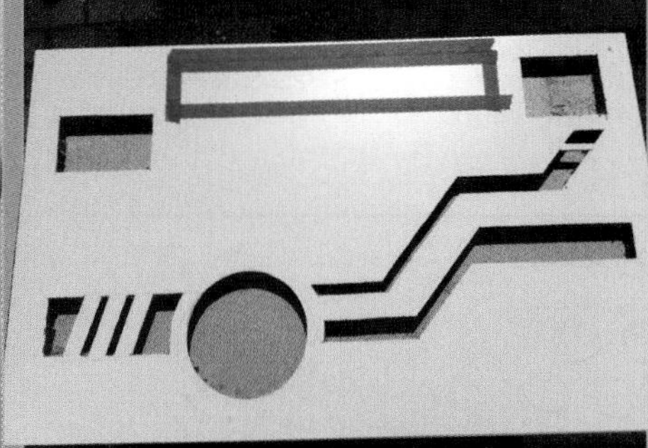

>STEP-02
Lights and controls

The desk itself is a cheap model with a hollow centre. Holes are cut into the surface and the components are placed inside. The cuts are filled in with paper and Plexiglass to recreate a flat surface.

>STEP-03
Desk assembly

A WS2812 LED strip is embedded into the desk to act as information lighting. Meanwhile, touch-sensitive pads are embedded to create interactive controls. A wireless charger is placed in the top-left to power the Magic Lamp.

THE GREAT RASPBERRY PI SPOOK-OFF

Get a look at these Raspberry Pi Halloween projects that are absolutely to die for…

Gather round, ghouls and girls, it's that time of the year again when scary rules supreme. Perhaps you're planning on dressing up to go trick-or-treating or marathoning a ghastly amount of horror films, but we've found some people who are deep in their lairs experimenting with a Raspberry Pi to create the spookiest projects the world has ever seen.

We've hunted down the most horrifying and wicked projects for your reading pleasure, but don't worry, the only dark art at work here is the odd bit of C programming. Beware, read any further and you'll be doomed to be inspired by these seven unholy projects… and have to read many more awful puns.

5	ABS-GHOUL-UTELY TERRIFYING
4	SPECTRE-CULARLY FRIGHTENING
3	DEADLY SCARY
2	GRAVELY CREEPY
1	QUITE SPOOKY

RASPBERRY PI HAUNTED HOUSE

Enter if you dare to the abode with home scare-tomation

STEWART WATKISS

Data centre manager, father, part-time Count Dracula
magpi.cc/2dqEMrU

t's late. The night grows dark and ou're near the end of your trick-or-treat run – but what's this? A house you've never seen before on your road. Eager for more sweets, you make your way to the door. A haunted house sign greets you, but you think it merely decoration. Approaching the door, you press the doorbell – only for glass to break and the light to go out. A door creaks, the sign you had dismissed flashes, and you hear screams as the lights come back on. Startled, you look to your right and realise monsters are partying in the garage next to you, celebrating another victim in their night of ghastly fun.

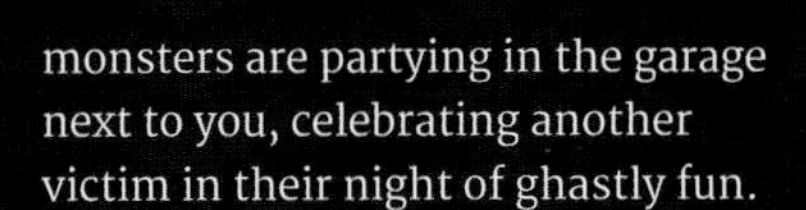

"I had been trying to think of something fun to do for Halloween and the Raspberry Pi was an obvious choice," the owner of this nightmarish house, Stewart, tells us. "I'd recently built a circuit for home automation using remote-control sockets and had the idea of using that to turn lights on and off automatically. I also spent some time looking around at shops to see what other Halloween props I could add to the project."

The system is deceptively simple, although there's a lot of different components to it. A dedicated doorbell is hooked up to a PiFace board that interacts directly with the Raspberry Pi and some Python code. Stewart chose the PiFace for this, instead of wiring up directly to the Raspberry Pi's GPIO pins, to make sure he didn't send any unwanted signals through the GPIO port – although with the right amount of research and careful wiring on a breadboard, you could do this without the PiFace. The PiFace directly controls the LEDs on a jack-o'-lantern and the haunted house sign, while the porch lights and the monster party lights are controlled by a wireless home-automation remote control that he directly soldered into.

"They are not designed to be used that way," Stewart mentions. "The solder joints were not very reliable and whilst they lasted for Halloween, they eventually came loose. Since I made the project, Energenie have released a Pi-mote Raspberry Pi board for their remote-control sockets, which is easier to use than having to solder onto the remote-control buttons."

Speakers play the appropriate sounds and music as dictated by the code, and the system is waterproofed as, well... Stewart lives in England. The results?

"I just managed to finish it in time for Halloween. We had friends coming over for our children's Halloween party who said they liked it, and the trick-or-treaters were certainly surprised by it. There was one young girl who was a little scared by it, but most thought it was fun rather than scary."

Above Surely it can't really be haunted... can it?

COMPONENTS LIST

CONJURE UP YOUR OWN VERSION

- PiFace
- Wi-Fi dongle (used during configuration and testing)
- 2× Reed relays (HE751A0510) – one for the on button, the other for off
- 2× LEDs
- 2× AA batteries with holder
- Doorbell
- Remote control socket with spare remote
- Plastic light-up pumpkin lantern (with test button)
- Plastic haunted house sign
- Waterproof box (or lots of wire to allow the Raspberry Pi to be installed indoors)
- Speakers (with amplifier)

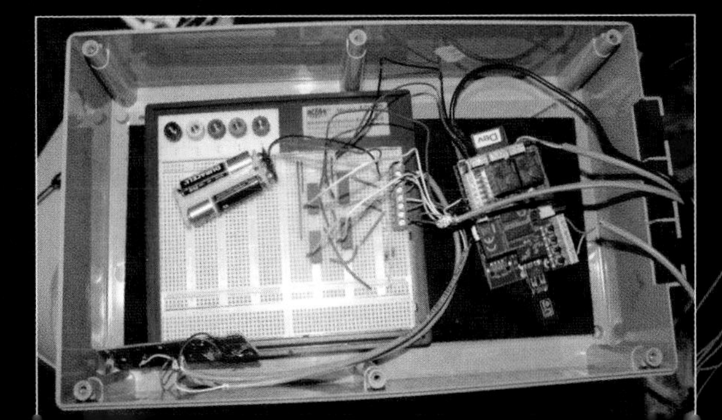

Below A simple box contains the Pi and all the electronics so that it's kept waterproof

SOCRATIVE ZOMBIE

A philosophical zombie, or a frightening, brain-munching head?

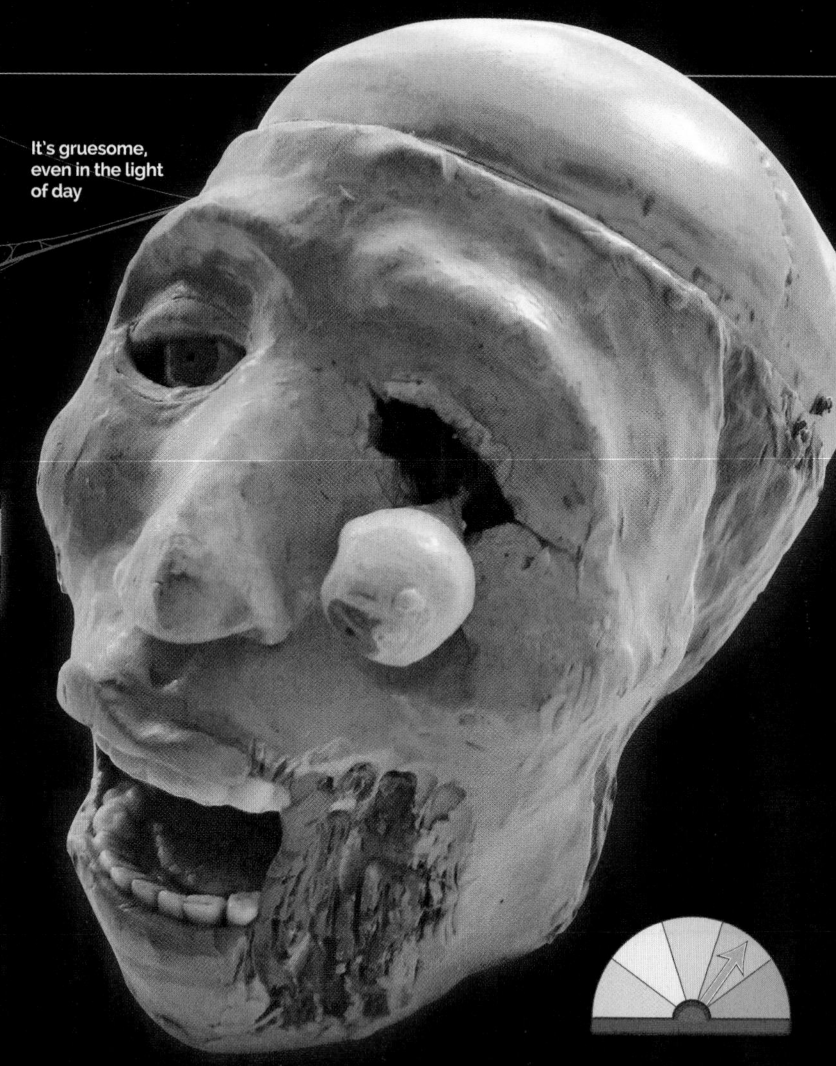

It's gruesome, even in the light of day

DAN ALDRED

Lead schoolteacher for Computing At School, raiser of the dead

magpi.cc/2dqFmWC

Out late at night, you should have known better than to enter the strange shed, but it was about to rain and you needed the shelter. A sense of unease comes over you as the door closes behind you. It's probably just because it's a bit of a creepy atmosphere. The winds begin to howl outside, but wait - that's not a howl, it's more of a gurgling groan. And it's coming from inside the shed with you. As you turn to confront the noise, you see an eerie glow from the corner of your eye. You fumble for your phone and turn the torchlight on to see the source of the noise and light… only to find an animated, undead head hungry for your flesh.

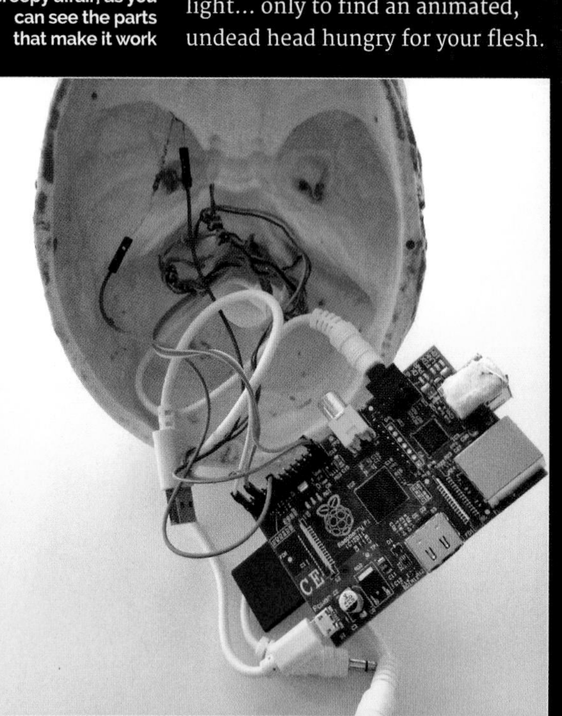

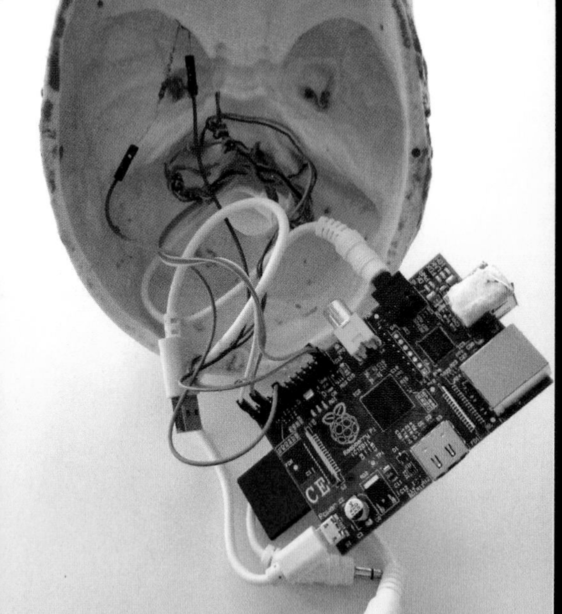

Below The inside of the zombie is a less creepy affair, as you can see the parts that make it work

Luckily, it's just a sculpture from a school project, but you get the picture. Its creator Dan Aldred tells us how he came up with such a horrifying idea:

"I wanted to create a Halloween hack that would scare people. Sheds are scary in the dark, but even more with a talking zombie head! I also wanted to create a interesting head that would ask my students questions related to their learning."

We assume they learnt the true meaning of fear alongside their new-found coding and soldering skills. The head is one of the few projects in this feature that makes use of sensors to know when someone is approaching it. In this case, a PIR motion sensor detects changes in temperature that correspond to a warm body entering its field of view. This means it unfortunately would not be able to sense its fellow undead. The sensor is placed in the mouth and controls a Python script which also hooks into LEDs and a speaker to complete the effect.

If you plan to replicate this project, Dan recommends a Raspberry Pi A+ due to its small size, and to create a cron job to start the program once the Raspberry Pi is powered up. How did it fare on the night?

"I had it in the classroom, it got dark about 4pm, and the students were very intrigued and excited," Dan tells us. "Then I moved it to my shed for the 31st and when the trick-or-treaters came around, they went in the shed and were scared. It made them jump; they really liked the zombie head."

COMPONENTS LIST

CONJURE UP YOUR OWN VERSION

- Zombie head
- PIR infrared motion sensor
- LEDs
- Speakers

PUMPKIN PI

Usually a delicious dish, can you stomach this version?

DREW FUSTINI

Software developer for element14 community, gourd sorcerer
bit.ly/1ilW2te

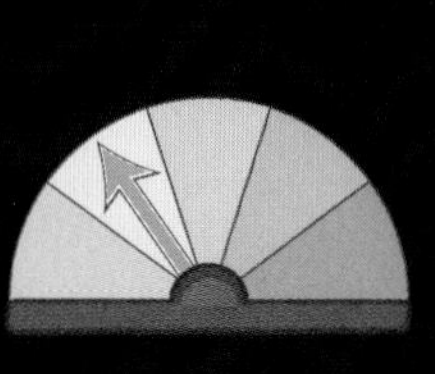

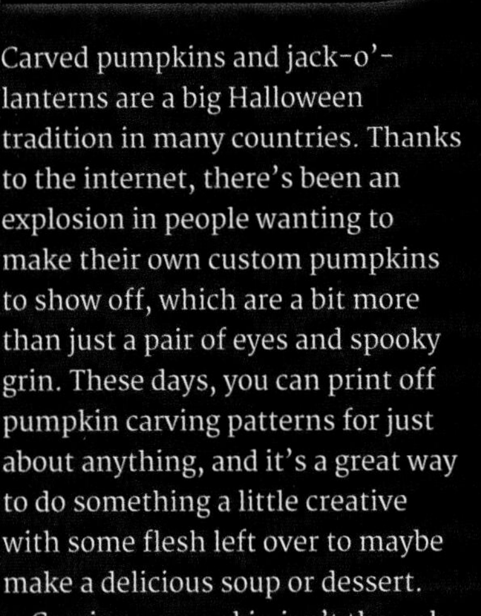

Carved pumpkins and jack-o'-lanterns are a big Halloween tradition in many countries. Thanks to the internet, there's been an explosion in people wanting to make their own custom pumpkins to show off, which are a bit more than just a pair of eyes and spooky grin. These days, you can print off pumpkin carving patterns for just about anything, and it's a great way to do something a little creative with some flesh left over to maybe make a delicious soup or dessert.

Carving a pumpkin isn't the only way to express yourself, however. To truly create a 'hack-o'-lantern', we need to add some electronics to its innards and dial up the spook-factor. That's exactly what Drew did with his Pumpkin Pi for the element14 community. Some of the projects he creates are inspired by upcoming holidays, and in this case Halloween was approaching.

The whole system is fairly simple: by activating a preset script from a web interface on his computer, the lights start rhythmically changing colour (check out the YouTube video to properly see it in action: **youtu.be/lIv8H7WPfQw**). The interface is mounted on the Pi and if you use his program for such a project, you can have multiple sounds and light sequences activating within the pumpkin.

The construction of the Pumpkin Pi requires a little more than just pressing a button, though. Taking a pre-carved pumpkin (you could carve one yourself), Drew then lined it with a large plastic food bag to make sure the electronics inside didn't get too damp from the pumpkin's moisture. A carving on the rear was used to pass the power cables through, and the breadboard with all the LEDs and such on was placed on the Raspberry Pi to save space. He also put on chopped-up drinking straws to diffuse the light better throughout the pumpkin. A speaker is attached and the pumpkin is done and ready for testing. If you want to make it a little more permanent, you can make use of a Pi Plate to solder the circuit and then mount it onto the Raspberry Pi.

The Pumpkin Pi is simple, but well thought out and put together. If you're going to be inspired by any of these Halloween projects, we'd recommend starting out with this one just to get the feel of creating a creepy contraption for your window or porch.

COMPONENTS LIST

CONJURE UP YOUR OWN VERSION

- A carved pumpkin
- Adafruit Pi Plate
- Adafruit Pi Box
- LEDs
- Resistors and transistors

Above A normal pumpkin, or a lost soul trapped in produce?

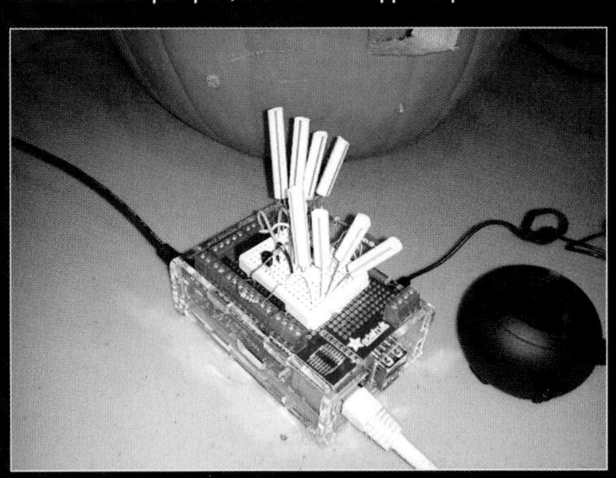

Above All you need to hack your pumpkin are some LEDs and some straws, apparently

Above left Significantly less scary with the lights on, nevertheless you can see the motion sensors mounted on crates that make it work

Above right Who's at the door?

SCARY DOOR (AND SCARY PORCH)

Don't get too close to this door if you value your sanity

CABE ATWELL

Electrical engineer, writer, crafter of cursed objects
bit.ly/1p6VQpW

You are entering the vicinity of an area adjacent to a location. The kind of place where there might be a monster, or some kind of weird mirror. These are just examples; it could also be something much better. Prepare to enter... The Scary Door.

Or not in this case, as this is not a real door. Or a *Twilight Zone* parody. While the Haunted House we started off this feature with shows the entrance to a spooky residence, this kind of project is what you might find inside as you wander around. It's a peculiar metal door, with a window you can see through. A knocking sound is coming from behind it; perhaps someone is lost? As you get closer, you see through the window a normal-looking lounge. You can't see anyone, but the knocking is still there and as you reach for the handle, a monstrous face appears.

Cabe's idea was to create a modern haunted house effect on the cheap that was different every time you saw it. As well as the pop-up scares, there's ghosts and monsters flying around in the 'window' (actually an LCD screen), and the scares and sounds you can create are as many as you can imagine. The knocking sound comes from pistons smashing against the door.

As well as the door, Cabe has previously created a Scary Porch, which he describes as "[an] exploration of my idea of consuming someone with light and sound, to the point where they wanted to run away." Unlike our Haunted House project from earlier, which was doorbell-activated, the porch could sense how far away you were from the door. As you started to approach, it would start playing creepy sounds and slowly turn on some bright red lights. As you got closer to the door, the louder the sounds became and the brighter the lights got, until screams and roars began playing when you were in knocking range.

"The Scary Porch was only set up in my shop," Cabe explains to us. "But, people did see it and did what I thought... they wanted to get away from the sound."

Both are quite elaborate projects and if you plan to make anything similar yourself, Cabe advises you exercise extreme caution unless you want to make yourself the centre of your Halloween display. This year he's toning it down a bit: "I plan to... make a wooded path, or [the] front yard a bit more scary."

At Cabe's house, we're sure it'll be more than just a bit scary.

COMPONENTS LIST

CONJURE UP YOUR OWN VERSION

- Too many to list here! Check out the link in the profile to find out what nearly $800 or more can get you in terms of spooky

SHOT THROUGH THE STOMACH

Take the scares around with you thanks to this gruesomely interactive costume

LUIS MARTIN

Maker, R&D engineer, major trauma victim
bit.ly/1KNZWot

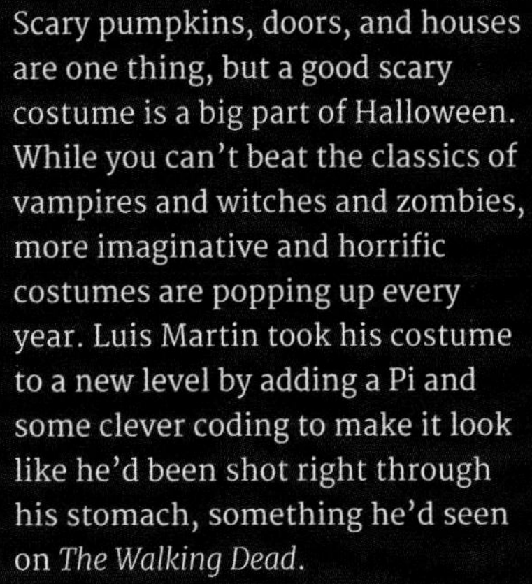

Scary pumpkins, doors, and houses are one thing, but a good scary costume is a big part of Halloween. While you can't beat the classics of vampires and witches and zombies, more imaginative and horrific costumes are popping up every year. Luis Martin took his costume to a new level by adding a Pi and some clever coding to make it look like he'd been shot right through his stomach, something he'd seen on *The Walking Dead*.

It's actually quite a simple and ingenious design. Using a Raspberry Pi as its main core, Luis took a Pi Camera Module and a 7-inch screen and had a live feed from the camera play onto the screen. By having the Pi and camera on his back, he was able to relay the live feed to the screen that was showing through his shirt, giving the illusion that there was indeed a hole in his stomach. Scary indeed – just don't ask him to turn around to ruin the effect.

It also involves a bit more than electronics, though: a later border was created around the edge of the screen to simulate the gruesome look of flesh to better create the effect through his clothes. With skin-tone paint added along with blood and detailing to get the right effect, he also cut up an old T-shirt and stained it with fake blood. "You have to be eager to stain your hands," Luis tells us. "Especially blood. The more blood in a zombie costume, the more realistic!"

With the shirt ready, Luis took a GoPro harness and had it hold the screen down to his stomach, as well as using it to attach the camera to the correct spot on his back for the illusion to work. This is then simply connected to the screen via the HDMI port on the Raspberry Pi - switch it on and you're ready to go!

It certainly sounds gruesome, and you'd think seeing a zombie walk around with a hole in his stomach would make everyone scream and run away. "Everyone wanted a picture through the hole, like some kind of blood-coated selfie?"

Kids these days, eh? You put a hole in your stomach and they're not even scared.

COMPONENTS LIST

CONJURE UP YOUR OWN VERSION

- Pi Camera Module
- 7-inch touchscreen
- HDMI cable
- GoPro chest mount harness
- Portable battery

Above Is there anything more indicative of modern culture than this image?

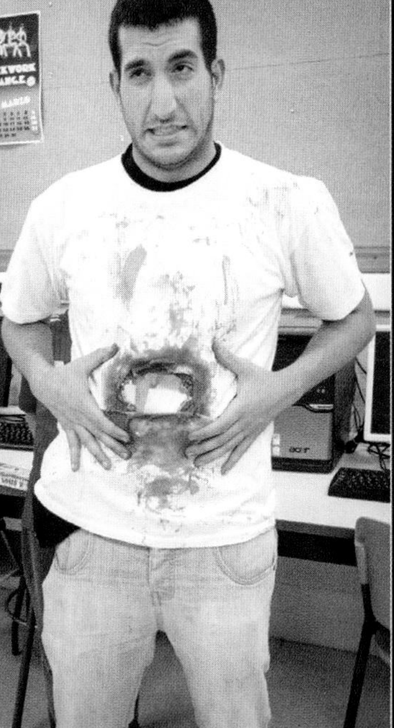

Left You don't have to pull a face, but it makes the picture look a bit better

Below The screen's fleshy border adds to the effect

HALLOWEENPI AT 3

A yearly tradition that will rattle your bones and help out the local food bank

CHRIS, PATRICK AND ELISHE

Solution architect, systems specialist, and srtist respectively, purveyors of haunted numbers
on.fb.me/1OuScjv

Scaring people as they come to the door is big business in spooks, it seems. We've seen porches, doors, and monster parties that give at least some warning or try to build a scary atmosphere, but the HalloweenPi is taking the jump-scare approach over building suspense.

To understand HalloweenPi, we need to learn about the history of Halloween at 3. A yearly tradition from the people at 3 Michelle Court, a display of their scariest Halloween-themed ideas is created to wow (and maybe frighten) trick-or-treaters or passers-by. Constantly trying to figure out a way to make each year better by adding to the display, Chris Kyte had a bit of a brainstorm:

"We were considering how to draw in a few more trick-or-treaters to our haunt. We had decided to start collecting canned food donations for our local food bank when I remembered the Raspberry Pi B+ I had received as a birthday present earlier in the year. I started to wonder if I could build a pneumatic prop or two in order to 'up our game'."

Currently, the massive tunnel houses a laboratory of rainbow-coloured mixtures in beakers and test tubes that react to black light, a projected puppet that compliments kids on their costumes, and all the other trappings of a Halloween-themed display. This new addition will have a motion-controller prop attached to it that will spring up and scare people as they arrive for Halloween at 3.

"The HalloweenPi Controlled Pneumatic Prop will be a really spooky piece," says Chris. "It will act as an ambassador to the haunt, reacting to the people who walk by: the prop will spread its wings wide and will scream a mighty scream! The way we've designed the props and pneumatics means that they are modular. They don't have to remain the same each year!"

The frights are for a good cause, though, as Hallowen at 3 takes donations for the local food bank. "The extra excitement generated by the pneumatic props should make a big difference to the number of people that show up. Hopefully, we'll see an increase in food donations as well."

We question how such an endeavour can be truly evil in the Halloween spirit with such a wonderful result, but we'll let it slide this time.

Below top The team are still hard at work on this year's project so they can be ready for the big day

Bottom What exactly happens at 3 Michelle Court?

COMPONENTS LIST

CONJURE UP YOUR OWN VERSION

- 4-channel relay board
- 2× PIR sensors
- Wireless key fob to arm and disarm the prop
- A pneumatic cylinder
- 12V pneumatic solenoid
- 12V amplifier

MULDER

Featured in this very magazine, this spooky skull comes alive

MIKE COOK
Writer, bone wizard
magpi.cc/1NqJnTz

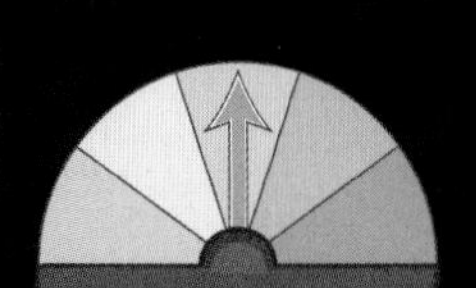

Zombie head? Too much flesh. Meet Mulder the skull, a very interactive head that you can control to scare the living daylights out of anyone who makes the mistake of passing by. With full control over his jaw, neck, and eyes, he can move around to watch anybody. Not only that, but you can light him up in a variety of colours and have him give out deadly screams or creepy owl hoots.

Mulder was made by Mike Cook as part of the Pi Bakery, and featured as a project you can create in issue 38 of The MagPi – head to magpi.cc to get started.

We won't spoil the surprise, but it involves a lot of soldering and tweaking as you install several servos and motors to articulate the eyes and jaw, along with several lights, a speaker system, and a way to control the neck. It's all controlled from an interface written in Python, the code listing and files from which are available in the tutorial.

We suggest you put a hidden camera near the skull so you can track trick-or-treaters as they approach your door. That's sure to scare them off, leaving more chocolate for you.

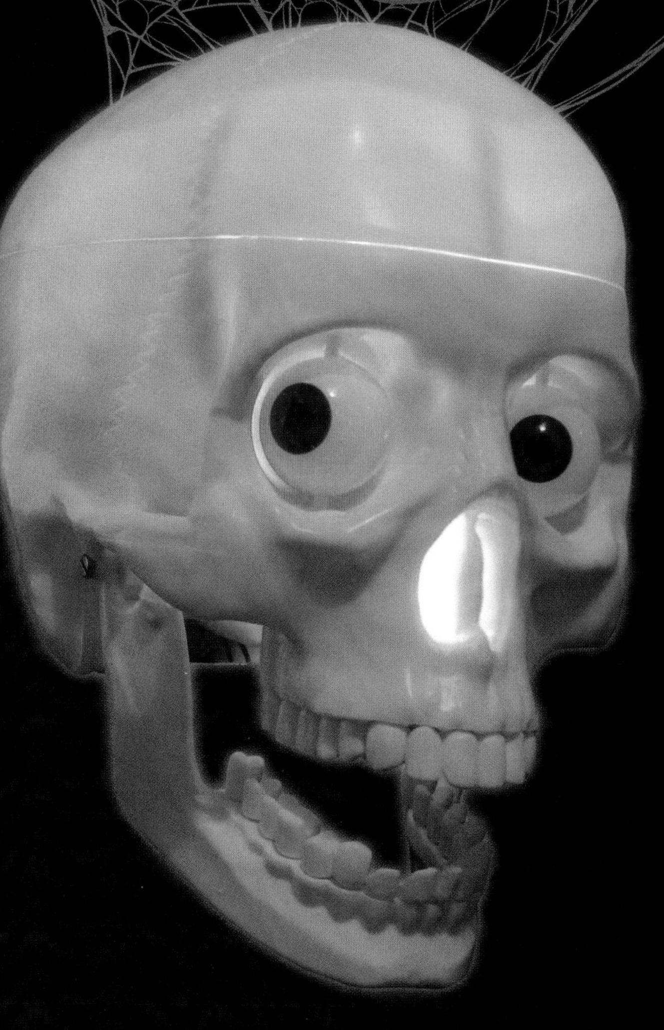

LIGHTS

Eyes	Nose
q	z
w	x
e	c
r	v
t	b
	n
	m

Right Eye
y
u

Cranium
a
s
d
f

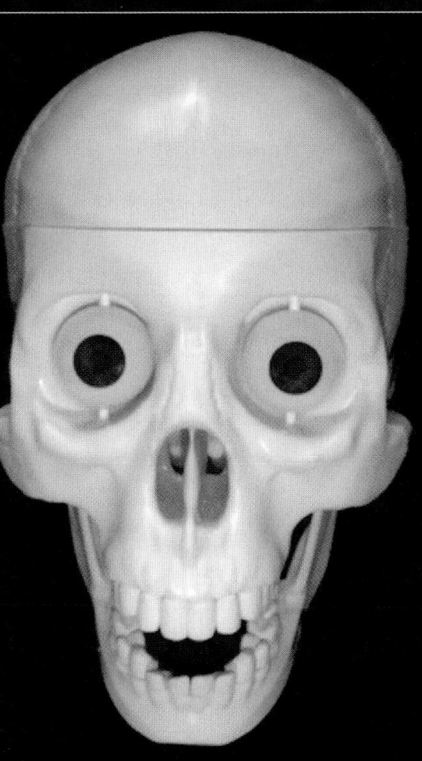

Movement

Jaw
o – Open
p – Closed

Eyes
1 – Forward
2 – Left
3 – Right

Right eye
4 – Forward
5 – Left
6 – Right

Left eye
7 – Forward
8 – Left
9 – Right

Neck
Forward
Nudge | Nudge
Stop
< – Full left
> – Full right

Sound h – Laugh j – Scream k – Door l – Kill ; – Thunder ' – Owl

Left Control Mulder with these simplish keyboard controls

Above In still images, Mulder looks quite tame and funny. In real life, it's a bit more scary

RESOURCES AND INSPIRATION

Not sure what to make with your Raspberry Pi for Halloween? Over the month of October, all the tech news sites will be inundated with Halloween-based stories, so keep an eye on them. Otherwise, you can head over to the Raspberry Pi tag of the Adafruit Learning System (bit.ly/1iroRHO), where you can get many great ideas for projects, along with the element14 community blogs and the Raspberry Pi Foundation's blog. Be inspired to be spooky!

SHOW US YOUR PROJECTS!

Are you doing something spooky for Halloween? Send us a picture or video to the MagPi Twitter account (@TheMagP1) or email us at magpi@raspberrypi.org and we'll include the best ones in our Community section next month! You should aim to be abs-ghoul-utely terrifying, but even a quite spooky will be good enough.

THE BEST RASPBERRY PI ZERO PROJECTS SO FAR

It took no time at all for people to start putting their brand new Pi Zero to work to power smaller and cooler projects

Well, the launch of the Raspberry Pi Zero was exciting, wasn't it? We sold out of all our copies and had to do a second print run, meaning there's a lot of Raspberry Pi Zeros out there already for people to start using in projects. Within days, people had done some incredible things: new hacks, updated hacks, proofs of concept... There was a lot of excellent stuff flying around. You could spend a good couple of hours going back through the #pizero hashtag for them all, but here's some of the best ones that we found while writing the magazine.

SEND US YOUR PROJECTS

ON TWITTER
@THEMAGPI

XBOX CONTROLLER PI ZER0

Bring new meaning to Xbox Media Centre by playing Doom built into a controller

There are many colloquial names for the original controller for the first Xbox. The Duke. The Bear. The Fire Hazard. Its size is attributed to the urban legend of being ergonomic for 'big American hands'; thanks to its size, however, it ended up being pretty perfect for Terence Eden's project.

"I wanted to play retro games on my TV," Terence tells us. "But I didn't want to buy yet another box to sit under there. I also didn't want to have to faff about with anything too complicated - wouldn't it be great, I thought, if I could fit an entire games console *inside* a controller?

Similar to our project idea (which ultimately resulted in a full tutorial you can find in this book), Terence

> "I wanted to play retro games on my TV"

thought originally about using the iconic NES controller. However, his wife pointed out that the larger Xbox controller would be perfect for what he had planned.

"So, this project was about stuffing a Pi inside a controller and using it to play *Doom*!"

Apparently it was a tight fit even for the Raspberry Pi Zero, meaning that some of the interior of the controller housing had to be shaved off to squeeze it in. "It's great that all the ports are along one side; that makes fitting it into tight spots much easier," Terence adds.

The component list was nothing fancy: just the standard cables needed to make the Zero work and the various assortment of tools needed.

Like everyone else, Terence has been inspired and is thinking how else he can make use of the Zero. "I'm curious as to whether it makes sense to use it as a door and window sensor. A Pi Zero is cheaper than a Z-Wave sensor so, as long as I can run power to it, I can place one on every door and window at home."

TERENCE EDEN
Web developer
shkspr.mobi

Fit a Pi Zero into a controller and you don't even need a console

USB OTG is a simple extension to the existing micro-USB spec. The connectors are really cheap: under £1 online. That said, it's pretty simple to make your own if you're confident with wiring and soldering. Terence spliced an old one directly into the controller lead

RetroPie is a brilliant resource for emulator fans, says Terence. He remembers the days when you had to scrabble around to get MAME to work, but this is a single disk image with everything built in. Magically, it even has kernel support for the Xbox controller via xpad – Terence thought he'd have to bodge that in for sure!

LAURA TREVAIL
Artist and tech explorer
twitter.com/lhtrevail

ENERGY MONITOR

The Internet of Things comes to the Zero with an energy consumption monitor

DANIELLE GRAYSTON
Software developer
twitter.com/Bladepanthera

"The project uses the Pi Zero as a tiny wee hub to connect my electronic devices at home to potentially anything," says Laura Trevail about the Pi Zero energy monitor. "It measures the device's energy consumption and publishes that data live, where it can be found and interacted with by Things elsewhere... While I'm brewing up [a drink], I can turn my kettle into something else somewhere completely different if I like, someone else can join me when I'm having a cuppa if they like, or use my inferred coffee consumption data (or whatever else I am sharing) to drive their own story in ways I may never have imagined."

So, a typical IoT device with a million uses from a simple concept! Apparently, Laura and Danielle spent the morning scouring two counties looking for a copy of *The MagPi*, and were surprised by how small the Pi Zero was when they finally got their hands on one.

The project makes use of Energenie, specifically an Energenie two-way PiMote and an Energenie MiHome monitor that uses David Whale's pyenergenie library (**magpi.cc/1jKpQ8L**).

Measure energy consumption using the Zero and a little extra hardware

PETER HOWKINS
Software engineer
marutan.net

RASPBERRY PI LAPTOP – ZERO EDITION

It's basically a full laptop, albeit very easy to open and maintain

A classic case for the Pi gets a revamp, thanks to the new size and spec of the Raspberry Pi Zero

Lego cases have been a major part of Raspberry Pi since it very first launched – especially when there was very little available in the way of cases at the very start. Taking that to its logical conclusion in a very short time, a Lego Pi-powered laptop was created, and everyone loved it.

"It's a small portable Raspberry Pi system, ideal for carrying to events without having to carry around a separate monitor and keyboard," its creator Peter Howkins tells us. "It combines two of my hobbies: Raspberry Pi and Lego. This is the third variation of my laptop; it started using an original Model B, then I rebuilt it to fit the B+ and Pi 2, and now it's using the Pi Zero."

Peter could not believe the price of the Pi Zero when he found out about it, but it really does drive down the cost of the overall Lego laptop build. It contains converters, hacked USB ports, a screen, a USB power pack, mini keyboard, cables, and an awful lot of Lego.

MATCHBOT

A great little robot that really shows off how versatile the Pi Zero really is

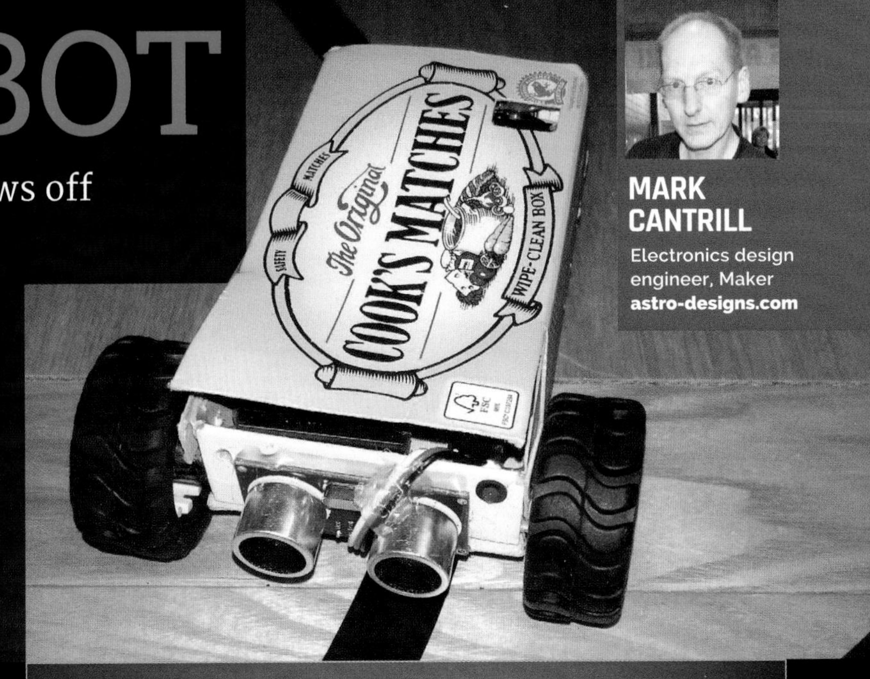

MARK CANTRILL
Electronics design engineer, Maker
astro-designs.com

In the last issue, we had an excellent 3D-printed Pi Zero robot, as made by Richard Hayler (**magpi.cc/1lLmeoi**). We didn't think we'd start seeing more robots until a few weeks down the line, but only a few days later, Mark's Zero-powered Matchbot crossed our Twitter feed.

"Matchbot, which was built in just a couple of days, is just for a bit of fun really," Mark tells us. "When the Pi Zero came out, I gave myself a challenge of building

> "Matchbot was built in just a couple of days"

something really tiny. I really wanted a break from other things that I've been working on recently, and a chance to join in the fun of Pi Wars. Plus, as a nice simple robot, I hope to use it to help get our two girls interested in the Raspberry Pi and physical computing."

While it would have been amazing in itself to use spare robot kit he had lying around, Mark actually repurposed the parts of a CamJam EduKit 3 to build it. "It's built from a large matchbox, two tiny geared motors, plus wheels, and the rest (motor drivers, sensors, and battery box) is mostly from a CamJam EduKit 3. There's also a 5V regulator so that it can use the motor battery to power the Pi."

As well as the motorised wheels, the Matchbot features ultrasonic distance sensors and a line-following sensor.

Fitting the robot inside a matchbox is a feat in itself. However, the control interface for the Matchbot is inspired – with no WiFi to talk to it remotely, Mark has programmed the distance sensors to change mode depending on how long you hold your hand out in front of it, with a flashing LED giving you an indication of what mode you've activated. On the day, at Pi Wars, it handled the line-following course very well!

The LED flashes twice for the line-following program, three times for the proximity test, while four and five flashes will exit the script and shut down the Pi respectively

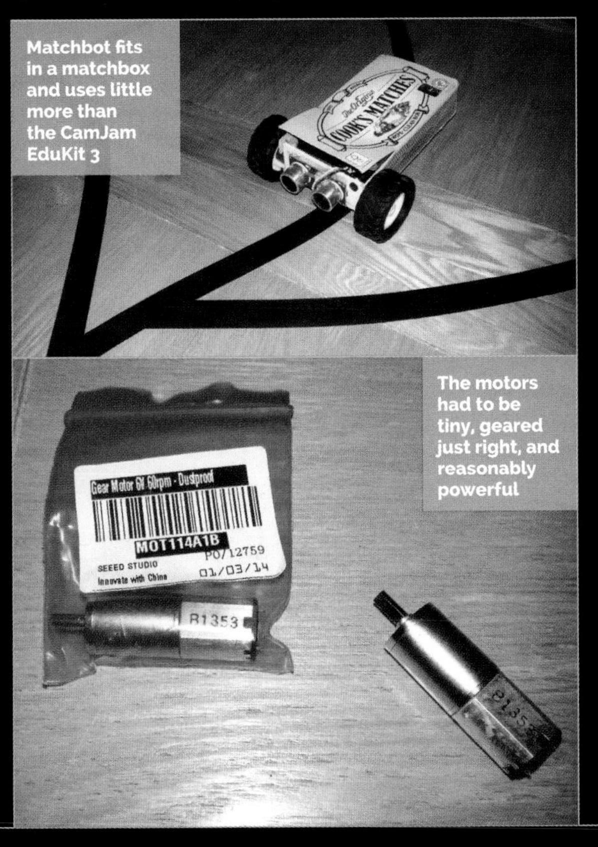

Matchbot fits in a matchbox and uses little more than the CamJam EduKit 3

The motors had to be tiny, geared just right, and reasonably powerful

SPANNER SPENCER

Spanner is the community manager for Element14, an online community for engineers.
magpi.cc/1m75kk9

PI ZERO RETRO GAMING SYSTEM

Spanner Spencer wasted no time hooking up the Pi Zero's RCA connection to a classic cathode ray tube television. The Pi Zero Retro Gaming system is the real deal...

Quick Facts

- It works like a dream with Xbox 360 controllers
- The whole project took only two hours to build
- The Pi Zero can be overclocked to 1GHz for gaming
- It uses RetroPie, part of the standard NOOBS installation
- The Pi Zero can even play some original PlayStation games

It's fair to say that the Pi Zero caused more than a bit of splash. Our new favourite smallest computer topped Twitter and caused chaos at British newsagents when it was cover-mounted on *The MagPi*. Even President Obama got a copy.

Those lucky enough to get a Zero quickly created some great projects and discovered its nuances. That the Pi Zero has RCA output was not lost on Spanner Spencer, community manager at Element14, who realised it could be inserted inside an old television.

"I picked up some crummy old Grundig for 20 quid at a charity shop in Huddersfield," says Spanner. "It's nice to think that the first ever Pi Zero games machine did its bit for charity.

"Initially, I soldered a couple of flying leads to the back of the composite phono socket," he continues, "but there was something skewey going on, and I didn't get a picture. Instead, I switched to using the composite video in on the SCART socket and then soldering the wires onto the PCB underneath to avoid external wiring.

"The video signal came from the Pi Zero's composite output, which I soldered directly. It's a tad permanent, and it would have been better to add some pins

Using RetroPie on a classic CRT television is a great way to play old console games

Attaching a USB joypad (like this Xbox 360 controller) enables you to play games with minimal setup

A USB hub is placed on the side of the television. New games can be then added to RetroPie without opening the TV

The wires from the Pi Zero are attached directly to the SCART board inside the TV

> The Pi Zero is small enough to tuck inside the television

and a plug to make the board easier to remove, but there you go."

The Pi Zero is small enough to tuck inside the television, but that makes it hard to access. However, RetroPie enables you to transfer games by via a USB drive, so Spanner decided to use a USB hub to provide an external connection.

"We cobbled together a powered USB hub from a pound-shop hub," he tells us, "[and] soldered a socket onto the power lines on the PCB and replaced the cable with a butchered micro-USB one. We also ran a second micro-USB cable out of the hub to power the Pi Zero, so both the hub and the board run from a single 5V power supply.

"Other than having to change the composite output from the default NTSC to PAL in the Pi Zero's config file, it all worked right out of the box. We're able to play classic computer and console games like the Mega Drive, SNES, Amiga, ZX Spectrum, and loads of others."

The Pi Zero turns out to be great for retro gaming. "Given the extra RAM overhead and being able to crank the Pi Zero up to 1GHz, it's coped with RetroPie beautifully," says Spanner. "For the older systems, you don't even need to overclock it, so make it easy on yourself if you're planning on playing Atari 2600 games."

Safety announcement! Working inside old CRT televisions is dangerous (and not in a cool way). It is important to wear safety goggles and to discharge the electricity completely. Residual charge in an old CRT television can easily kill you. Please don't open an old TV set if you don't know what you're doing; it's wiser to connect the RCA from the Pi Zero to a SCART cable and plug this into the television, or use a newer HDMI monitor for your retro-gaming system.

A cheap USB hub was adapted to provide external access to the Pi Zero inside the television

PUTTING A PI ZERO INSIDE A TELEVISION

>STEP-01

Pi Zero RCA output

The Pi Zero comes with composite RCA output connectors on the board. Two wires are connected from the Pi Zero to pins 18 and 20 on a SCART socket.

>STEP-02

USB connection

Spanner took apart a USB hub and modified it to share power with the Pi Zero. A section of the TV is cut away to provide external access to the USB ports.

>STEP-03

NTSC to PAL

Pi Zero's config file needs to be changed to get colour on a UK PAL television. Edit the config file and uncomment the line `sdtv_mode=2`. The system is now ready to play games.

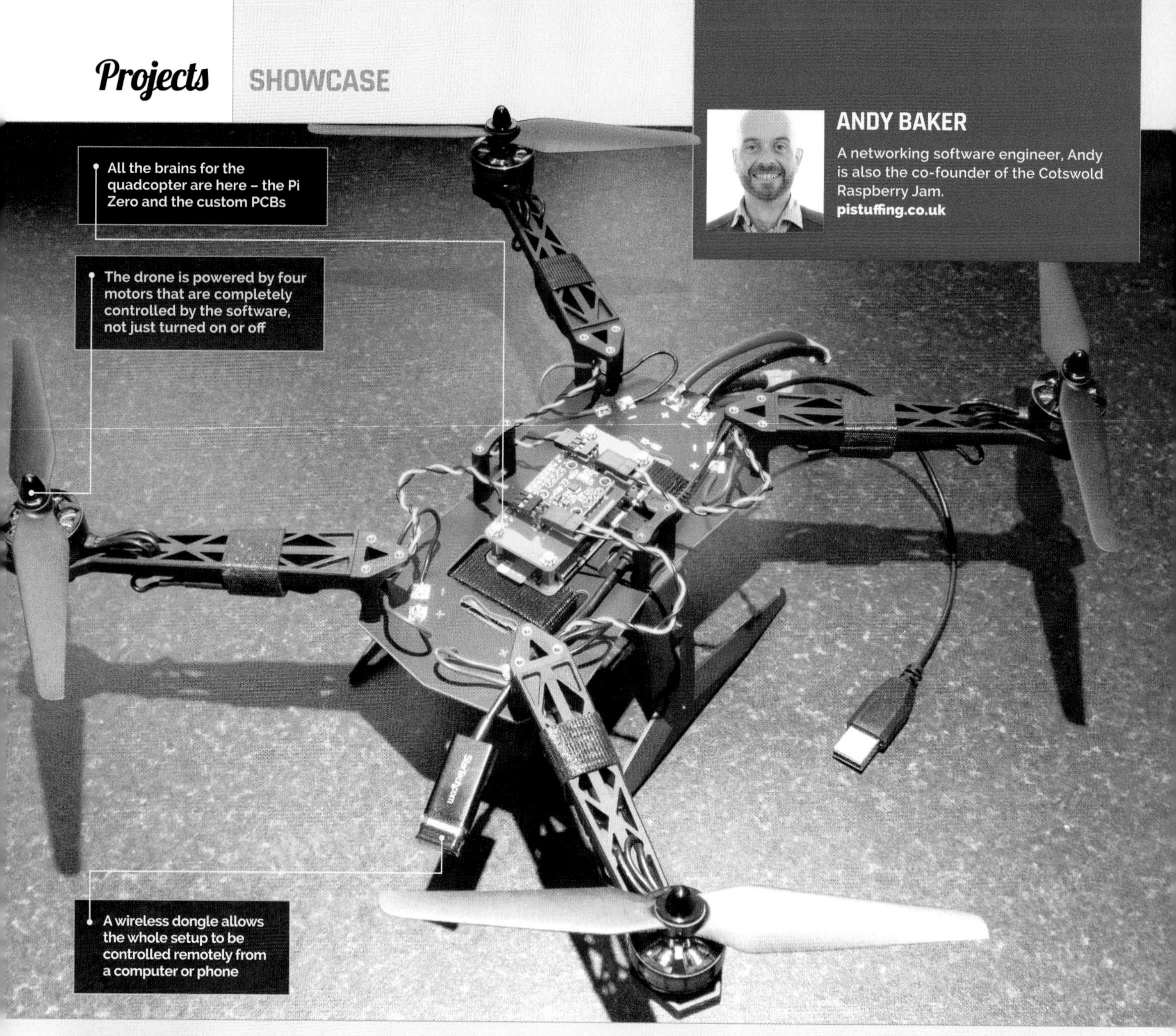

All the brains for the quadcopter are here – the Pi Zero and the custom PCBs
The drone is powered by four motors that are completely controlled by the software, not just turned on or off
A wireless dongle allows the whole setup to be controlled remotely from a computer or phone

ANDY BAKER

A networking software engineer, Andy is also the co-founder of the Cotswold Raspberry Jam.

pistuffing.co.uk

ZOE THE ZERO

The first in what will more than likely be a swarm of Pi Zero-powered drones, Zoe the Zero is the continuation of a long-held dream

Quick Facts

- Andy claims it's taken him three years so far
- An older version appeared in *The MagPi* #19
- It couldn't actually fly for the cover image, though
- Raspbian Jessie fixed a number of programming errors
- It's only his second Pi project

When we were planning issue 40 of *The MagPi* with its cover-mounted Pi Zero, we had a big brainstorm about the kind of projects we could do for features, and maybe also as future covers. One thing that we noted was that the Pi Zero could be great for powering quadcopters and other drones. In just over a month since the issue hit shelves, Andy Baker managed to start the trend and create his own drone.

"I completed my first Pi project (a wheeled 'Turtle' robot) in December 2012," Andy tells us. "I wanted to move on to something that was a real challenge, and quadcopters were just starting to appear commercially. I was completely ignorant of how they worked, so I wanted to fill that gap in my understanding and have some fun at the same time."

Andy has spent the last few years building, testing, and experimenting to create his very own quadcopter from scratch: "I haven't finished yet, primarily because I actually wanted to work it out all by myself, without borrowing anyone else's code or guidance. There was a lot of experimentation and learning involved, including a lot of wasted time taking the wrong direction and backing up when I hit a metaphorical brick wall – or, more precisely, when I couldn't stop

The turtle was Andy's first Raspberry Pi project back in 2012

The Pi Zero looks a bit dwarfed by Zoe, but powers it just fine

the quad from hitting a physical brick wall."

The Raspberry Pi Zero helped Andy bring Zoe back and make it operational again after a few tweaks. The years-long creation wasn't always so quick or simple, though.

"Other than having a custom HAT PCB, the physical build is very simple due to the off-the-shelf combination of frame, motors, and props," says Andy. "But the software interfacing to hardware was a major challenge and the testing is expensive; the innate instability of a quadcopter means any imperfections ultimately end with a crash and corresponding hardware damage. Despite it 'only' costing about £200 to build the Pi Zero quadcopter from scratch, it's cost me more than ten times that over the last few years to reach this stage."

Interestingly enough, Andy doesn't plan to really use the drone as such, instead treating it as a challenge to just make it work.

"If it ever reaches that stage, I'll almost certainly shelve the project as complete and start on something new – perhaps a fusion reactor, or infinite improbability drive. But at the moment, there's plenty of interesting stuff I can add to the very basic quad I have now to keep me interested for a long time yet."

While it may have taken Andy years, there's now a lot more info and kits available to take a few shortcuts with. Hopefully, in the future, we can show you how to create your own quadcopter.

OPERATING ZOE

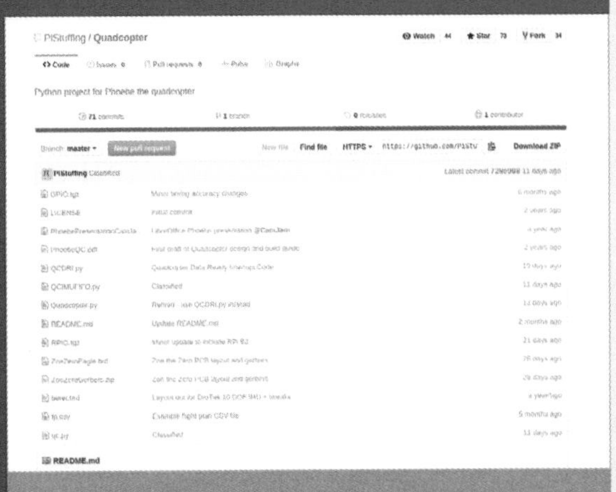

>STEP-01
Starting flight

A preprogrammed flight plan begins for Zoe, with targets for what it should do. This includes ascending at a specific speed for a specific amount of time, hovering, etc.

>STEP-02
In-flight checks

The sensors on the drone provide input as to what it's doing, as a way to make sure everything is operating as it should during the plan.

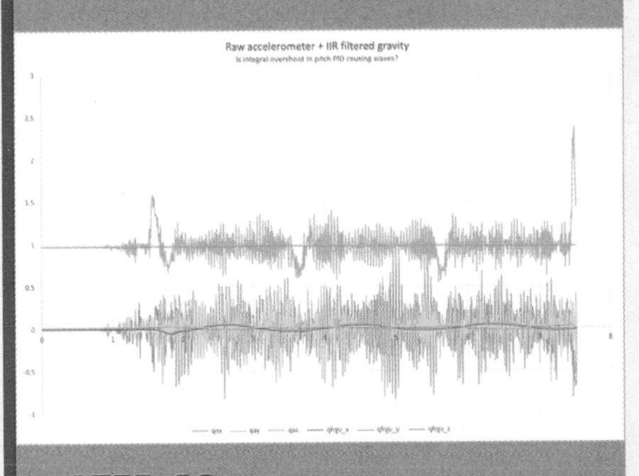

>STEP-03
Flight corrections

A lot of maths 'glues' the flight plan and data input together to make sure everything is on track, correcting any mismatch in the props/motors.

IDEIN, INC

Yasuyuki Yamada , Koichi Nakamura and Yukimasa Sugizaki make up the team at Idein, Inc, which works on AI technology.

idein.jp

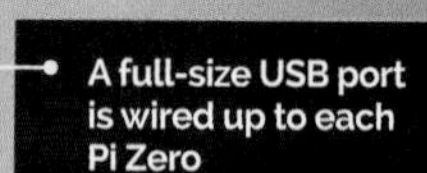
A full-size USB port is wired up to each Pi Zero

16 Pi Zeros working in parallel means 16 1GHz cores and 8GB of RAM are available

The board is powered by one supply on the rear that can activate all 16 Pi Zeros

Quick Facts

- The board works with any number of Pi Zeros
- From idea to completion, the cluster took six weeks to build
- A Compute Module is used in the Actbulb
- The team have been studying the VideoCore GPU for future projects
- The board is 20cm × 20cm × 5cm, even with Pis attached

PIZERO CLUSTER BOARD

Turn your Raspberry Pi Zeros into a number-crunching cluster of computers with this custom-made board

When the Raspberry Pi Zero was being made, Eben Upton mentioned to us how one box of Pi Zeros holds hundreds of them. Hundreds of cores and hundreds of gigabytes of RAM – a crate of power, if used correctly. We never managed to work out the FLOPS one box could theoretically process, even if that might not be feasible. However, a Japanese company also saw the power of the Pi Zero in numbers and has created the PiZero Cluster Board, which allows up to 16 Pi Zeros to do parallel computing. We spoke to Koichi Nakamura, representative director of Idein, Inc, about the cluster board:

"When I was playing with Raspberry Pi Zero, I realised that costs of cables and adapters are relatively expensive, and found a solution that used micro USB plugs for cradles. I used this idea to create our computer cluster... I think it's useful for many other projects, [but it was] originally designed and developed for our internal purposes."

Idein is currently developing the Actbulb, a Pi-powered sensor suite that fits into standard lightbulb sockets to use in any way you see fit. Sensors include a microphone and cameras; it's also internet-enabled and has an audio speaker.

"Since we are developing products using Raspberry Pi, we need a cluster of many Pis for software development and tests," Koichi explains to us. "It's also useful to set up many other devices... We plan to create a cluster to enable setup of hundreds of our devices a day."

Above The Pi Zero is plugged in via its micro USB power and data ports. Each unit also requires an SD card with an operating system installed

Below The Pi-powered sensor that necessitated the creation of the Pi Zero cluster board. It attaches to standard light fittings

It's had a huge reaction online, with many people excited by the idea of the board. However, Koichi believes it's quite a simple project:

"PiZero Cluster Board is just a collection of 16 identical circuits. Each circuit draws one Ethernet port and one USB port from [each] Raspberry Pi Zero's micro USB port, using an SMSC LAN9512 chip. There are also 16 power supply circuits to generate 5V and 3.3V from a 12V single power source for Raspberry Pi Zero and LAN9512. All 16 circuits are the same."

> We plan to create a cluster to enable setup of hundreds of our devices a day

With Pi Zeros in short supply, the team were unable to secure enough to complete the cluster at first. Fortunately, we at *The MagPi* managed to call in every favour, pull every string, and beg, plead and borrow to get them the remaining 15 Pi Zeros they needed for tests.

The insides of Actbulb are a lot more complex than a normal light bulb

Due to the popularity of the board and its many uses, Koichi plans to put it on Kickstarter once they're ready to crowdfund it. It will be an improved version of the prototype we've seen online.

"In our current plan, the number of Raspberry Pi Zeros and USB ports is reduced to 14," Koichi tells us. "We'll also add an on-board Ethernet switch to the board, and the number of ports is reduced to two." This improvement will reduce the number of Ethernet ports and cables required, and so lower the board's overall cost.

CREATE A CLUSTER

>STEP-01
Set yourself up

To start with, all you need to do is slot in your Raspberry Pi Zeros. It works with as few as one and as many as 16 at a time.

>STEP-02
Hook it up

The next step is to connect it all up. The Ethernet switch and cables should go in first, followed by the AC adapter to power it.

>STEP-03
Work in parallel

That's it! Turn it on and you can program it using MPI or any other methods that utilise multiple Pi Zeros at the same time.

TUTORIALS

Follow along to these hand-picked projects and learn how to make something truly amazing

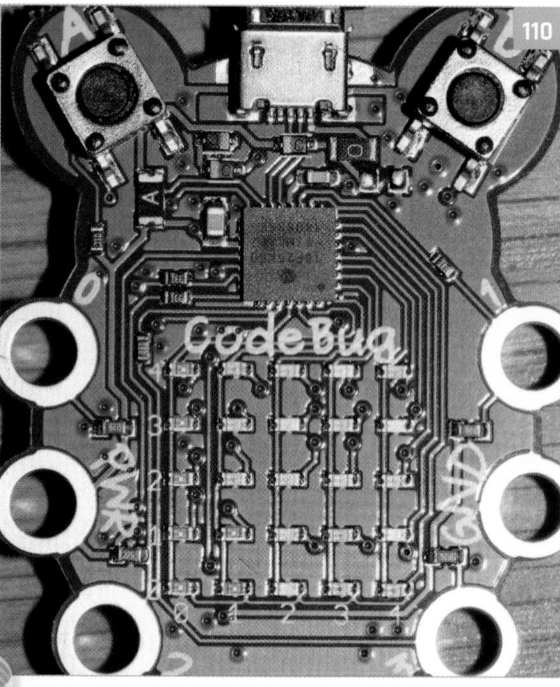

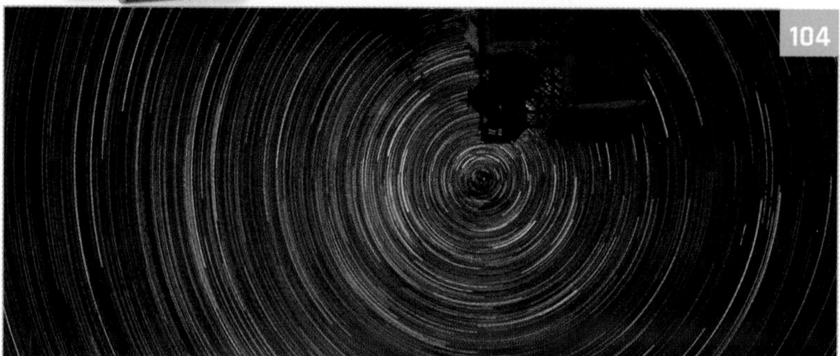

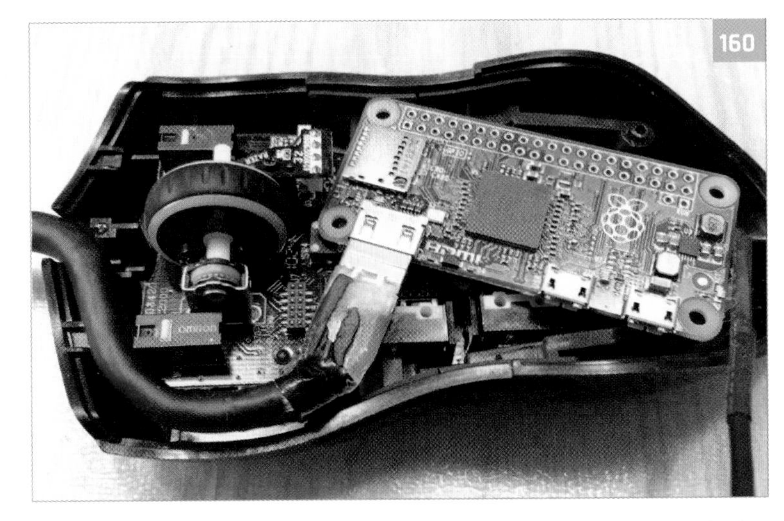

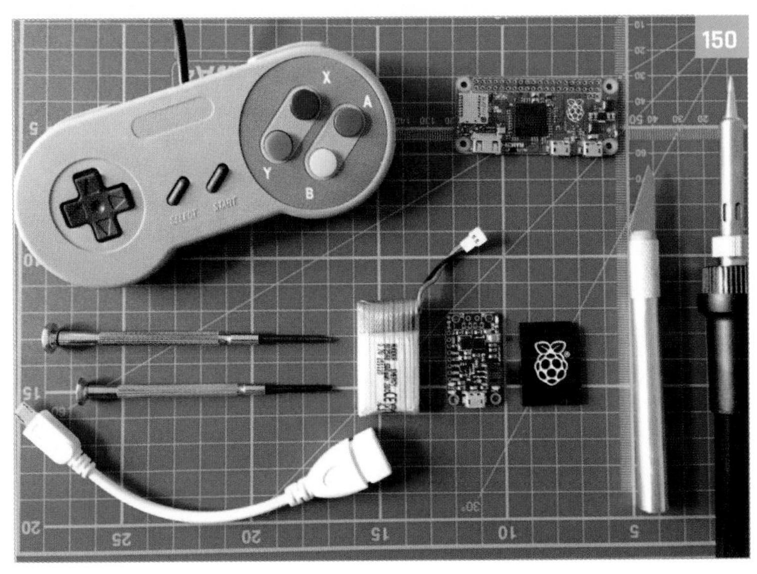

Tutorials

ROB ZWETSLOOT

An avid coder and Raspberry Pi enthusiast with a history of building many things with a Raspberry Pi
magpi.cc

GET STARTED WITH SENSE HAT

You'll Need

- Sense HAT - magpi.cc/1TGGUt5
- Sense HAT library
- Raspbian - magpi.cc/1MYYTMo

The exciting new sensor add-on for the Raspberry Pi is very easy to use once you know how. We'll show you how, then.

This issue we've had a bit of a Sense HAT blow out, with our interview with the creators early on in the mag, and a review of it later on. It's an amazing piece of kit and hopefully by now you've been able to snag yourself one.

While it's definitely easy to use, there's a few things you need to learn first to get it going as it's reliant on programming it via Python scripts at the moment. The commands are very simple though, so we can show you in only a couple of pages how to start getting the most out of your new toy!

Learn how to use the features of the Sense HAT, and figure out how to make this smiley face

All you need is a Raspberry Pi to use the Sense HAT - no other gadgets!

>STEP-01

Installing the Sense HAT

Getting the Sense HAT ready to use is quite simple. Turn off your Raspberry Pi and make sure your Raspbian SD card is inserted if it isn't already. Place the Sense HAT on the GPIO pins, carefully aligning them before pressing down firmly so that it properly attaches to the Raspberry Pi. Once that's done, turn the Raspberry Pi back on. If it's attached properly, the LEDs on the SenseHAT will light up in a rainbow pattern during boot time. When it gets to the desktop, the pattern might turn off but that's normal.

>STEP-02

Sense HAT library

The Sense HAT won't work straight away on every Pi. You may need to download a custom script that will install the necessary libraries for Python to access it if you're using a much older version of Raspbian, and update some of the core kernel code so that it runs properly. You can download and install the update by opening the terminal and running these commands:

```
$ sudo apt-get install sense-hat
$ sudo pip-3.2 install pillow
```

After both commands have run their course (they might take a few minutes each to complete) you'll need to reboot the Raspberry Pi. You might as well do this from the command line with:

```
$ sudo reboot
```

>STEP-03

Get started with Python

We can start controlling the Sense HAT by writing code in Python. As the Sense HAT is using the GPIO pins, we need to have administrative privileges to execute the scripts. This means opening IDLE using

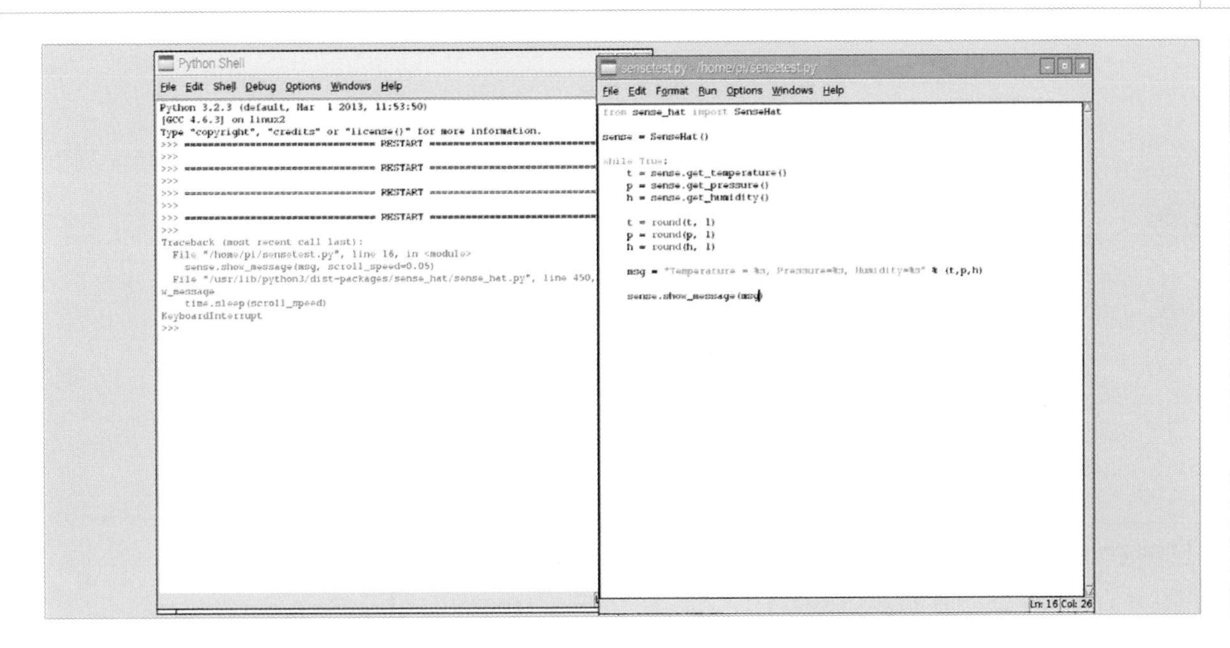

EASIER PAINTING

Set colours to specific letters using lists (e.g., red could be r=[255,0,0]). You can go even further and create a matrix of letters that can display an image

Left You can set sensor outputs as variables to then be printed out on the LED, combining all the functions of the HAT

sudo in the command line with:

```
$ sudo idle3 &
```

Open up a new window to start writing a Python script. Each Sense HAT script needs to begin with two lines to import the relevant Python module, and then a line to turn it into a variable that makes writing the code easier.

```
from sense_hat import SenseHat

sense = SenseHat()
```

>STEP-04

Text and pictures

The easiest thing to start off with is to get text scrolling along the LED display. The library for the Sense HAT will automatically turn a string of words into a scrolling banner across the matrix. A line like the following will create it:

```
sense.show_message("Hello World!")
```

You can control the scroll speed and colours as well. You can also manipulate the individual LEDs by telling the script which pixel to change, and give it an RGB colour variable with something like:

```
sense.set_pixel(0, 0, [0, 0, 255])
```

Put this in a variable set the top left corner pixel as blue

>STEP-05

Environmental sensors

Using two of Sense HAT's sensors, you can measure temperature (in degrees C), pressure (in millbars) and relative humidity (as a percentage). You can get the three individual measurements with:

```
sense.get_temperature()
sense.get_pressure()
sense.get_humidity()
```

You'll have to attach them to a variable thought (e.g., t = sense.get_temperature()) so that you can print out the reading or display it on the LED matrix.

>STEP-06

Motion sensing

The gyroscope, accelerometer and magnetometer can be used to detect motion in real time. This is a little trickier to use than the other parts, as it involves understanding how the three-dimensional values represent the orientation of the Raspberry Pi, and then how the accelerometer can be used to figure out the movement within space. Both the gyroscope and accelerometer functions (get_orientation(). values() and get.accelerometer_raw().values() respectively) will return three values from which you can use however you please.

This handy guide will explain all you need to know on the motion sensors: **http://bit.ly/1UBdEmA**

SLOW DOWN THE TEXT

You can edit your scrolling text's speed by adding the scroll_speed option. Use something like: `sense.show_message("Hello World!", scroll_speed=0.5)`

Below The most basic script you can write, but it's very useful to get to grips with the basic coding of the Sense HAT

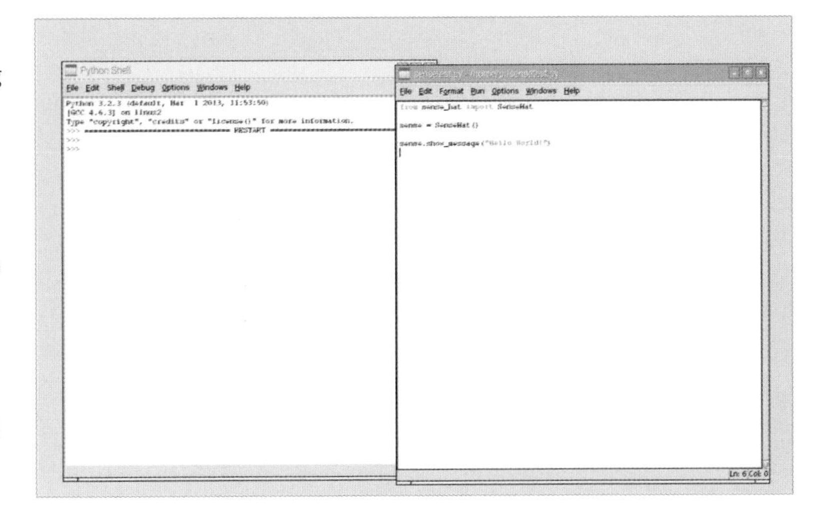

ROB ZWETSLOOT

Tech writer, avid coder, and Raspberry Pi enthusiast with a history of building many things with Raspberry Pi
magpi.cc

Create simple images or more advanced pixel art to represent your favourite thing

The 8×8 display on the Sense HAT may be simple, but it has a wide range of colours and is fully programmable

PIXEL ART ON SENSE HAT

Make use of Python and the Sense HAT's LEDs to read and display 8×8 pixel art

You'll Need

- Raspbian **magpi.cc/1MYYTMo**
- Sense HAT **magpi.cc/1TGGUt5**
- Pixel art

INSPIRATIONAL CODE

This tutorial was inspired by reader Mike Legg on Twitter, who created code to cycle through all 100 characters on Johan Vinet's sheet. View the Python code for this here: **bit.ly/1GOVoBp**

We know what you're thinking: 8×8 pixel art doesn't seem like a whole lot of pixels. And if you were thinking that, you'd be right. That's 64 pixels to try to convey something – simple for low-complexity objects, but for proper pixel art it seems like a tall order. If you think back to the early days of gaming, though, there are plenty of examples of sprites that didn't use many pixels at all and looked... passable. The main limitations in those days were the number of colours you could have on screen at once, and with the Sense HAT we have the power to use a full RGB spectrum, utilising every pixel to make something a bit better than on the old Atari 2600. Grab a sprite, and let's go!

>STEP-01
Get the Sense HAT ready

If you've upgraded to the newer version of Raspbian, Jessie, all you need to do is switch off the Raspberry Pi, remove the power cable, and then plug the Sense HAT on top of the Pi. Turn it back on and it's ready to use. If you haven't made the update, you'll need to install a few extra libraries first. Open the terminal and run the following commands:

```
sudo apt-get install sense-hat
sudo pip-3.2 install pillow
```

...and then reboot the Raspberry Pi (which you can also do in the terminal with `sudo reboot` if you wish!)

>STEP-02
Find some art

There's a few ways you can do this: using Google or searching on something like DeviantArt with the right keywords ('8×8 pixel art' is a good start) and you should be able to find a suitable sprite for showing off on your Sense HAT. You could also experiment with a square picture (from something like Instagram) to see what the code will spit out, or you can draw your own pixel art in something like Swanky Paint. For testing this tutorial, we grabbed one of the 100 characters from a sprite sheet created by Johan Vinet (**twitter.com/johanvinet**), which can be found here: **bit.ly/1jxaJ3m**.

>STEP-03

Prepare the art

The Sense HAT can only display 64 pixels, and our code assumes the image you have is going to be exactly that. On a normal computer, use an image editor such as the free software GIMP to prepare the image. Remove any borders (you may need to zoom right in to make sure) by cropping the image and save it to a file name you'll remember with the extension .png or .gif. This is especially important if the 8×8 art you have isn't actually saved as an 8×8 image; for instance, if each 'pixel' in the art is six pixels wide, like in our code.

>STEP-04

Study the pixel art

As mentioned above, your pixel art may not be actually saved by the pixel. In the code we've created, it takes this into account. The easiest way to check the width of the pixels is to look at the resolution of the image. In our case, it's 48×48, which means that each 'pixel' is six real pixels wide (and high, because it's a square). You can check this in GIMP by using a square pixel brush and increasing the size until it's the same as the pixels in your image. Alternatively, once you've cropped the image, you can scale the image to be 8×8; this may not have the desired results, though, as it tries to squash everything together.

>STEP-05

Load it all on the Raspberry Pi

Put the image on the Raspberry Pi and open it in the image viewer to make sure it transferred fine. We did this by plugging the SD card directly into the computer we prepared the image on and copied it to a directory called 'SenseHAT' in the home folder, but you can always put it on a USB stick and copy it over from within the Pi or upload it to your cloud storage and download it to the Pi.

>STEP-06

Write the code!

Follow along to the code listing and tweak it to suit your own pixel art, whether this means you need to change the location of the file in the code (our code assumes you've put it in a folder called 'SenseHAT' in Raspbian's home directory) or if you need to change the width of each pixel to 1 or higher. Press F5 to run the code, and it will then display the image on the Sense HAT for three seconds before turning itself off.

Pixelart.py

Language
>PYTHON

```
from sense_hat import SenseHat
import time
from PIL import Image
import os

# Open image file
image_file = os.path.join(
os.sep,"/home","pi","SenseHAT","pixelart.png")
img = Image.open(image_file)

# Generate rgb values for image pixels
rgb_img = img.convert('RGB')
image_pixels = list(rgb_img.getdata())

# Get the 64 pixels you need
pixel_width = 6
image_width = pixel_width*8
sense_pixels = []
start_pixel = 0
while start_pixel < (image_width*64):
    sense_pixels.extend(image_pixels[start_pixel:(
start_pixel+image_width):pixel_width])
    start_pixel += (image_width*pixel_width)

# Display the image
sense = SenseHat()
sense.set_rotation(r=180)
sense.set_pixels(sense_pixels)
time.sleep (3)

sense.clear()
```

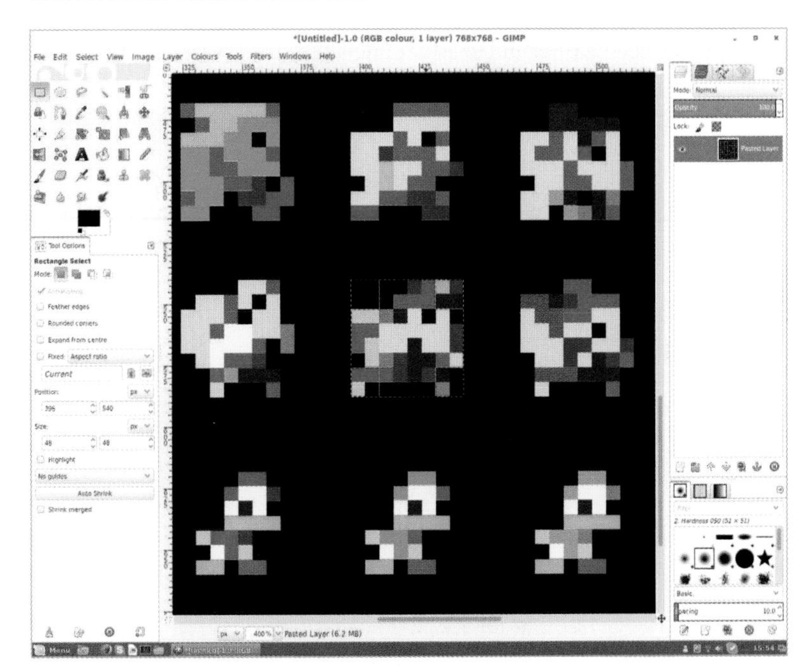

Above Rob is very vain, and (carefully) cut out an image of his alter-ego M. Bison to display on the Sense HAT, taken from Johan's sprite list

Nice big lights are easy to solder on and use within the code as well

The board slots neatly over the Raspberry Pi – it will completely cover an A+!

ROB ZWETSLOOT

Tech writer, avid coder, and Raspberry Pi enthusiast with a history of building many things with Raspberry Pi.
magpi.cc

USE THE TRAFFIC HAT WITH GPIO ZERO

As one of the boards that GPIO Zero supports, the Traffic HAT is a perfect way to show off the library...

You'll Need

- Traffic HAT **magpi.cc/1Mma7oD**
- GPIO Zero **magpi.cc/1MmajnP**
- Soldering iron (optional)

The Traffic HAT is a great little kit: a GPIO-mounted add-on for the Raspberry Pi that makes learning how to program for physical computing a little easier and bit more fun, along with nice big components that can also help you learn the basics of soldering.

With the release of GPIO Zero, the Traffic HAT is now easier than ever to program, whether you want to use it manually or make use of the handy Traffic HAT function built into GPIO Zero. Follow along with us as we teach you how to make the most of both the HAT and GPIO Zero.

>STEP-01

Prepare the Traffic HAT

You can buy the Traffic HAT pre-soldered so that you don't have to worry about it, but it's a great beginner kit for learning how to solder. You only need to install the main features you'll be using: the three LEDs, the push-button switch, and the buzzer.

Make sure to follow the outline guides on the board as to how to place them. The buzzer's positive side is indicated on the component, and the board also has a guide showing which side it should be attached to. The LEDs should be soldered so the flat edge of the bulb meets the flat edge of the outline.

Above We wrote the code on a computer and moved it to the Raspberry Pi, but there's no difference from writing it on the Pi itself

>STEP-02

Install the Traffic HAT

Make sure your Raspberry Pi is turned off. Slot the HAT over the GPIO pins, with the board itself lying across the Raspberry Pi. This way, it shouldn't be poking over the edge like a plank and will look like a normal addition to the Pi.

Once that's done, you can turn on your Raspberry Pi. Once booted up into Raspbian, you'll need to make sure GPIO Zero is installed. This can be done by using the following commands in the terminal:

```
sudo apt-get install python-pip python-w1thermsensor python-spidev

sudo pip install gpiozero
```

>STEP-03

Basic GPIO Zero

The LEDs have a GPIO number attached, as do the button and buzzer. We can use that in conjunction with GPIO Zero to activate the LEDs manually in the GPIO Zero style. Open up a new Python script in IDLE

Above You can also install the GPIO Zero software under Python 3; in fact, it's recommended by the creator. However, you'll need to change the print lines in our code

and start it with the following code, so it knows what functions to use:

```
from gpiozero import LED
```

Then write in the following so the red LED, connected to GPIO 24, lights up:

```
led = LED(24)
led.on
```

Press F5 to run it and see the results. **Buzzer** and **Button** are the other functions that you can import for the Traffic HAT.

>STEP-04
Dedicated GPIO Zero

A slightly easier way of programming the Traffic HAT with GPIO Zero is by using the actual Traffic HAT function built into Zero. You can make use of it by changing the first import line to:

```
from gpiozero import TrafficHat
```

This makes use of **buzzer**, **button**, and **lights** functions to manage those respective parts of the HAT. The lights are then described as **green**, **amber**, and **red** in the code, for when you want to activate them. We'll now create a little script to perform a traffic light sequence in Python.

>STEP-05
Setting up

Looking at the code on this page, we have a simple setup by importing **TrafficHAT** and **time**. We'll need the latter to simulate the kind of delay you normally get on real traffic lights. Set the Traffic HAT code to be known as the variable **th** and we're ready to begin our loop.

Create a simple **while** loop that will continuously run. Start it by having the green light show, and use another **while** loop to stop the code until the button is pressed. It will stay green forever unless you press the button or interrupt the program.

TrafficLights.py

Language >PYTHON

```
from gpiozero import TrafficHat
from time import sleep

th = TrafficHat()

try:
      while True:
            # Traffic light code
            # First, turn the green LED on
            th.lights.green.on()
            print "Press the button to stop the lights!"

            # Next, we want to wait until the button is pressed
            while(th.button.is_pressed == False):
                #While not pressed do nothing
                pass

            # Button has been pressed!
            th.lights.green.off()
            # Amber on for a couple of seconds
            th.lights.amber.on()
            sleep(2)
            th.lights.amber.off()
            # Turn the red on
            th.lights.red.on()
            # Buzz the buzzer 20 times with 0.1 second intervals
            th.buzzer.blink(0.1,0.1,20,False)
            sleep(1)
            th.lights.red.off()
            # Red off and blink amber 4 times with 0.5 second intervals
            th.lights.amber.blink(0.5,0.5,4,False)

except KeyboardInterrupt:
      exit()
```

> A GPIO add-on that makes learning how to program for physical computing a little easier

>STEP-06
Light timing

The bit of code after the button is pressed may seem a little complicated at first glance, but under closer inspection it should be fairly straightforward. It emulates the way traffic lights work at a pelican crossing, activating the amber light for a few seconds before giving a steady red light.

When the red light appears, the buzzer will beep for a few seconds before the red light is turned off and the amber appears, this time flashing itself, before reverting back to green. At this point, the **while** loop starts again, waiting for a button prompt.

DANA FLINN & BRETT HAINES

Dana Flinn (left) is a project administrator in Public Relations at Wolfram Research, and Brett Haines (right) is a junior software engineer in the Research & Development department.
magpi.cc/1Otb5Af

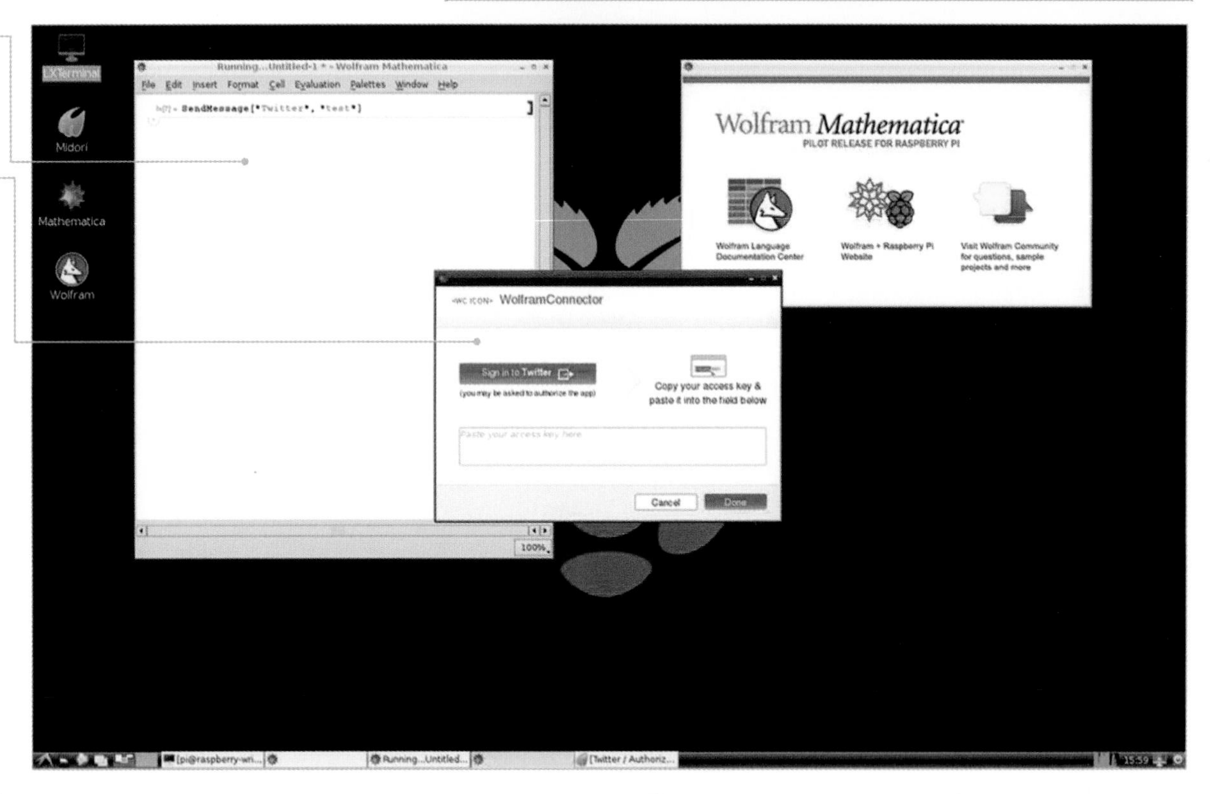

A single function in the Wolfram Language can send a tweet from your Pi

Authorisation is only required once for the Wolfram Language to tweet on your behalf

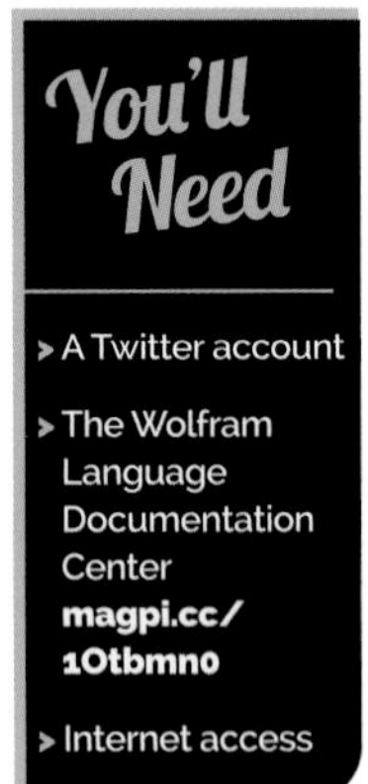

TWEET FROM YOUR RASPBERRY PI WITH THE WOLFRAM LANGUAGE

Dana Flinn and **Brett Haines** walk you through how to easily send tweets in the Wolfram Language, using the SendMessage function

The Wolfram Language is a powerful knowledge-based language that makes computation accessible to everyone, and is an easy language to dip your toes into as a first-time programmer. To send tweets from Twitter on your Raspberry Pi, all you need is a single function. We'll be using SendMessage, which is a multipurpose function in the Wolfram Language that gives Raspberry Pi users the ability to seamlessly tweet from their device.

Using the SendMessage function, we'll walk you through how to apply the symbolic language and tweet using your Raspberry Pi. Don't feel limited to just tweeting with this function, though! SendMessage can also be used to generate an email, update a Facebook or LinkedIn status, and generate a beep.

PYTHON VS WOLFRAM

Wolfram allows for much easier access to Twitter compared to Python so, depending on your needs, Wolfram may be all you need.

>STEP-01

Prepare the syntax

First, you need to launch your copy of Mathematica on your Raspberry Pi and open a blank notebook. With over 5,000 functions built into the Wolfram Language, it can seem intimidating at first. However, using the Documentation Center will make it simple to find the right function for your project.

In the Wolfram Language, all functions use square brackets and have names that start with capital letters. The function needed for this project is SendMessage, which is rather straightforward. It's used to send a message to a specified channel, which in our case is Twitter.

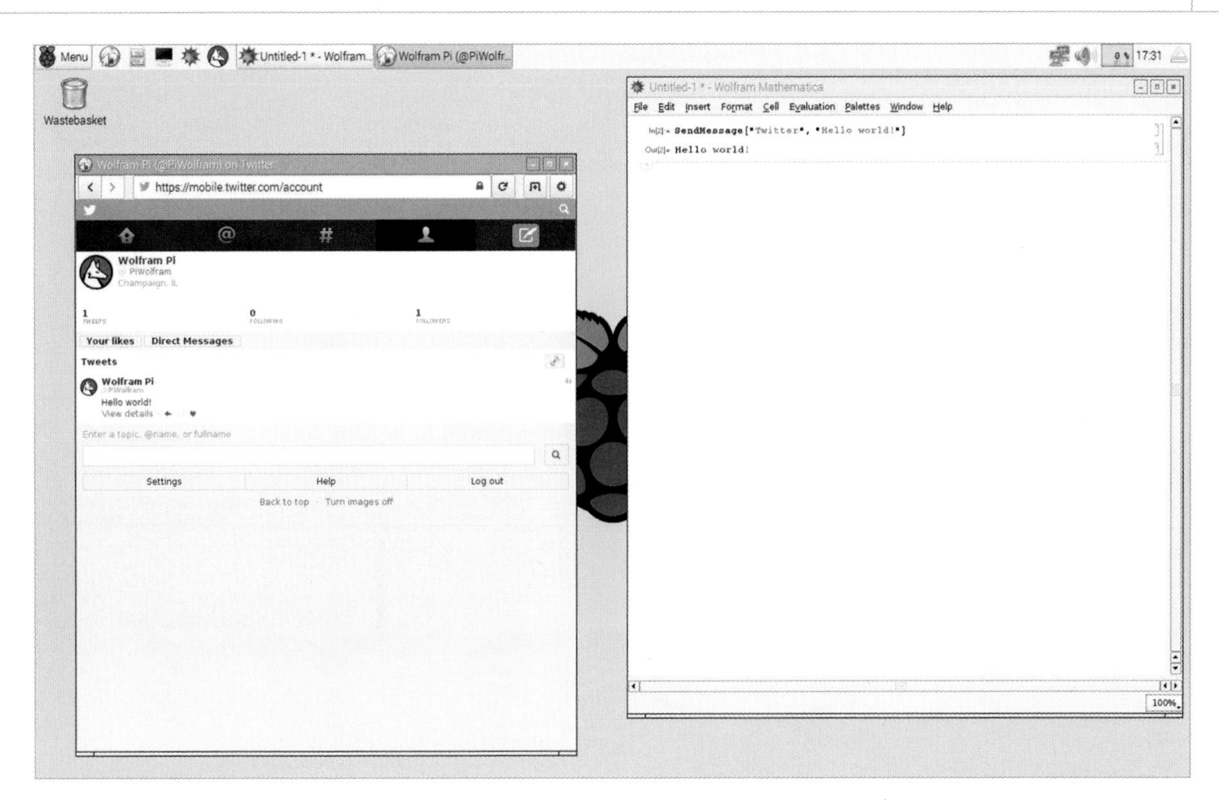

MORE IN WOLFRAM
Find more projects from the Wolfram team over on the Wolfram site: magpi.cc/1SCpu2o

Left You can tweet whatever message you want and it will appear instantly – limited to 140 characters, of course!

>STEP-02

Setting up your code

To set up your code, open Mathematica on your Pi and type the SendMessage function, then the text you want your tweet to say. So, from the Documentation Center, we know it should be set up like this:

```
SendMessage["Twitter", "Tweet text"]
```

Where it says **"Tweet text"**, the text can be changed to anything you want posted to your Twitter account.

>STEP-03

Evaluate your code

Once you've typed that in, press **SHIFT+ENTER**. This will run your code in Mathematica and prompt an authorisation dialogue to allow the Wolfram Language to send tweets on your behalf. Once authorised, a tweet is sent to your account. Select 'Done' after entering the access key, and the tweet will appear in your Twitter stream.

>STEP-04

Create a variable

The previous example showed a static string being tweeted. However, this is far from all the Wolfram Language is capable of. Much like other programming languages, it allows users to set variables, in which we can store whatever we like. To create a variable, just type the name you want to give it, an equals sign, then whatever you want to assign to the variable, like so:

```
myVariable = "Some string here!"
```

Unlike several other programming languages, you don't need to specify what kind of data is being stored in your variables – the Wolfram Language is smart enough to figure out what it is and how to use it on its own!

>STEP-05

Using StringJoin

You can combine strings using the **StringJoin** function. Just like SendMessage, StringJoin is used by putting the strings you want to join in between square brackets ([and]), separated by commas. So, to join "Hello " and "world", you'd enter:

```
StringJoin["Hello ", "world"]
```

This isn't limited to static strings – variables can be joined to strings too, like so:

```
StringJoin["Hello ", myVariable]
```

>STEP-06

Combining it all

Now it's time to put it all together. We can take a variable, store a string to it, join it to another string, then send it to Twitter:

```
myName = "WolframLanguage"
SendMessage["Twitter", StringJoin["This
tweet brought to you by ", myName]]
```

Now that you know how functions work in the Wolfram Language, it's easy to dive into the documentation and explore the thousands of functions built in. Now go forth and code!

JAMES SINGLETON

James is a software developer and engineer. He founded Computing 4 Kids Education (C4KE) and Yo Flow online gym inductions.
computing4kids.com
unop.uk

TIME-LAPSE PHOTOGRAPHY

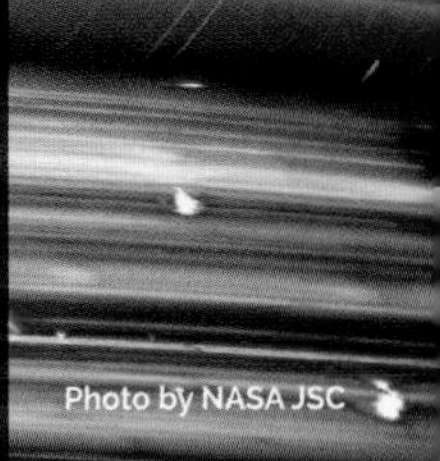

Photo by NASA JSC

Make a device to capture photographs at regular intervals. Then turn these images into a video

You'll Need

- Raspberry Pi Camera Module **magpi.cc/1UaFuuW**

Time-lapse photography reveals exciting things about the world which you wouldn't otherwise be able see. Things that happen too slowly for us to perceive: bread rising and plants growing; the clouds, sun, moon, and stars crossing the sky; shadows moving across the land. In this tutorial, we'll be making a Raspbian-based device that lets you watch things that are too slow to observe with the naked eye. To do this, we will capture lots of still photographs and combine these frames into a video with FFmpeg/libav, which can then be accessed via a web browser.

The top of the camera is at the other end of the ribbon cable connection

The metal contacts on the ribbon cable should face away from the Ethernet socket

>STEP-01

Connect the Camera Module

First, connect the camera module to the Raspberry Pi with the included ribbon cable. Locate the correct socket; it's on the top of the Raspberry Pi circuit board and is the one furthest away from the micro-USB power connector. The socket is handily labelled 'CAMERA' on the newer Raspberry Pi models. Lift up the outside of the socket to release the clamp, then insert the ribbon cable with the metal contacts facing towards the micro-USB power connector. Finally, hold the ribbon cable in position and push the outside of the socket back down to clamp the cable in place.

>STEP-02

Enable and test the camera

Power the Raspberry Pi up. You now have a choice: boot to the command line, open a terminal window, or establish a secure shell (SSH) connection. Enable the camera by running this command from a terminal to launch the Raspberry Pi configuration tool:

```
sudo raspi-config
```

Then select the 'Enable Camera' option. You can test the camera by running the following command:

```
raspistill -o testimage.jpg
```

The red LED on the camera module should light up for 5 seconds and a JPEG image will be saved to the current directory. If the camera is mounted upside down, then you can use the vertical and horizontal flip command-line switches (**-vf** and **-hf**).

>STEP-03
Install and configure software

Install a web server to access your images remotely. Run this command to install Apache:

```
sudo apt-get install apache2
```

Remove the default page to see the contents of the directory:

```
sudo rm /var/www/index.html
```

Visit the IP address of your Pi (e.g. **http://192.168.1.45** – you can find this by using **ifconfig**) and you should see an empty directory listing. If you run the following command and refresh the page, you should see an image file listed. You run this as a superuser so you can write to the directory.

```
sudo raspistill -o /var/www/testimage.jpg
```

Click on the file link and you'll see the image in your browser.

>STEP-04
Capture the images

Set up your scene and check the positioning of the camera.

```
sudo raspistill -w 1920 -h 1080 -o /var/
www/testimageFullHD.jpg
```

The width and height have been changed to capture a smaller image in 16:9 aspect ratio. This makes things easier later. The top and bottom are cropped,

Below Some bread dough ready to prove. Watch it rise in your video. Be careful not to move the bowl or camera during filming

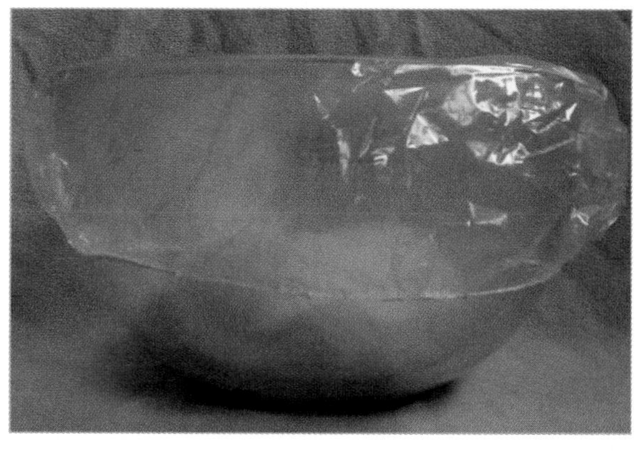

```
pi@raspberrypi ~ $ sudo avconv -i /var/www/frame%04d.jpg -crf 4 -b:v 10M /var/www/video.webm &
[1] 3761
pi@raspberrypi ~ $ avconv version 9.14-6:9.14-1rpi1rpi1, Copyright (c) 2000-2014 the Libav devel
  built on Jul 22 2014 15:08:12 with gcc 4.6 (Debian 4.6.3-14+rpi1)
Input #0, image2, from '/var/www/frame%04d.jpg':
  Duration: 00:00:30.64, start: 0.000000, bitrate: N/A
    Stream #0.0: Video: mjpeg, yuvj420p, 1920x1080, 25 fps, 25 tbr, 25 tbn
[libvpx @ 0x1b72c40] v1.1.0
Output #0, webm, to '/var/www/video.webm':
  Metadata:
    encoder         : Lavf54.20.4
    Stream #0.0: Video: libvpx, yuv420p, 1920x1080, q=-1--1, 10000 kb/s, 1k tbn, 25 tbc
Stream mapping:
  Stream #0:0 -> #0:0 (mjpeg -> libvpx)
Press ctrl-c to stop encoding
frame=  133 fps=  0 q=0.0 size=    6294kB time=5.32 bitrate=9691.9kbits/s
```

Above Shell running the rendering process on the Raspberry Pi. This will take some time, so you may prefer to use a faster machine

so make sure that your subject is in frame. Run this to start the capture:

```
sudo raspistill -w 1920 -h 1080 -t 10800000
-tl 10000 -o /var/www/frame%04d.jpg &
```

This takes a photograph every ten seconds (10,000 milliseconds) for three hours (10,800,000 milliseconds). The ampersand (**&**) at the end runs the process in the background.

>STEP-05
Prepare to make the video

You can render the video on the Raspberry Pi, but it'll be very slow. A better way is to transfer the files to a more powerful computer. In any case, you'll need to install the tools on the rendering machine; for the Pi, enter:

```
sudo apt-get install libav-tools
```

This installs a fork of FFmpeg, but you can also use the original FFmpeg. To copy the images to a remote machine, you can download them from the web server using wget or curl. For example:

```
wget -r -A jpg http://192.168.1.45
```

Or if you don't have wget...

```
curl http://192.168.1.45/frame
[0001-0766].jpg -O
```

Change the IP address and numbers accordingly.

>STEP-06
Make the video

The final step is to make the video. Run this command to start the rendering process:

```
sudo avconv -i /var/www/frame%04d.jpg
-crf 4 -b:v 10M /var/www/video.webm &
```

When this has finished, you'll be able to view the video in your browser. The default frame rate is 25fps. This compresses three hours of frames at ten-second intervals to about forty seconds of video. You can adjust this with the **-framerate** command-line option. The bitrate (**-b**) has been set high, and the Constant Rate Factor (**-crf**) low, to produce a good-quality video.

MAKE AN ANIMATED GIF

Instead of video, make an animated GIF with ImageMagick. Use smaller images, captured less frequently.

sudo convert /var/www/frame*.jpg /var/www/anim.gif &

OTHER VIDEO FORMATS

WebM is an open video format that can be displayed directly in most browsers. However, other video formats are available.

WESLEY ARCHER (AKA RASPBERRY COULIS)

Self-taught Raspberry Pi enthusiast, now writing guides for Pi Supply's Maker Zone to help others get involved in gadgety goodness!
magpi.cc/2dtoUBL
@RaspberryCoulis

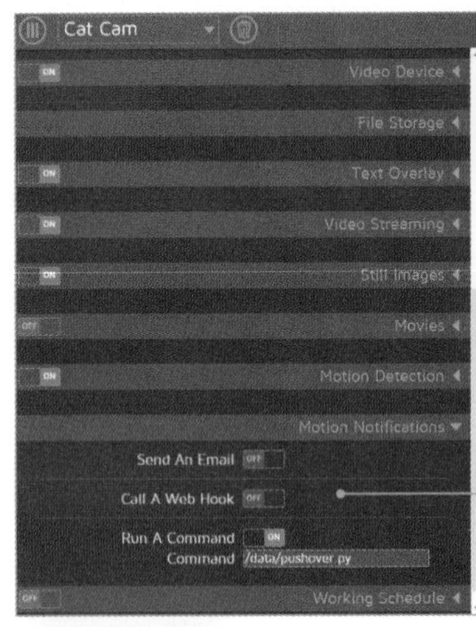

Busted! This is what your camera sees (and records) when motion is detected

This is where you'll tell MotionEyeOS to run your Python script

You'll Need

- MotionEyeOS **magpi.cc/1UCw1Jk**
- Raspberry Pi Camera Module
- Pushover app for iOS or Android with full licence (£3.99/$4.99) **pushover.net**

ADD PUSH NOTIFICATIONS TO MOTIONEYEOS

MotionEyeOS is perfect for using your Pi as a CCTV camera. Want to detect movements while you're out? Then read on...

One benefit of MotionEyeOS is its ability to detect motion and capture images and movies of what triggered it. You can also access a live stream of your camera online, even when you're not home, which is handy if you want to check in every now and then. When away from home, being notified of any movement is very useful, and MotionEyeOS has a nifty option for custom notifications.

This guide will assume you have already set up and configured MotionEyeOS. A Pushover licence is required, which costs £3.99/$4.99. For help, check out the MotionEyeOS wiki here: **magpi.cc/1UCvYwV**.

Motion Notifications

Send An Email	OFF
Call A Web Hook	OFF
Run A Command	ON
Command	/data/pushover.py

Right Make sure you turn on 'Run A Command' and then include the path to your script!

>STEP-01

Create an application in Pushover

Pushover has a great, easy to use API. Before we start, we need to register an application with it. Click on Register Application under the Your Applications heading on the Pushover website (**pushover.net**). Give your app a name – something like RaspiMotion – and then make sure the type is Application. Give your app a quick description (e.g. 'Push notifications sent by my Raspberry Pi') and, if feeling creative, upload a custom icon which will show in your Pushover client app whenever a notification is sent.

>STEP-02

Get your API token and user key

Once you have created your application, you should have access to an API token/key. This is a unique combination of numbers and letters – please keep this a secret! You'll also need your user key, which is shown once you log into Pushover's website. Okay, so you have an app and your API and user keys. You'll now need to download (or recreate if you so

Language
>PYTHON

DOWNLOAD:
magpi.cc/20DHpYW

pushover.py

```
import httplib, urllib

conn = httplib.HTTPSConnection("api.pushover.net:443")
conn.request("POST", "/1/messages.json",
  urllib.urlencode({
    "token": "APP_TOKEN",                     # Insert app token here
    "user": "USER_TOKEN",                     # Insert user token here
    "html": "1",                              # 1 for HTML, 0 to disable
    "title": "Motion Detected!",              # Title of the message
    "message": "<b>Front Door</b> camera!",   # Content of the message
    "url": "http://IP.ADD.RE.SS",             # Link to be included in message
    "url_title": "View live stream",          # Text for the link
    "sound": "siren",                         # Define the sound played
  }), { "Content-type": "application/x-www-form-urlencoded" })
conn.getresponse()
```

wish) a simple Python script to tell your Raspberry Pi to work its magic once the script is called upon by MotionEyeOS.

>STEP-03
Create your Python script

MotionEyeOS is not like Raspbian. You cannot use certain commands as you would normally, such as **git clone**, so we'll have to create our Python script manually; you can also drag and drop using WinSCP if preferred. We also don't need to use **sudo**, as we're already logged in as root by default. Our script needs to live in the **data** folder, so let's go there and create **pushover.py** using nano:

```
cd /data
nano pushover.py
```

Once here, you'll need to copy and paste or type in the code listing, while also including your API token and user key where required.

>STEP-04
Make your script executable

As with any script, we need to make sure it can be executed, otherwise it's nothing more than a fancy collection of text! You can do this either from the command line or from within WinSCP. From the command line, make sure you're in the **data** folder and then type:

```
chmod +x pushover.py
```

Or, if using WinSCP, select the **pushover.py** file in the **data** folder, then press **F9**. In the window that appears, change the permissions to **0755** and then click 'OK' to confirm.

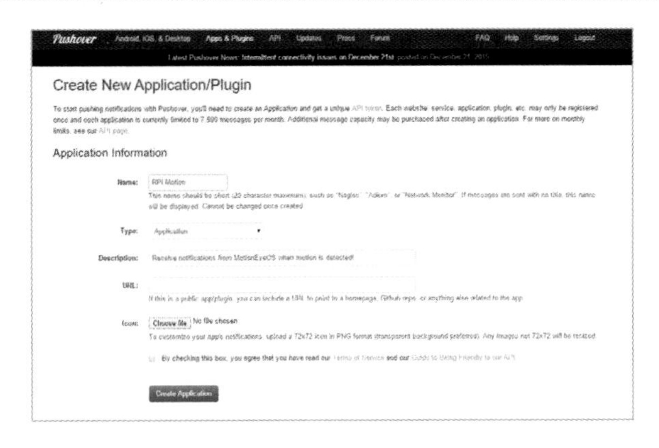

Left Create an app via Pushover.net to get the ball rolling. It's pretty self-explanatory

>STEP-05
Configure MotionEyeOS to use your script

Now that we have our script, we need to tell MotionEyeOS to use it when it detects motion. To do this, log in, go to the Motion Notifications menu and turn on the 'Run A Command' option. You then need to specify which command to run, which will be the Python script you just created – this is **/data/pushover.py**. Click Apply once done, to confirm the changes.

>STEP-06
Test it out!

Hopefully, by now you have created your Python script, made it executable, told MotionEyeOS to use your script when it detects motion, and have the Pushover app installed on your smartphone or tablet. We now need to test that it works! Wave your hand in front of your camera (or you can do a dance if you're feeling energetic!) and then shortly afterwards you should receive a notification via Pushover, warning you that motion has been detected!

Feel free to experiment with the script to customise the message displayed and sound played in Pushover.

JAMES SINGLETON

James is a developer, engineer, and author. He helps people find software jobs in the environmental sector with 'Cleanweb Jobs'.
unop.uk
cleanwebjobs.com

It's all powered by the Raspberry Pi, timed to go off when you need it to

A discarded globe from a charity shop is the perfect thing to create the wake-light

The main light for the alarm is much brighter than the Sense HAT LEDs

You'll Need

- Sense HAT **magpi.cc/1TGGUt5**
- BlinkyTape LED strip (or NeoPixel / DotStar)
- An unwanted globe
- Plastic bottle
- Sticky pads
- Blu-Tack or putty

PI GLOWBE
THE PI-POWERED WAKE-LIGHT

Turn a globe into a glowing orb and use it to help you wake up in the dark winter months

During the winter, or even at any time of the year, it can be difficult to get up in the mornings. If you wake before dawn, your body still thinks it's night (because it is). You can buy wake-lights that trick your body into waking up by simulating a fake sunrise; they get gradually brighter as your alarm approaches. These can be quite expensive, so why not make your own with a Pi and some LEDs? To celebrate the Astro Pis on the ISS, we've built one using a Sense HAT inside a globe that was found in a charity shop – perhaps an unwanted Christmas present, now repurposed!

>STEP-01
Make an LED bulb

Create a bulb by wrapping an LED strip around a plastic bottle. You could skip this, but the Sense HAT is not bright enough to make a lamp. Cut the top off an empty plastic bottle, cover it in sticky pads and wrap the LED strip around it in a spiral. You can secure the ends further with tape. Have the connection end at the wider opening so that you can route the power cable to the Pi and then out through the centre. We'll mount the Pi on top of the upside-down bottle end, so ensure it's flat.

>STEP-02
Destroy the world
Remove the Earth from its mount by pulling the pegs of the holder out of the holes in the Arctic and Antarctic. Next, split it in half along the equator by pulling the two hemispheres apart. It should disassemble fairly easily with a little force applied in the correct places. You'll want to fashion a new mount to stop the globe rolling around, whilst still allowing the power cable to exit from the bottom hole - you could use the inside of a roll of tape. You can cut a small slot with a knife to allow the wire to enter.

>STEP-03
Mount inside globe
Attach your new LED bulb to the inside of the globe. Mount the neck of the bottle over the lower hole with Blu-Tack or putty; it should be sturdy enough to support the weight of the Pi resting on top of it. Mount the Sense HAT on the Pi, and then place both on top of the upturned bottle. Attach a USB WiFi dongle to the Pi (unless you're using wired Ethernet), otherwise it will wake you at the wrong time. This is because the Pi requires internet access to set its clock.

>STEP-04
Route the power
You'll probably need to cut and reconnect the power cable to fit it through the hole. The official Pi power supply uses bell wire, which makes it easy to reconnect with a screw terminal (choc block). Unfortunately, it doesn't supply enough power to use the LEDs at full brightness and also run the Pi. Cut the cable and insert the supply end through the hole. Tie a knot in the cable to stop it from being pulled back through. Separate the two power cores from both ends and strip the insulation. Reconnect with a choc block, matching the polarity.

>STEP-05
Download the code
Clone the code from the GitHub repository into your home folder:

```
git clone https://github.com/jpsingleton/pi-glowbe.git
```

If you're only using part of the hardware or a different LED strip, you can adapt the code to your needs. You may also need to install the Sense HAT software if you're running an older version of Raspbian – follow the instructions at **magpi.cc/1KboHnN**. You may also want to disable the LEDs on the Pi so they don't disturb your sleep. Newer models can do this in software, otherwise you could tape over them, or even de-solder them if you're brave enough.

wakeup.py

DOWNLOAD:
magpi.cc/1TUKdz7

```python
from BlinkyTape import BlinkyTape
from sense_hat import SenseHat
from time import sleep
import optparse

# Default Blinky Tape port on Raspberry Pi is /dev/ttyACM0
parser = optparse.OptionParser()
parser.add_option("-p", "--port", dest="portname",
                  help="serial port (ex: /dev/ttyACM0)",
                  default="/dev/ttyACM0")
(options, args) = parser.parse_args()

if options.portname is not None:
    port = options.portname
else:
    print "Usage: python wakeup.py -p <port name>"
    print "(ex.: python wakeup.py -p /dev/ttyACM0)"
    exit()

sense = SenseHat()
bt = BlinkyTape(port)

# wake phase - gradually get brighter, linearly
sleepTime = 18 # 18 sec for 30 min in 100 steps
maxPower = 100 # flickers or cuts out above 100

for y in xrange(maxPower):
    sense.clear(y * 2, y * 2, y * 2)
    for x in xrange(sleepTime):
        bt.displayColor(y, y, y)
        sleep(1)

# on phase - at full brightness for the same time
sense.clear(255, 255, 255)
for z in xrange(maxPower * sleepTime):
    bt.displayColor(maxPower, maxPower, maxPower)
    sleep(1)

# tidy up
sense.clear()
```

>STEP-06
Set up your schedule
We'll run the code with cron. It should start about half an hour before you get up and probably only on weekdays. Launch the cron configuration by typing the following into a terminal:

```
crontab -e
```

Next, set it up by adding the following line to the end:

```
15 6 * * 1-5 python /home/pi/pi-glowbe/wakeup.py
```

This will run the code every weekday at 06:15, so change it to meet your needs. Save the file and exit the editor (**CTRL+X**, **Y**, then **ENTER** in the default nano). Once happy, reassemble everything and wait for morning!

TONY GOODHEW

Taught programming since 1967 (IBM 1130 with FORTRAN IV). BBC Micro teacher trainer, now using Raspberry Pi and Arduino.

PROGRAM CODEBUG WITH PYTHON 3

You'll Need

- CodeBug **magpi.cc/1MelyfA**
- USB Micro B cable (included)
- Python libraries: python3-serial & python3-codebug-tether
- CodeBug script: codebug-tether.cbg **magpi.cc/1MelBYR**

Move on from Blocky programming and control your CodeBug with all the power of Python...

The CodeBug is simple to set up and start programming with the Scratch-like Blocky interface on the website. Once you have mastered this, you'll probably want to move on to the next stage and take full control with a more powerful language like Python 3. This allows you to include more ambitious data structures, such as lists and tuples, and build larger projects with procedures. Your expert started to wonder how good a game you could build with just a square of 25 LEDs and a switch. This is his first attempt.

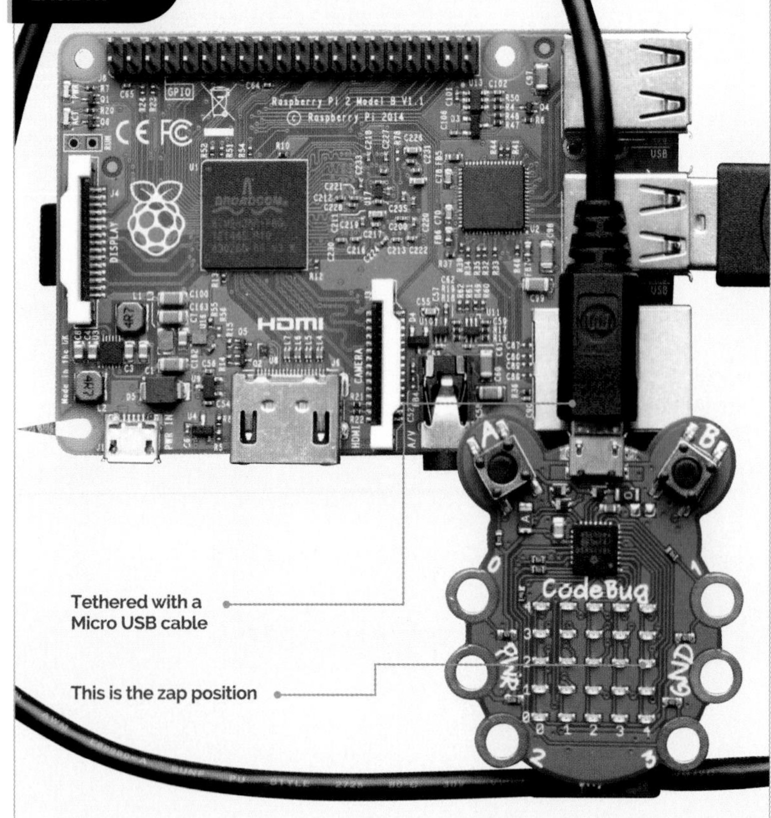
Tethered with a Micro USB cable
This is the zap position

>STEP-01

Game rules

We need a simple game in which you press a button when a target is in a certain position. Back in the late 1970s, your expert used to set a 'Zap the Rat' game as homework while teaching Commodore PET or Ohio Scientific Basic. You have to click a button as a moving 'rat' target passes a certain 'zapping point' on a circuit. In this version, the speed increases each time you successfully hit a rat, and you need to hit three rats with as few attempts as possible. It would be nice to display the hits while the game is running, and a final score to show how many times you missed the target. Can all of this be fitted on a 5×5 LED display?

Above This shows the rat at (4,0), the zap position marker, and hits counter at two zaps

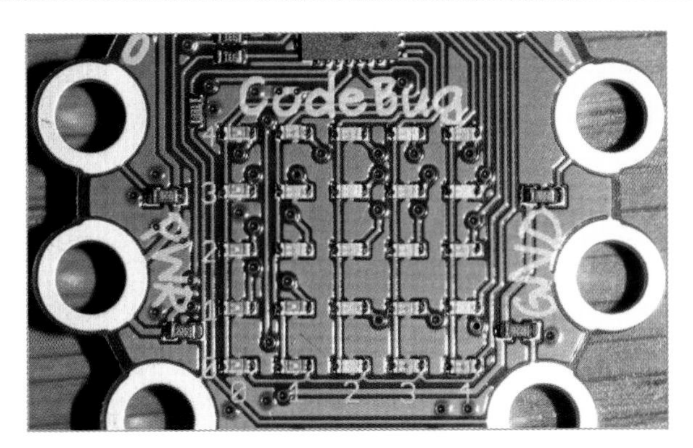

Above The final score: seven missed opportunities to zap the rats

>STEP-02
Planning the display

The circuit will be all the outside edge LEDs, with the rats starting their run from the bottom-left corner: (0,0). The zap cell will be at (4,2), with a permanently lit LED at (3,2) to mark it. Hits can be indicated by a column of lit LEDs rising from (1,1) to (1,3). Button 'B' will be used to zap the rat. The final score can be displayed with either a character 'O' to indicate no missed zap opportunities – quite difficult to achieve – or lit LEDs (0 –25) for each miss. For a 'hit' to register, the button must be pressed while the zap position LED is lit; holding the button down won't work.

>STEP-03
Setting up the CodeBug

To run the CodeBug in tethered mode, you'll need to download and install a program called **codebug_tether.cbg**. Once installed in the normal way, the CodeBug temporarily becomes a slave device to your Raspberry Pi and obeys instructions sent from Python 3. (This is rather like using Nanpy to control an Arduino from a Pi.)

Two additional Python libraries, **python3-serial** and **python3-codebug-tether**, need to be installed on the Pi. Point your browser to **magpi.cc/1MeIWdR** and follow the excellent instructions from Thomas Macpherson-Pope.

Open IDLE 3 and type in the **Zap_the_rat.py** Python script. Save it and run it.

>STEP-04
Things to do

There are several modifications and additions you could make to the script:

- Randomise the rat's starting position
- Randomise the direction in which the rat runs around the circuit
- Improve the zero final score to a square, expanding and contracting from position (2,2) to the edge and back again five times as a celebration.

Zap_the_rat.py

Language
>PYTHON

```
# Zap the Rat - Python3 Game for Tethered CodeBug
# Tony Goodhew - 5 Oct 2015
import codebug_tether
import time
cb = codebug_tether.CodeBug()
cb.clear()

# Circuit LED co-ordinates - round the edge from bottom-left
LEDx =(0,0,0,0,0,1,2,3,4,4,4,4,4,3,2,1)
LEDy =(0,1,2,3,4,4,4,4,4,3,2,1,0,0,0,0)
for i in range(0,-66,-1):  # Display game title
    cb.write_text(i,0,'Zap the Rat', direction="right")
    time.sleep(0.1)

score = 0               # Rats zapped!
opps = 0                # Zap opportunities
p = 0                   # Position of rat on circuit (0-15)
delay = 0.05            # Initial delay between rat moves
old_sw = 0                        # Last value of switch B
running = True                    # Loop control variable
cb.clear()
cb.set_pixel(3,2,1)               # Show Zap position

while running:
    cb.set_pixel(LEDx[p],LEDy[p],1)   # Show rat
    if p == 10: opps = opps +1        # Incr opps - in (4,2)
    time.sleep(delay - score * 0.007) # Wait - gets faster
    sw = cb.get_input('B')            # Read switch B
    pixel = cb.get_pixel(4,2)         # Rat in Zap position?
    cb.set_pixel(LEDx[p],LEDy[p],0)   # Hide rat
    if old_sw == 0 and sw == 1 and pixel == 1: # Hit?
        score = score +1              # Increment hits
        cb.set_pixel(1,score,1)       # Show hits
        if score == 3:                # Game over?
            running = False           # Stop looping
        p = -1                   # Position of next rat
    old_sw = sw                  # Store switch value
    p = p + 1                    # Update rat position
    if p > 15:                   # Rat pointer out of range?
        p = 0                    # Reset to start position

cb.clear()  # Game over - display opportunities
opps = opps - 3  # Remove successful opportunities
print("Missed Opportunities were ",opps)
if opps > 25:  # Reduce missed opps to 25 max
    opps = 25
if opps == 0:
    cb.write_text(0,0,'O') # Zero missed opps
else:
    for x in range(0,5):   # Display missed opps
        for y in range(0,5):
            if opps > 0:
                cb.set_pixel(x,y,1)
            else:
                cb.set_pixel(x,y,0)
            opps = opps - 1
time.sleep(5)
cb.clear()  # Tidy display
```

RICHARD HAYLER

Richard is a mentor at CoderDojo Ham, and his school Code Club was one of the winning teams in the Primary Astro Pi competition.
magpi.cc/1lLmeoi
coderdojoham.org | @rdhayler

PLAYING IT BY EAR WITH PIANO HAT

You'll Need

- A Piano HAT **magpi.cc/1OALwNT**
- The Piano-HAT library **magpi.cc/2dXkylM**
- Headphones or an external speaker

The latest HAT from Pimoroni is a great way to unleash your ivory-tinkling tendencies. Let's use it to build a relative pitch tester

Relative pitch is the ability to identify a given musical note by comparing it to a reference note. Unlike perfect pitch, relative pitch can be improved with training. The Piano HAT is a versatile piece of hardware that we can use to create a fun game that tests people's skill in recognising different notes. It was inspired by Zachary Igielman's legendary PiPiano and it turns your Pi into a functional musical keyboard. Each of the 16 capacitive keys also has an LED so you can create you own 'learn to play' tutorials or just give your performances a visual appeal.

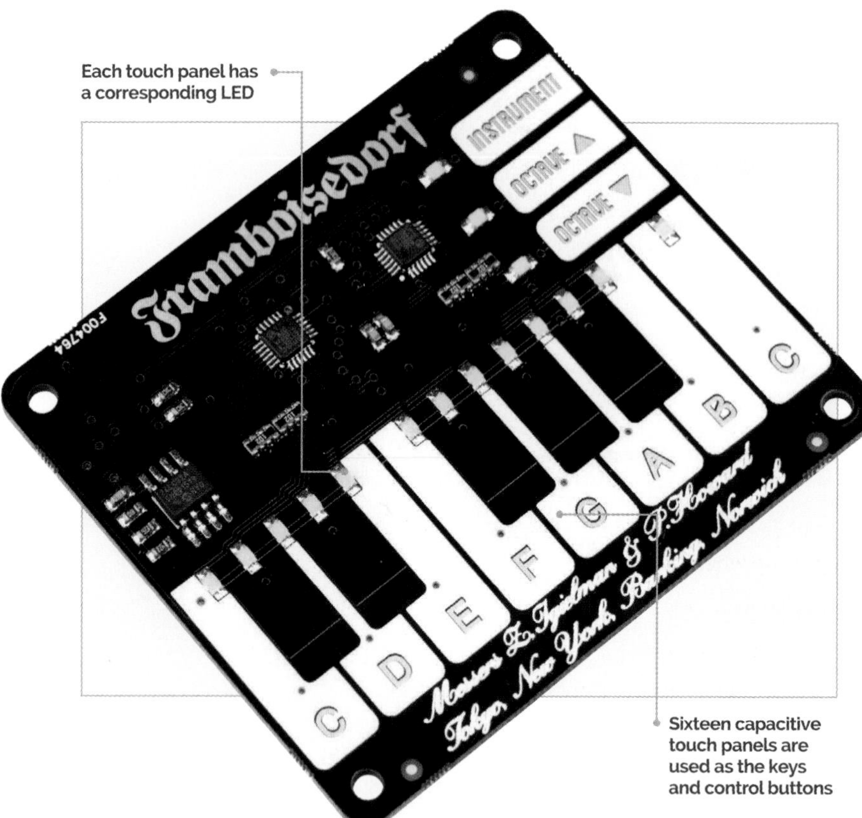

Each touch panel has a corresponding LED

Sixteen capacitive touch panels are used as the keys and control buttons

>STEP-01

Getting started with Piano HAT

Like most HATs, this one is straightforward to use. Simply plug it carefully onto the GPIO pins of your Pi. Then install the Piano-HAT Python library. This requires the I²C bus on the Pi to be enabled, and there are plenty of instructions for this online. But to make life super-easy, those Pirates at Pimoroni provide a handy script that takes care of everything:

```
curl -sSL get.pimoroni.com/pianohat | bash
```

>STEP-02

Wired for sound

There are two options for getting audio output from a Pi. If you are using a HDMI monitor or a TV that has built-in speakers, the audio can be played over the HDMI cable. If not, you can switch to use headphones or a speaker plugged into the headphone jack. The Pi will normally auto-detect the available outputs, but sometimes it gets this wrong. To force audio to use a specific output, you can use this command:

```
amixer cset numid=3 2
```

The second number determines the output: HDMI = 2, jack = 1, auto = 0.

>STEP-03

Play it again

The Piano-HAT library has a nice collection of demonstration Python scripts. A good one to start with lets you use the Piano HAT as... a piano!

```
sudo python Pimoroni/pianohat/
simple-piano.py
```

Language
>PYTHON 2.7 & 3

DOWNLOAD:
magpi.cc/2dXjJj9

Relative_Pitch.py

```
import pianohat # import libraries we need
import pygame
import time, random

pygame.mixer.pre_init(44100, -16, 1, 512) #Configure pygame sound
pygame.mixer.init() #Initialise pygame mixer
pygame.mixer.set_num_channels(16)
pianohat.auto_leds(True) # LEDs light when keys pressed
# A dictionary mapping sounds and notes onto keys
NOTES = {'0':['C','./sounds/piano/39172__jobro__piano-ff-025.
wav'], # C
  '1': ['C Sharp', './sounds/piano/39173__jobro__piano-ff-026.
wav'], # C sharp
  '2':['D','./sounds/piano/39174__jobro__piano-ff-027.wav'], # D
  '3':['D Sharp','./sounds/piano/39175__jobro__piano-ff-028.wav'],
# D sharp
  '4':['E','./sounds/piano/39176__jobro__piano-ff-029.wav'], # E
  '5':['F','./sounds/piano/39177__jobro__piano-ff-030.wav'], # F
  '6':['F Sharp','./sounds/piano/39178__jobro__piano-ff-031.wav'],
# F sharp
  '7':['G','./sounds/piano/39179__jobro__piano-ff-032.wav'], # G
  '8':['G Sharp','./sounds/piano/39180__jobro__piano-ff-033.wav'],
# G sharp
  '9':['A','./sounds/piano/39181__jobro__piano-ff-034.wav'], # A
  '10':['A Sharp','./sounds/piano/39182__jobro__piano-ff-035.wav'],
# A sharp
  '11':['B','./sounds/piano/39183__jobro__piano-ff-036.wav'], # B
  '12':['C','./sounds/piano/39184__jobro__piano-ff-037.wav'] # C
}

def handle_note(channel, pressed): # handler for key presses
    global note
    global correct
    if channel < 13 and pressed: # Only for note keys
        if str(channel) == note: # Did the player get it right?
          print('correct, it was a ' + str(NOTES[note][0]) )
          pianohat.auto_leds(False)
          for x in range(16): #
Flash all the lights to celebrate
            pianohat.set_led(x,
True)
          time.sleep(0.05)
          for x in range(16): # Them turn them off
            pianohat.set_led(x,False)
          pianohat.auto_leds(True)
          correct = True
        else:
          print('wrong, try again')

def play(note): # Play a note from the dictionary
        pygame.mixer.Sound(NOTES[note][1]).play(loops=0)
        time.sleep(1)

pianohat.on_note(handle_note) # Set keys to use our handler

while True:
  print('Here comes a C')
  time.sleep(1)
  play('0') # Play a C
  time.sleep(2)
  correct = False
  print('Now identify this note')
  time.sleep(2)
  note = random.choice(list(NOTES)) # Pick a random note
  play(note)
  print('press the key for the note you heard')
  count = 6 # Set countdown timer
  while count > 0 and correct == False:
    time.sleep(1)
    print(str(count) + ' Seconds remaining')
    count -=1
  if not correct: # If they didn't get it right, tell them the
answer
    print("time's up, it was a " + str(NOTES[note][0]))
```

If you press the Instrument key, you'll notice that the sounds change from pianos to percussion. The Piano-HAT library itself does not map any of the keys to a particular sound; that is all done using Python. The sounds themselves are WAV files, which are played using the Pygame library.

Let's map our own sound to one of the Piano HAT's keys. Find a short WAV file online (or create your own using Sonic Pi) and save it as **mysound.wav**. Then type in the code from **Listing_l1.py** (on page 52) and run it: your sound should play when the D key is pressed.

>STEP-04
A little light music

You'll notice that the relevant LED lights up when any key is pressed. This is the default behaviour, but can be disabled using:

```
pianohat.auto_leds(False)
```

Add this line immediately before the **handle_note** function in **Listing_l1.py**. Now we can add code so that only the D key's LED will work. Insert

```
pianohat.set_led(2,True)
```

...before the **pygame.mixer.Sound** line and

```
pianohat.set_led(2,False)
```

...after it.

Now rerun the program to verify that only the D lights up when tapped.

>STEP-05
Use a dictionary

Mapping keys to sounds using a bunch of **if…** statements is easy but rather long-winded. For our relative pitch test, we want to associate the key (an integer) with the note (a text string) and the sound

to be played (also a string). A simple way is to use a Python construct called a dictionary. A real-world dictionary has an index of words, and each word has definitions. In a Python dictionary, the word is called the 'key', and the definitions the 'values'.

Listing_12.py uses a simple two-item dictionary to map sounds and names (the values) onto the C and D keys (the keys). Give it a try.

>STEP-06

Putting it all together

We've now explored everything needed for our relative pitch tester: we'll use the piano sounds that come with the Piano-HAT library for our notes.

Type up the code from the **Relative_Pitch.py** listing (on page 51) and run it with **sudo**. A reference note (a C) is played, then, after a pause, the note to be identified. The player then has 6 seconds to press the correct key for the note they just heard. If they get it right, all the LEDs will flash in celebration, otherwise they're asked to try again.

As an extension, how about using different, selectable instruments?

> In a Python dictionary, the word is called the 'key', and the definitions the 'values'

Listing_11.py

```
import pianohat
import pygame
import signal

pygame.mixer.pre_init(44100, -16, 1, 512)
pygame.mixer.init()
pygame.mixer.set_num_channels(16)

def handle_note(channel, pressed):
        if channel == 2:
                pygame.mixer.Sound('./mysound.
wav').play(loops=0)

pianohat.on_note(handle_note)
signal.pause()
```

Listing_12.py

```
import pianohat
import pygame
import signal

pygame.mixer.pre_init(44100, -16, 1, 512)
pygame.mixer.init()
pygame.mixer.set_num_channels(16)
NOTES = {0:['Sound1','./mysound.wav'],
              2: ['Sound2', './mysound2.wav']}

def handle_note(channel, pressed):
        if channel == 0 or channel == 2:
            pygame.mixer.Sound(NOTES[channel][1]).play(loops=0)

pianohat.on_note(handle_note)
signal.pause()
```

JASPER HAYLER-GOODALL
The brains behind one of the winning AstroPi entries and a regular helper at CoderDojo Ham and CodeClub! He's ten.
coderdojoham.org
cranmereprimary.org.uk

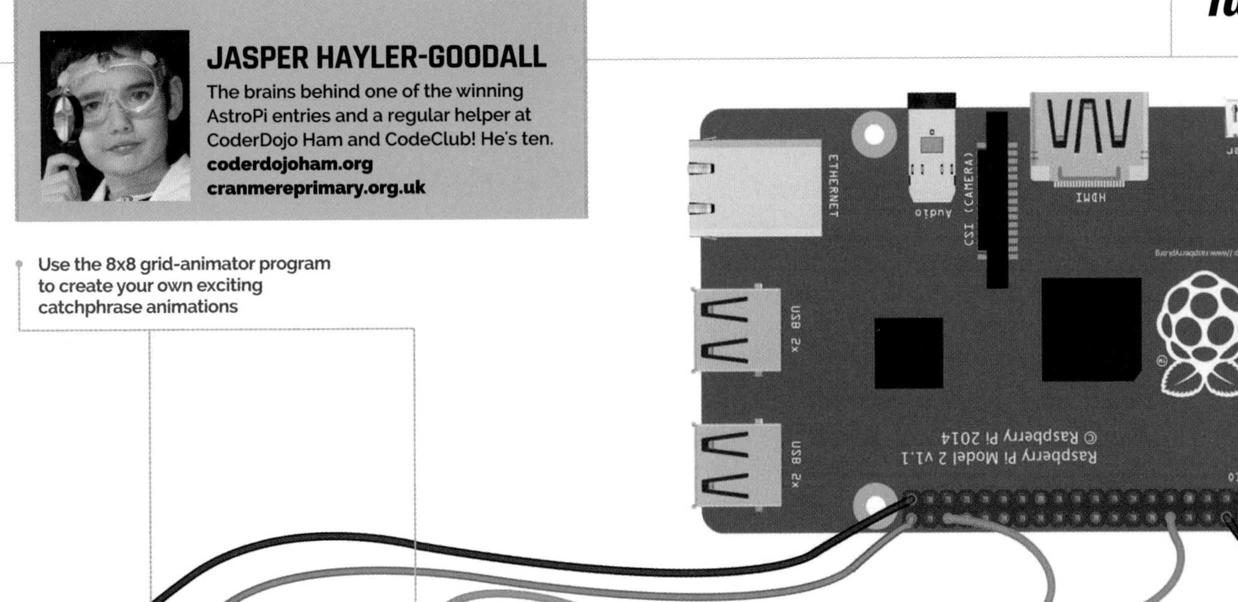

Use the 8x8 grid-animator program to create your own exciting catchphrase animations

Only three wires are needed to connect the Pi to the UnicornHAT

PIPHRASE!

You'll Need

- A Unicorn or Sense HAT **shop.pimoroni.com**
- A tall 40-pin header (for Sense HAT) **shop.pimoroni.com**
- Some jumper wires, two buttons, and a breadboard
- The 8x8 grid animator program **magpi.cc/2dXmlbn**
- The Fuzzy Wuzzy library **magpi.cc/2dXlOvH**

Make your own version of the popular TV show, Catchphrase. All you need are a few components and a LED matrix, in this case the Unicorn HAT...

Catchphrase is a TV game show where contestants try to guess the well-known phrase or saying being visualised on a big screen. In this project, you will be making a similar game, using either a Sense HAT or a Unicorn HAT to display the animation. We have mainly written this project for a Unicorn HAT, but with a little modification it can work with the Sense HAT. To make the game two-player, we have added some buttons to see who is the fastest at guessing the catchphrase.

>STEP-01
Put your hat on

Later on, we will attach a breadboard to use some buttons, so we'll need access to the Pi's GPIO pins. Therefore you shouldn't just place the Unicorn HAT directly onto the GPIO pins; instead, connect it using jumper wires. Surprisingly, the Unicorn HAT only uses three pins (5V, GND, and GPIO 18), so these are the only ones we need to worry about.

If you have a Sense HAT, remove the header already attached and replace it with a tall one instead. This should leave some pins sticking out of the top of the Sense HAT, which will be enough to attach the wires.

>STEP-02
Download the animator program and get creating

When you download the 8×8 grid animator program, make sure you use the appropriate one for your HAT. If you have a Unicorn HAT, use the command:

```
sudo python 8x8grid-unicorn.py
```

To create an animation, simply select a colour from the palette on the right, and click on a circle on the grid to turn that colour on. Add another frame by pressing the >> button; this will duplicate the current frame. If you need to clear the frame, press the 'clear frame' button. You can also play your animation on

Maingame-Uni.py

```
import unicornhat as uh #import the necessary modules
import time, random,signal
import catchphrases_uni as cp # the file with our
animations
import RPi.GPIO as GPIO
from fuzzywuzzy import fuzz

def halfthing(num,colour): #turns on half the LEDS to
indicate who pressed button first
        uh.clear()
        for x in range (num,num+4):
                for y in range(0,8):
                        uh.set_pixel(x,y,colour[0],col
our[1],colour[2])
        uh.show()

def  pressed(num): # Function to be run when buttons
pressed
        global running
        running = False # stops animaton from playing
        halfthing(num,(255,0,0))
        get_answer(3) # call with goes set to 3

def b21pressed(channel): # Run when button on GPIO 21
pressed
        pressed(0)

def b16pressed(channel): # Run when button on GPIO 16
pressed
        pressed(4)

def get_answer(goes): # Asks the player for their
answer
    answer = raw_input('Name that catchphrase? ')
    match = fuzz.ratio(answer, picked) # compare
answer to catchphrase title
    if  match >=85:
        print 'Correct!'
    elif match >= 60 and match < 85: # if it nearly
matches
        goes=goes-1
        if goes==0:
            print('run out of goes')
```

the LEDs and delete frames. When you are happy with your animation, click 'export to py' and it will be saved as **animation8x8.py**.

>STEP-03
Tinkering with the animations

You will then need to rename the file (to your own choice of name) by using the command line:

```
mv animation8x8.py yourchoice.py
```

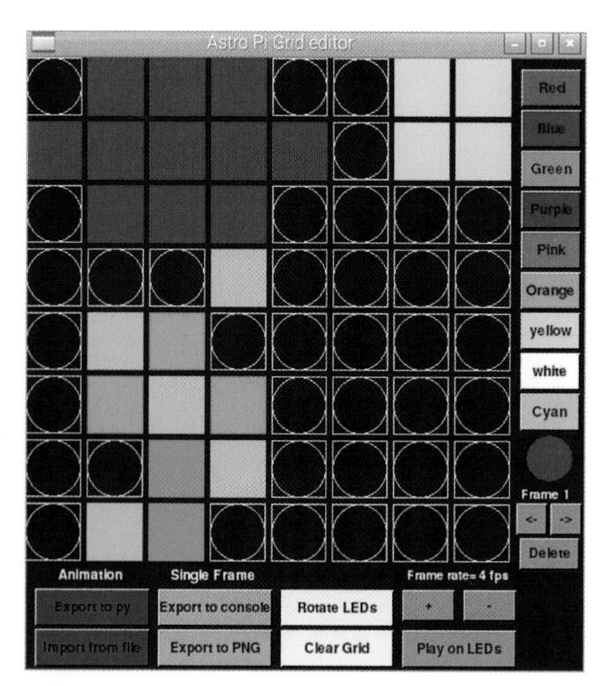

Right Use the 8x8 grid-animator program to create your own exciting catchphrase animations

You should then repeat step-02 until you have at least three animations. Make sure you rename them after each export.

Now we need to copy the animations into the catchphrase code. First of all, open up **yourchoice.py** (or whatever you called it) in IDLE, then find the line which has **frames=[** on it. Highlight this all the way to the final **]**, then copy and paste it into a new file called **catchphrases.py**. Do the same with the rest of the animations and paste them into the same file. At the end, you'll need to use a Python dictionary and a list to link the animations to their name; an example **catchphrases.py** is included in the GitHub repository for this project.

>STEP-04
Connect and test buttons

To connect the buttons to the Raspberry Pi, you need three jumper wires, one breadboard, and two buttons. To make the circuit, follow the image on page 55; to test the buttons, use the **listing1.py** code. If using a Sense HAT, make sure you use the same GPIO pins (16 and 21).

>STEP-05
Fuzzywuzzy matching

Fuzzy matching is about finding out how close one string is to another. Open up a Python shell (either using the command line or IDLE) and then import the **fuzzywuzzy** library.

```
>>>from fuzzywuzzy import fuzz
```

Language
>PYTHON 2.7

DOWNLOAD:
magpi.cc/2dXnpBO

```
        else:
            print 'Close.. Try again (' +( str(goes) +
' guesses remaining)')
            get_answer(goes)
    else:
        print "That's not right"
    print 'Press ^C to exit'

def show_catchphrase():  # Display an animation on the
LED matrix
    picked = random.choice(cp.ANSWERS.keys()) # Pick
random animation from file
    for i in range(3):
        for x in cp.ANSWERS[picked]:
            if running:
               uh.set_pixels(x) # display a frame from
animation
               uh.show()
               time.sleep(0.25) #pause before next
frame
        time.sleep(1) # pause before we play animation
again
    return picked

GPIO.setmode(GPIO.BCM) #set GPIO
numbering to BCM
GPIO.setup(21,GPIO.IN, pull_up_
down=GPIO.PUD_UP) #Set these pins as
inputs
GPIO.setup(16,GPIO.IN, pull_up_down=GPIO.PUD_UP)
#set callback functions that are run when button
pressed
GPIO.add_event_detect(21,GPIO.FALLING,callback =
b21pressed,bouncetime=300)
GPIO.add_event_detect(16,GPIO.FALLING,callback =
b16pressed,bouncetime=300)
try:
        running = True # use this to stop animation
when button pressed
        picked = 'blank'
        picked = show_catchphrase()
        signal.pause() #stops the code from exiting
except KeyboardInterrupt: # catch ^c
        exit() #exit the code
```

Fuzzywuzzy gives you a score out of 100 for how close two phrases are.

```
>>>fuzz.ratio('hello world','catchphrase')
18
>>>fuzz.ratio('piphrase','pyphase')
80
```

We can use this to check how close the player's answer is to our catchphrase (because we don't want to be too mean!).

>STEP-06
The final code

Now we need to put everything we've learned together to create the catchphrase game. Type the code from the main listing (above) into a file called **piphrase.py**, then run it using:

```
sudo python piphrase.py
```

The program should make an animation play three times on the Unicorn HAT while waiting for someone to press either button. When one of the buttons is pressed by a player, their side of the Unicorn HAT lights up. They then need to type in the catchphrase they think is being shown. The program will the tell them if their answer is correct or incorrect. The player might also be shown the message 'try again' if their answer falls somewhere between 60 and 80 percent correct according to the fuzzy matching.

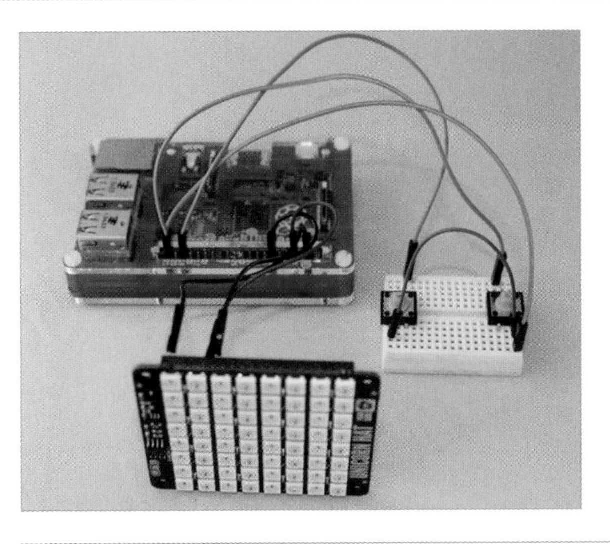

Left This project will work with a Sense HAT or a Unicorn HAT. If you're using a Unicorn HAT, it should be connected like this

listing1.py

```
import RPi.GPIO as GPIO #import the necessary modules
import time

GPIO.setmode(GPIO.BCM)  #set GPIO numbering to BCM
GPIO.setup(16,GPIO.IN, pull_up_down=GPIO.PUD_UP)
GPIO.setup(21,GPIO.IN, pull_up_down=GPIO.PUD_UP)

while True:
    print('b1= '+str(GPIO.input(16))+ ' b2= '+str(
GPIO.input(21)))
    time.sleep(0.1)
```

RICHARD HAYLER

Richard is a mentor at CoderDojo Ham. His school CodeClub was one of the winning teams in the Primary School Astro Pi competition.
magpi.cc/1lLmeoi
coderdojoham.org

MAGIC PRESENTATIONS WITH SKYWRITER

You'll Need

- Skywriter HAT or board **shop.pimoroni.com**
- Skywriter API library **magpi.cc/2dXntBn**
- Python AutoPy library **magpi.cc/2dXmbpZ**
- LibreOffice Impress **libreoffice.org**

Amaze your audience with baffling magical powers or mastery of the Force using a Skywriter HAT

Let's face it: simply using a Raspberry Pi to run the slides for your talk will make the audience think you're pretty cool. But if that's not impressive enough, why not dazzle them further by using your telekinetic powers to flip through the presentation and annotate the slides by drawing in the air? You don't even need to be a graduate of Hogwarts or the Jedi Academy: just get yourself a Skywriter device and some simple Python, and you're ready to rock.

The Skywriter device uses a grid of transmitting electrodes to generate an electric field that propagates around the surface in three dimensions. When you move your hand above the Skywriter, it disturbs this field and these variations are detected by the receiver electrode grid. These measurements can be used to calculate the position and movement direction of your hand.

>STEP-01
Connect the Skywriter device

If you have a Skywriter HAT, this just connects onto the GPIO pins like other HATs. If you have the larger Skywriter board, you'll need to connect six GPIO pins to the matching pins at the top, as shown below.

Below You can use longer wires or a ribbon cable to locate the Skywriter board away from the Pi if needed

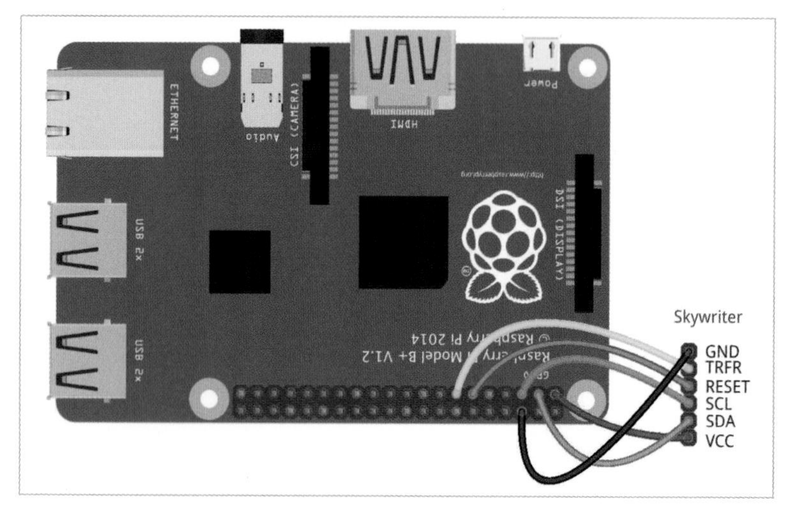

>STEP-02
Install the software

Make sure you have the latest version of Raspbian, with all updates installed. As usual, those helpful Pimoroni Pirates supply a single script to handle the installation, including the full Python API. Like most HATs, the Skywriter needs the I²C bus on the Pi to be enabled, so if you haven't already got this activated on your Pi, you'll need to reboot before the Skywriter will work.

```
curl -sSL get.pimoroni.com/skywriter | bash
```

You'll also need the AutoPy Python library and its dependencies, so install these with:

```
sudo apt-get install libx11-dev libxtst-dev
```

...and then:

```
sudo pip install autopy
```

>STEP-03
Test your Skywriter

The Python API has example scripts to help you become familiar with the way Skywriter works:

```
cd Pimoroni/skywriter
sudo python test.py
```

Now wave your hand around in the air just above your Skywriter. You should see three columns of scrolling numbers corresponding to your hand's position in a three-axis (x/y/z) box over the device. The Python library is preconfigured to recognise certain gestures: a flick (swiping over the Skywriter), a tap or touch (bring your hand down to just above the surface), and, trickiest of all, the Airwheel (wiggle a finger in a circular pattern above the Skywriter). It takes a while to get the hang of reproducing these gestures so that they are always detected, so spend some time practising. You can edit the **test.py** script and comment out the **@skywriter.move()** function (which displays the x/y/z numbers) to make it easier to see when you've nailed one of the gestures.

>STEP-04

Configure your presentation software

Now it's time to get your presentation software ready. LibreOffice Impress is very similar to Microsoft PowerPoint and works well on the Raspberry Pi. If you don't need the other applications in the LibreOffice suite, you can just install Impress and the core components using:

```
sudo apt-get install libreoffice-impress
```

You're going to use Python code to detect gestures via the Skywriter and generate keyboard taps to control Impress in the normal way. The only extra configuration necessary is to activate the functionality that lets you draw on slides with the mouse. This is done by selecting Slide Show>Slide Show Settings and checking the 'Mouse pointer as pen' box.

>STEP-05

Use the code

Type up the code from the listing (right) and save it as **magic_control.py**. You can do this using IDLE or with another text editor of your choice. Start LibreOffice Impress and open your presentation. Then minimise Impress and run your code either through Idle or via the command line:

```
sudo python magic_control.py
```

Now flip back to Impress and get ready to start your talk or presentation.

>STEP-06

Dazzle your audience

Start the slideshow by flicking upwards across the Skywriter. You can navigate through the slides by flicking left to right (forward), or right to left (backwards). To end the presentation, flick down across the Skywriter.

To annotate a slide, you need to activate the drawing function. Do this using a tap/touch: you'll now be controlling the mouse with your hand movements, leaving a trail on the screen just like you're drawing with a pen. This takes practice, so make sure you've spent some time preparing in advance! When you've finished drawing, tap/touch again to disengage the pen function.

We all know that, under the pressure of a live performance, things can go wrong. If you want to quickly disable Skywriter control of the presentation, use a double-tap to quit the Python program.

Magic_Control.py

Language
>PYTHON

DOWNLOAD:
magpi.cc/2dXnBko

```
#!/usr/bin/env python
import skywriter
import signal
import autopy
import sys

mouse_down = False
#work out how big the screen we're using is.
width, height = autopy.screen.get_size()

@skywriter.move()
def move(x, y, z):
  #print( x, y, z )
  global mouse_down
  if mouse_down: # Only run if we're in drawing mode
      x = (x) * width
      y = (y) * height
      # scale to screen size
      x = int(x)
      y = height - int(y)

      if( y > 799 ):
       y = 799

      autopy.mouse.move(x, y)
      #print( int(x), int(y) )

@skywriter.flick()
def flick(start,finish):
  print('Got a flick!', start, finish)
  if start == "east": # Back through Impress slides
    autopy.key.tap(autopy.key.K_LEFT)
  if start == "west": # Forward through Impress slides
    autopy.key.tap(autopy.key.K_RIGHT)
  if start == "north": # Start slideshow
    autopy.key.tap(autopy.key.K_F5)
  if start == "south": # Quit slideshow
    autopy.key.tap(autopy.key.K_ESCAPE)


@skywriter.double_tap()
def doubletap(position):
  print('Double tap!', position)
  sys.exit() # Emergency stop


@skywriter.tap()
def tap(position):
  global mouse_down
  print('Tap!', position)
  if mouse_down: # Toggle mouse up/dwon
      autopy.mouse.toggle(False)
      mouse_down = False
  else:
      autopy.mouse.toggle(True)
      mouse_down = True

#@skywriter.touch()
#def touch(position):
#  print('Touch!', position)

signal.pause()
```

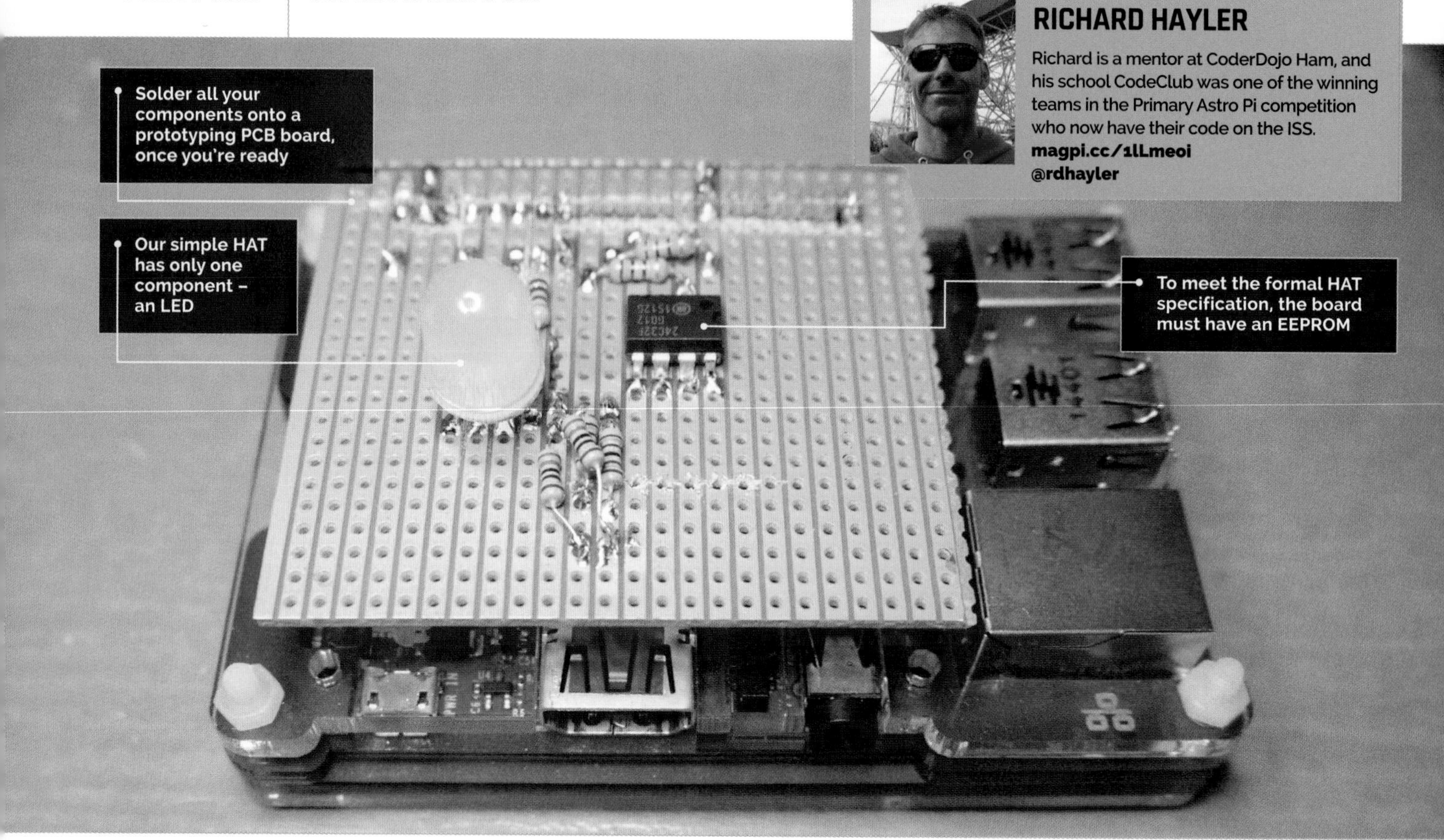

Solder all your components onto a prototyping PCB board, once you're ready
Our simple HAT has only one component – an LED
To meet the formal HAT specification, the board must have an EEPROM

RICHARD HAYLER

Richard is a mentor at CoderDojo Ham, and his school CodeClub was one of the winning teams in the Primary Astro Pi competition who now have their code on the ISS.
magpi.cc/1lLmeoi
@rdhayler

MAKE YOUR OWN PI HAT

You'll Need

- An EEPROM (a CAT24C32 is recommended) **magpi.cc/1RwAaQP**
- A breadboard and some jumper leads **magpi.cc/1RwAdMt**
- Some LEDs **magpi.cc/1RwAiQi**
- The Pi HAT specification repository **magpi.cc/1OAHaGk**

There are some amazing HATs available to enhance the hardware capability of your Pi. Ever wondered how to design and build a prototype HAT? This tutorial will show you how to get started

HATs first arrived with the launch of the Raspberry Pi Model B+ in 2014. Since then, there have been some amazing and wonderful HATs, many of which have featured in previous issues of *The MagPi*: theUnicorn HAT, Piano HAT, Sense HAT, and Explorer HAT. Officially, HAT stands for 'Hardware Attached on Top,' although your expert suspects that the acronym came after the name. What else would you call an add-on board that sits on top of the Pi?

Although you can manufacture and sell boards that don't conform to the HAT standard, there are many advantages in doing so. Having the same physical dimensions makes it easy to ensure your board will fit with most Pi cases, and the inclusion of an EEPROM allows the operating system to identify the HAT and set up any required hardware at startup.

These instructions will work with either the latest version of Raspbian (Jessie) or the older Wheezy. As usual, run a **`sudo apt-get update`** and **`sudo apt-get upgrade`** before starting. Then enable kernel support for I²C using:

```
sudo raspi-config
```

Choose 'Advanced Options', then tap down and select 'A7 I2C'. Make sure 'Yes' is highlighted for the

Left Build your circuit on a breadboard or Explorer HAT first to make sure it works, allowing you to make changes

WHAT IS AN EEPROM?

EEPROM stands for 'Electrically Erasable Programmable Read-Only Memory' and is a chip used in electronic devices to store small amounts of data.

answers to both questions. Alternatively, if you're using Jessie, you can set this up using the Raspberry Pi configuration tool available through the GUI.

You will then be prompted to reboot. Once your Pi has restarted, install the I²C tools package with:

```
sudo apt-get install i2c-tools
```

Now it's time to construct your EEPROM circuit on a breadboard. Put together the circuit as shown in **Fig 1**. If you're not using a 24C32, you may need to connect to different pins for SDA and SCL. Check the data-sheet for your IC to make sure you get this correct. You also need to give the HAT some functionality: in the interests of keeping things simple, the circuit of Fig 1 just contains a tri-colour RGB LED, but you can use whatever components you wish, depending on what you want your HAT to do.

Power up the Pi. You may notice that the LED is already on (perhaps just faintly). This is because the Pi doesn't know what is connected and so the GPIO output is 'floating'. This is something our HAT will deal with by preconfiguring the pins that it uses. The code snippet overleaf (**myoh-rgb.py**) provides some simple Python for interacting with the LED; you'll need to install the wonderful gpiozero library to use it.

Next, check to see what I²C devices have been detected on the second I²C bus:

```
i2cdetect -y 1
```

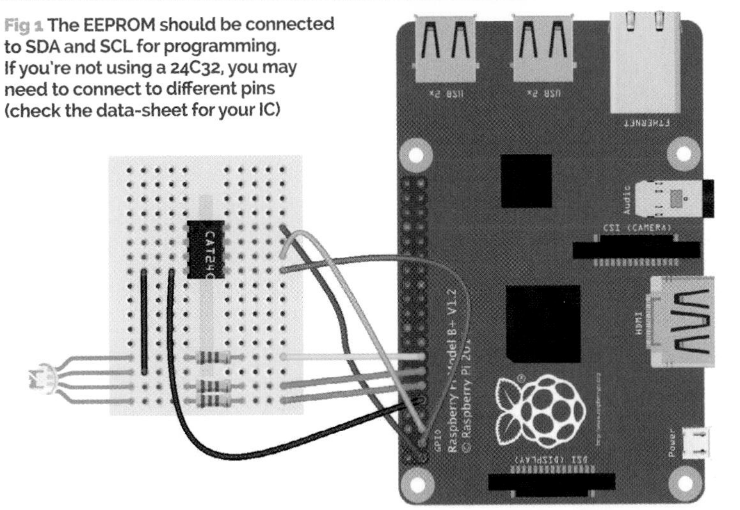

Fig 1 The EEPROM should be connected to SDA and SCL for programming. If you're not using a 24C32, you may need to connect to different pins (check the data-sheet for your IC)

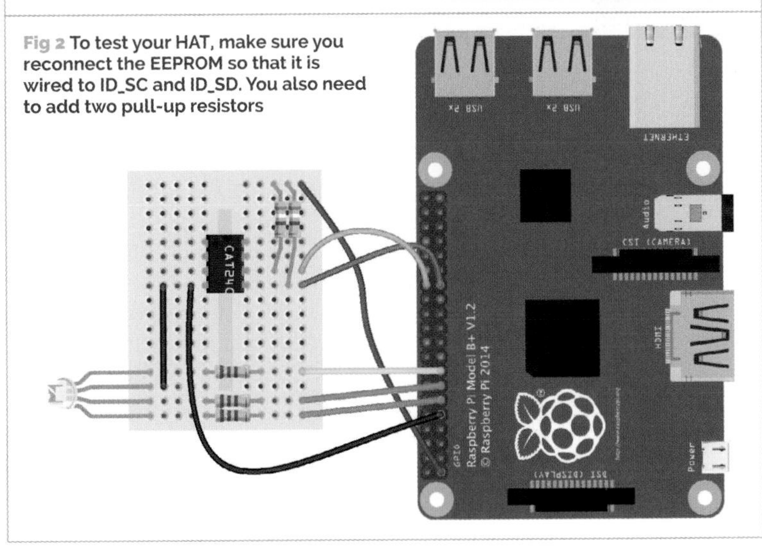

Fig 2 To test your HAT, make sure you reconnect the EEPROM so that it is wired to ID_SC and ID_SD. You also need to add two pull-up resistors

STATIC WARNING!

EEPROMs can be easily damaged by static electricity, so try to ground yourself before handling them. Ideally, wear an anti-static wrist strap, or at the very least leave that nylon sweater in the wardrobe.

You should see a table displaying the devices found on your I²C bus. Assuming you have nothing else connected, all but one of the entries should be empty, as represented by 2 dashes: – –. Normally, your EEPROM should show up in the leftmost column (0) as the number 50, next to the 50 on the horizontal axis.

If you don't see this or the command returns an error ('No such file or directory'), try the other bus:

```
i2cdetect -y 0
```

If your EEPROM still isn't showing up, check your connections and that you have I²C support enabled.

Now you need some software. Clone the HATs reference material and tools from GitHub (**magpi.cc/1OAHaGk**). It's well worth reading this documentation, as it explains the thinking behind the HAT specification in lots of detail.

You're also going to use the handy EEPROM tools to flash your chip. First of all, compile the eepmake tool:

```
cd hats/eepromutils
make
```

Then modify the eepflash script, which assumes that the EEPROM is on the first I²C bus; if yours is, then you can obviously skip this step. Copy the **eepflash.sh** and then modify with your favourite text editor:

```
cp eepflash.sh eepflash1.sh
nano eepflash1.sh
```

Change all mentions of `i2c-0` to `i2c-1`, and `i2c-0/0-0050` to `i2c-1/1-0500`, then save the file.

Now you need to modify the supplied template with your own settings. Open the **eeprom_settings.txt** file in your favourite editor and modify the various fields. Most are self-explanatory and you can read more about each one in the specification. However, the UUID is particularly important and must comply to RFC 4122, so that every HAT can be uniquely identified and can therefore be used as a per-board serial number. It also allows HATs to be stacked.

Once that's done, you need to convert the human-readable text file into binary data that can be written to the EEPROM.

```
./eepmake eeprom_settings.txt eeptest.eep
```

Then dump this data to the EEPROM - this is the actual flashing bit and you'll see a warning asking you if you're sure you want to go ahead:

```
./.eepflash1.sh -w -f=eeptest.eep -t=24c32
```

Make sure you use the version of the script we modified earlier. If you're using a different type of EEPROM, change the `-t` parameter accordingly.

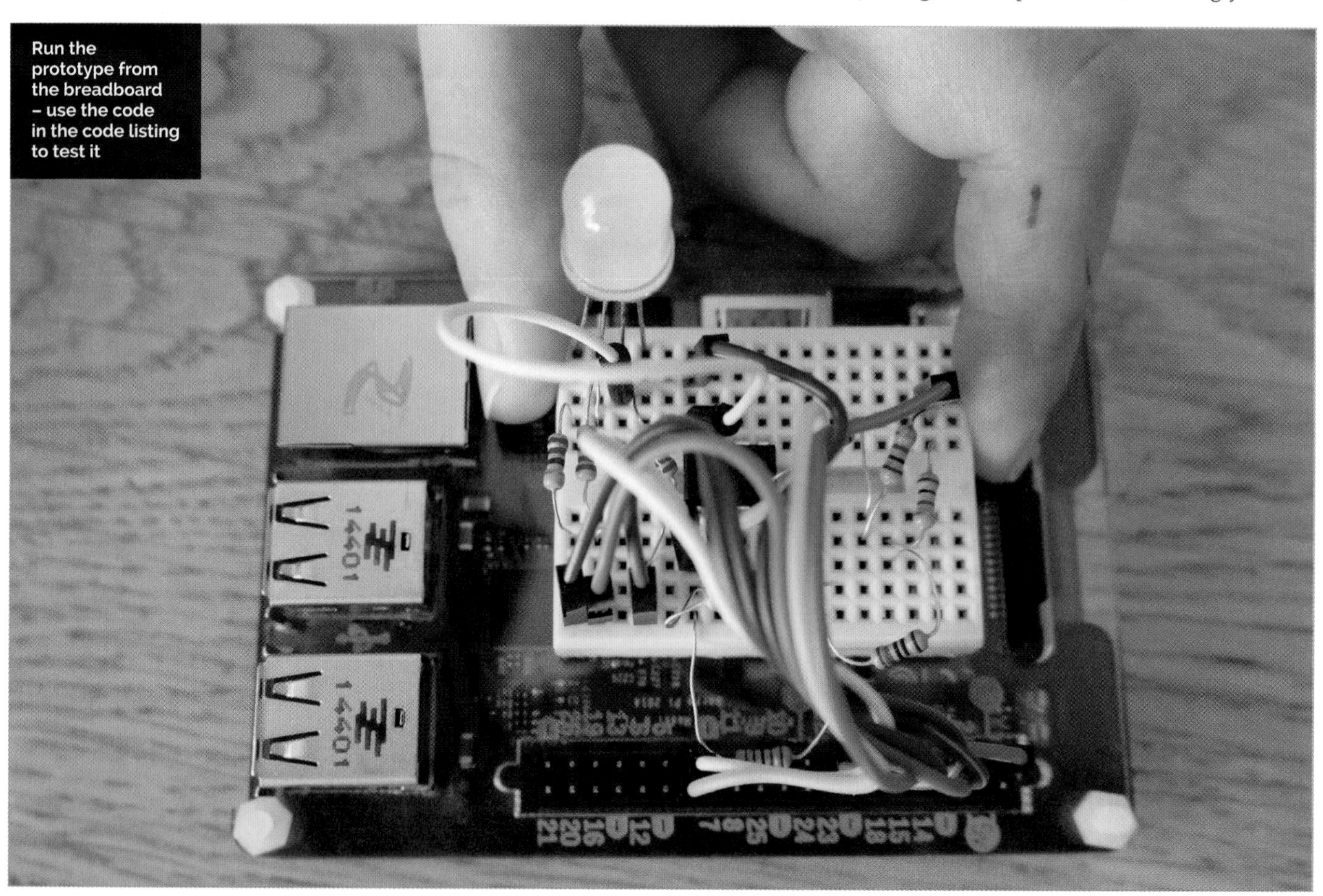

Run the prototype from the breadboard - use the code in the code listing to test it

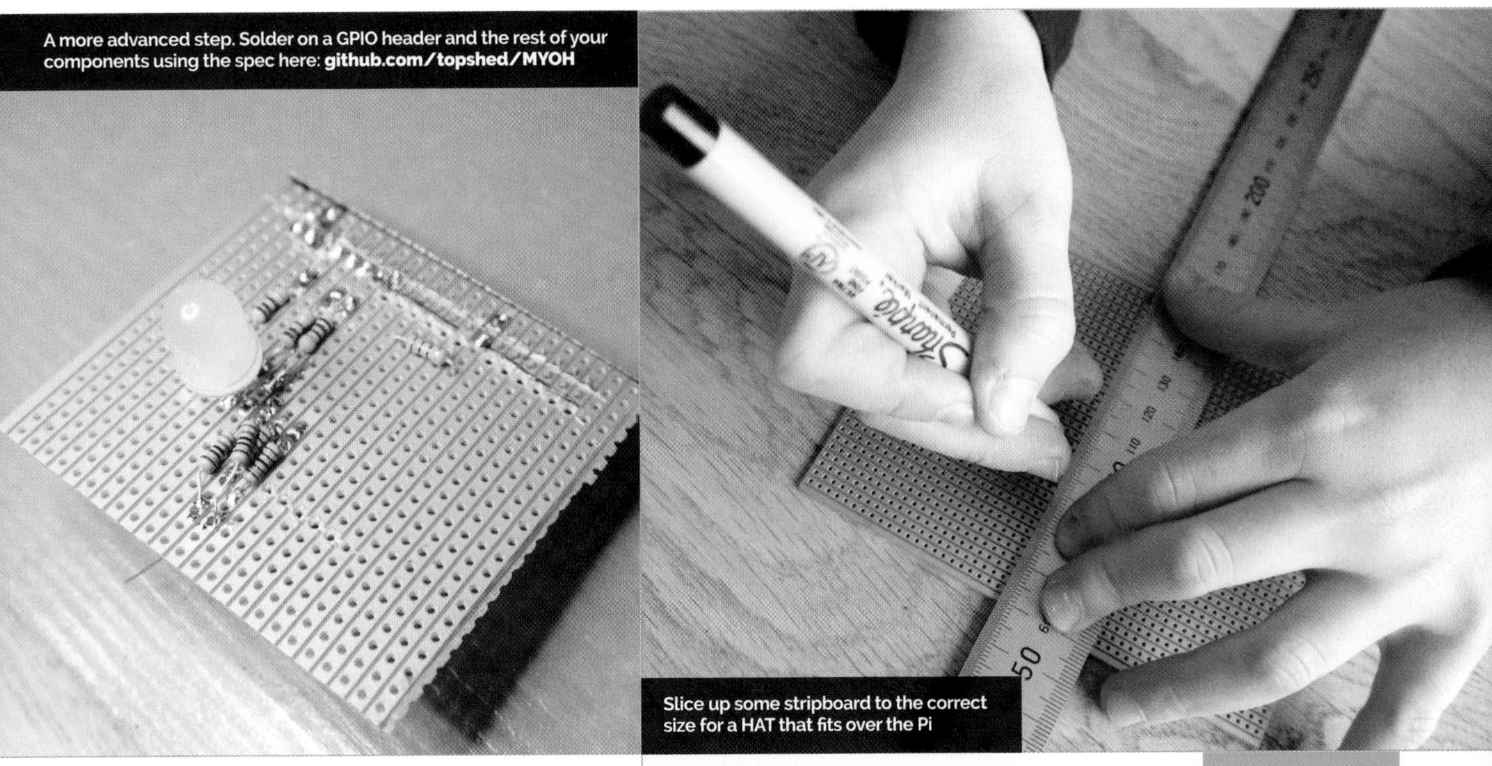

A more advanced step. Solder on a GPIO header and the rest of your components using the spec here: **github.com/topshed/MYOH**

Slice up some stripboard to the correct size for a HAT that fits over the Pi

To test your new creation, you need to modify your circuit so that the EEPROM is connected to the Pi as it would be if it were part of a HAT. GPIO pins 27 and 28 are reserved for HAT detection, so power down your Pi again and move the appropriate wires as shown in **Fig 2**. Then add the 3.9kΩ pull-up resistors which ensure that the pins are not 'floating'.

Now reconnect the power to your Pi and let it boot. If everything has worked, the directory **/proc/device-tree/hat** should be present, and the contents

> See what other amazing add-ons you can create!

of its files should match the details in the default **eeprom_settings.txt** file. You should also see that the GPIO pins used by the RGB LED have now been preset, so it should not be lit at all.

Congratulations! You have now programmed an EEPROM that the Pi recognises as meeting the specification for a HAT.

As a final test, run the **myoh-rgb.py** code and check that the RGB LED flashes through its sequence of colours. Clearly, this is a very basic HAT; there are loads more possibilities for using the ability to have the Pi preload the necessary drivers, so that more complicated hardware can be easily supported. The Sense HAT is a great example of this technique.

Now that you've made a simple HAT and got to grips with the process, see what other amazing add-ons you can create!

If you want to completely follow the whole HAT design process, you now have the option to make the transition from breadboard to proper circuit board. The Raspberry Pi Foundation specification also sets the physical properties of the board, right down to the radius of the rounded corners and the inclusion of slots for the camera and display cables. For prototyping, you probably needn't worry about this too much; a simple stripboard design is available in the GitHub repository for this tutorial, and is pictured in the main image. If you want to take things even further, the marvellous Fritzing CAD software has a built-in PCB template that can help you produce a final design suitable for manufacture.

myoh-rgb.py

Language
>PYTHON 3

DOWNLOAD:
magpi.cc/1RwCo40

```
from gpiozero import RGBLED
from time import sleep

led = RGBLED(22,27,17)

led.on()
sleep(0.5)
led.off()
led.red = 1
sleep(0.5)
led.red =0
led.green=1
sleep(0.5)
led.green = 0
led.blue = 1
sleep(0.5)
led.blue=0
```

EVERYDAY ENGINEERING PART 8

SIMON MONK

Simon Monk is the author of the *Raspberry Pi Cookbook* and *Programming the Raspberry Pi: Getting Started with Python*, among others.
simonmonk.org
monkmakes.com

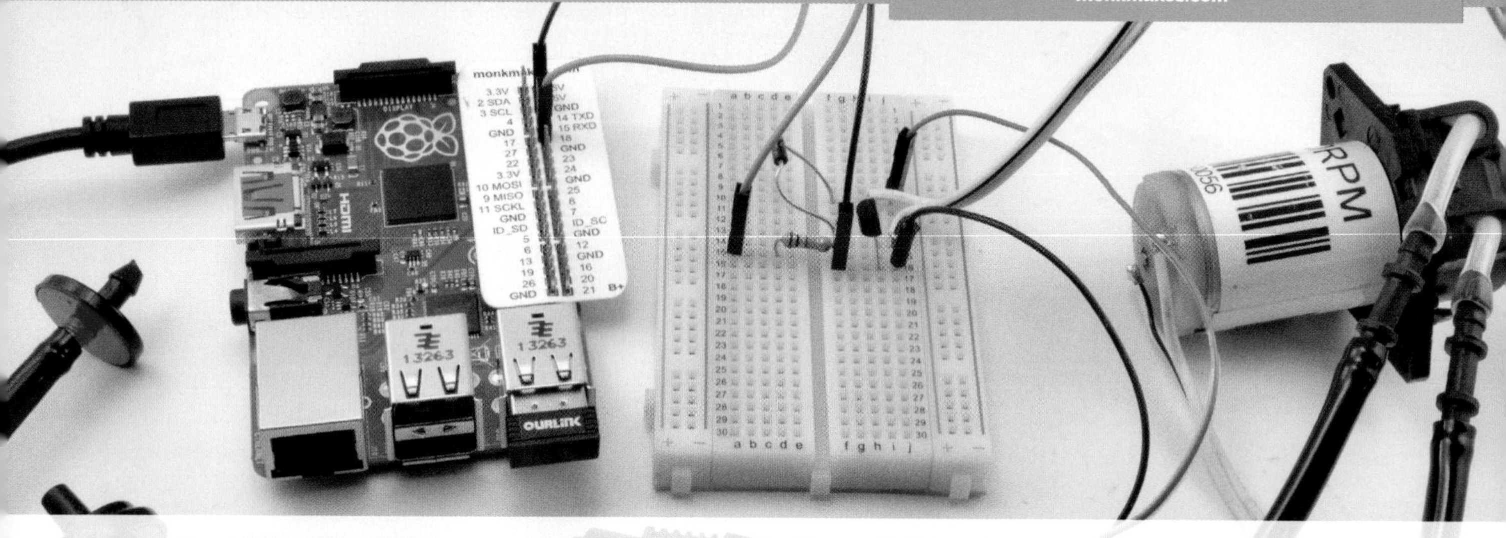

WEB-ENABLED PLANT WATERER

Above Watering can meets the Internet of Things

You'll Need

- Half-size breadboard
- 12V peristaltic pump
- 2× male-to-female jumper wires
- 2× male-to-male jumper wires
- 1k ohm resistor
- MPSA14 transistor (CPC: SC10647)
- 1N4001 diode
- DC barrel socket to screw adaptor (CPC: CN19646)
- 12V DC 1A power supply (this just supplies power to the pump)
- Tubing and connectors

Solve real-world electronic and engineering problems with your Raspberry Pi and the help of renowned technology hacker and author, Simon Monk

This project automates the watering of your plants. You can use it indoors to take care of house plants while you are away, or with a water butt and outdoor containers.

The interface is used to control the duration and start time of your watering, over your local network or even over the internet.

12V Pump

12V DC

MPSA14 Transistor

MPSA14 Transistor

As you'll see from the list of required components on the left, this project uses a small circuit built on breadboard, and a peristaltic pump to take water from your water butt to your containers.

You can find a pump on eBay, where it will cost about £6 from China or twice that from the UK. The pumps are intended for use in an aquarium. They consume about 300mA, a little too much for an old favourite transistor like the 2N3904, so a MPSA14 Darlington transistor, which can cope with 1A, is used instead.

The pumps are usually supplied without leads attached, so you will probably need to solder leads on. If you plan to use the pump outdoors, then solder twin speaker cable or the like to the pump terminals; it must be long enough to allow you to have the pump outside, and your Raspberry Pi and the rest of the electronics indoors.

The pump needs its own 12V DC power supply, which is

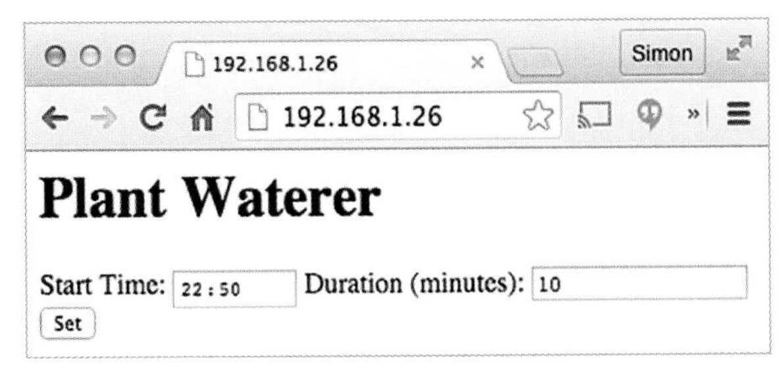

Above Controlling the waterer from a browser

connected to the breadboard using a DC barrel socket to screw adaptor and two male-to-male jumper wires.

The tubing and fittings that we used came from a low-cost supermarket as a 'Micro Irrigation System'. This packet contained a few metres of tubing as well as small posts for anchoring the pipes, and small joining sections that were perfect for connecting the pump to the tubing.

The breadboard, jumper wires, and resistor are probably best bought as an electronics starter kit. The Monk Makes Electronic Starter Kit for Raspberry Pi includes these parts. Most starter kits for the Raspberry Pi will include the breadboard, jumper wires, and some resistors.

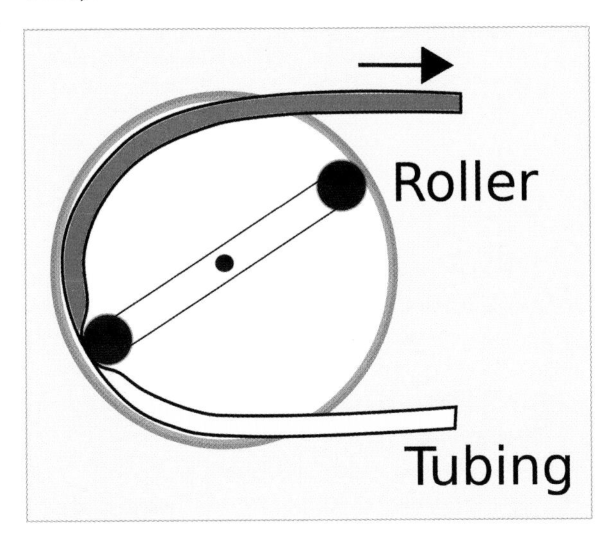

Above Peristaltic pump

Peristaltic pumps

Peristaltic pumps use a motor to drive a gearbox that in turn drives a pair of rollers that squeeze the flexible but strong pipe to push the water through the pump.

These pumps have the advantage that they are 'self-priming'. That is, you do not need to get the air out of the intake tube before they start pumping; they will eventually pull the water through. The other advantage they have is that when the motor stops, it effectively seals the pipe, so no water will flow through it even if the water is under a bit of pressure.

Building your waterer

As with all projects, it is a good idea to test the project out and get everything working while the parts are all still in your workspace. Once you know all is well, you can install the project in its final location.

BUILDING THE PROJECT

This is a pretty straightforward project to build. There are just three components on the breadboard. As well as the electronics, you will also need to find a way to attach the pump to your water container and, if it is in the open, keep the rain out of the pump.

>STEP-01

Solder leads onto the pump

Bell wire or speaker cable is just fine. To make it easier to push the loose ends into the breadboard, tin them with solder so that they don't bunch up when you try to insert them into the breadboard.

>STEP-02

Build the breadboard

When inserting the components into the breadboard, make sure that you get the transistor and diode the correct way around. The transistor has one curved side that should be facing to the left, and the diode has a stripe on one end that needs to be towards the top of the breadboard. The resistor can be connected either way around. To prevent accidental shorts between the resistor and diode leads, it is a good idea to shorten one or both of the leads.

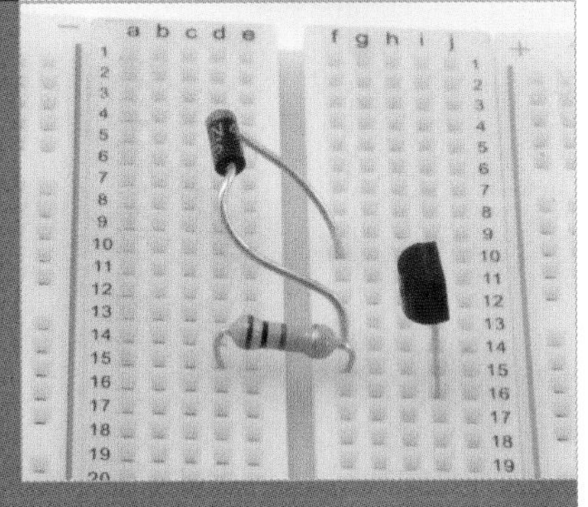

>STEP-03

Connect the breadboard

Attach male-to-male jumper wires to the screw terminals of the barrel jack adaptor. Use red and black leads, and make sure that you attach the red lead to the screw terminal marked '+'. Fit the other end of the jumper wires into the breadboard.

The wires to the pump motor should also now be fitted to the breadboard, and the female-to-male jumper wires used to connect the breadboard to GND and 18 on the Raspberry Pi GPIO header.

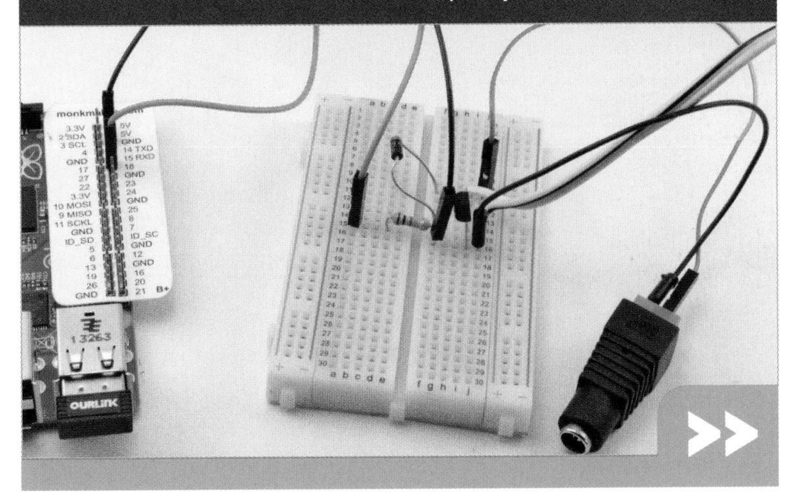

>STEP-04
Testing

Before installing the project, test it out using two short lengths of tube attached to the pump and two glasses, one containing water. Jump ahead to the software section and set the start time for a minute ahead of the current time. Wait for the pump to start, then make sure that it will pump water from one glass to the other. This will also tell you which tube is the inlet and which is the outlet.

Make sure that the tubes are really well connected to the pump. If any air at all can get in, then the pump will not work properly.

>STEP-05
Installation

Our example setup is temporary. The Raspberry Pi lives indoors, with the lead to the pump fed out through a window. The inlet tube to the pump fits under the water butt lid and down into the water. The outlet goes off to the plant container.

Now that the hardware side of the project is complete, we just need to get the software running. The program is written in Python and uses a library called Bottle to provide the web server feature of this project. If you made either the Web Door Lock or the Teenager Alarm Clock from issues 32 and 33 of *The MagPi*, you should already have Bottle installed. If not, to install Bottle, make sure that your Raspberry Pi has an internet connection and then run the commands:

```
sudo apt-get update
sudo apt-get install python-bottle
```

Waterer_Server.py

```
from bottle import route, run, template, request
import thread, time
import RPi.GPIO as GPIO
import datetime

# Change these for your setup.
PUMP_PIN = 18

# Configure the GPIO pin
GPIO.setmode(GPIO.BCM)
GPIO.setup(PUMP_PIN, GPIO.OUT)
GPIO.output(PUMP_PIN, 0)

# Glogal variables
start_time = "22:00"
duration = "30"

# Handler for the home page
@route('/')
def index():
```

You can download the program for this project from your Raspberry Pi command line, using the command:

```
git clone https://github.com/simonmonk/pi_magazine.git
```

To run the program, change to the directory where the code for this project lives and then run the program using the commands below:

```
cd /home/pi/pi_magazine/08_waterer
sudo python waterer_server.py
```

This will start a web server running on your Raspberry Pi. You can check this by opening a browser window on another computer or your phone and entering the IP address of your Pi. Open the terminal and type **ifconfig** to find yours. If all is well, a webpage will be displayed, inviting you to enter a start time and duration for the watering.

How the code works

The Python code for this program is pretty heavily commented. You will probably find it handy to have the code up in an editor while we go through it.

The program starts by importing the **Bottle**, **thread**, **time**, **RPi.GPIO** and **datetime** libraries that it needs. The constant **PUMP_PIN** is used to specify which GPIO pin is to be used to control the pump. Change this value if you want to use a different pin.

Two global variables are used: **start_time** and **duration**. The variable **start_time** contains the

Language
>PYTHON

```
    global start_time, duration
    # Change the start_time and duration

    local_start_time = request.GET.get('start_time', '')
    if local_start_time != "":
        start_time = local_start_time
    local_duration = request.GET.get('duration', '')
    if local_duration != "":
        duration = local_duration
    return template('home.tpl', start_time=start_time,
duration=duration)


def update(thread_name):
    global start_time, duration
    watering = False
    end_timestamp = 0
    while True:
        # Get the time formatted as a string for comparison
        # with the alarm time
        current_time = time.strftime("%H:%M")
        # If its time to start watering, do so, but not if
        # you are already watering
        if current_time == start_time \
and not watering:
            print("Starting Watering")
            watering = True
            GPIO.output(PUMP_PIN, 1)
            end_timestamp = time.time() + int(duration) * 60
        # Check to see if its time to stop watering
        if watering and time.time() > end_timestamp:
            print("End Watering")
            watering = False
            GPIO.output(PUMP_PIN, 0)

        time.sleep(1) # allow other threads to run

# start a separate thread to check the time
thread.start_new_thread(update, ("update_thread",))

# Start the webserver running on port 80
try:
    run(host="0.0.0.0", port=80)
finally:
    print('Cleaning up GPIO')
    GPIO.cleanup()
```

time for the next watering to take place; this is in the format of a string containing two numbers for the hour (24-hour clock) followed by a colon, followed by two digits for the minute. The **duration** is the number of minutes that the watering should last. Both of these variables will be set using the web interface for the project.

started by the command **start_new_thread**, which causes the **update** function to effectively run independently of the rest of the program. The **update** function checks the current time against the start time and if they are the same, it starts the watering process by turning on the GPIO pin that is connected to the pump via the transistor.

"Since this Python program is mostly acting as a web server, the code to check the start time happens in a separate thread of execution"

The next section of the code supplies the web interface. Bottle uses the **@route** directive to indicate that the function that immediately follows it is a handler for web requests. So the default route page of '/' is handled by the function called **index**. The **index** function uses Bottle's templating mechanism to return the HTML contained in the template file called **home.tpl**. You will find the HTML template used in the project contained in the code directory for it (**bit.ly/1NezVHT**).

When you enter values into the **Start Time** and **Duration** fields on the webpage, they will be passed as parameters when the form is submitted. These are extracted in the **index** function and as long as they are not blank (empty-string), they are used to set new values of **start_time** and **duration**.

Since this Python program is mostly acting as a web server, the code to check the start time happens in a separate thread of execution. This thread is

The last few lines of the program start up the web server on port 80. The **try** / **finally** clause is used to set the GPIO pins back to inputs when the program is quit using **CTRL+C**.

Using your waterer

You can use a web browser on a computer, or on a smartphone if it is connected to your Wi-Fi network. For this reason, the Raspberry Pi needs to have a network connection, which also allows the Pi to synchronise with an internet time server. If you find that your Raspberry Pi is an hour out, then you may need to use the **raspi-config** tool to set the time zone.

If you enjoy a bit of web design, the first thing you will probably want to do is to add some styling to the webpages. The place to do this is in the template file **home.tpl**. If you are network-savvy, then you could also set up port forwarding to allow access to the waterer from the internet at large.

EVERYDAY ENGINEERING PART 10

SIMON MONK

Simon Monk is the author of the *Raspberry Pi Cookbook* and *Programming the Raspberry Pi: Getting Started with Python*, among others.
simonmonk.org
monkmakes.com

USB WiFi adaptor

An accurate DS18B20 temperature sensor

PIPE TEMPERATURE MONITOR

Solve real-world electronic and engineering problems with your Raspberry Pi and the help of renowned technology hacker and author, **Simon Monk**

You'll Need

- Encapsulated DS18B20 (eBay, Adafruit, Proto Pic)
- 4.7k resistor (often supplied with DS18B20)
- Three-way screw terminal block
- 3× female-to-male jumper wires
- USB WiFi adaptor
- Small food container as an enclosure
- Drill

At this time of year, our roof spaces can get pretty chilly and if there are pipes up there, there is a chance they could freeze. As anyone who's put a bottle of wine in the freezer to cool and then forgotten about it knows, ice takes up more space than water and can burst pipes as it expands. This is often only discovered when the ice thaws again and your bedroom has water dribbling through the ceiling.

This project monitors the temperature of your pipe and uses the If This Then That (IFTTT) web service to alert you by email or other mechanism of your choice if the temperature falls below a threshold that you set.

IFTTT is a web service that allows you to set up triggers that then cause an action. For example, you could create an IFTTT 'Recipe' that sends you an email (Action) whenever someone mentions you on Twitter (Trigger). As well as actions and triggers from all sorts of social media and email services, IFTTT can also be set up to work with physical events like the temperature measured by a temperature sensor falling below some threshold.

The way this works is that the Raspberry Pi sends a web request to IFTTT as a trigger and then IFTTT performs whatever action you have specified for it. In this case, the trigger is to send an email.

The various channels available to IFTTT often require their own logins, so IFTTT will from time to time ask you to enter a user name and password for a particular channel.

⚠ WARNING!

Do not rely solely on this project to protect your pipes from frost. This is a DIY project intended to illustrate the principles of making a temperature monitor and is in no way guaranteed to protect your home.

> DS18B20 is a digital device, accurate to ±0.5 degrees C

As you'll see from the list of required components, this project does not call for any soldering. The leads to the temperature probe are connected to the Raspberry PI GPIO pins using a combination of electrical terminal block and female-to-male jumper wires. You will find the screw terminal block at any DIY or hardware store that sells electrical supplies.

DS18B20 temperature sensor

The DS18B20 is a sensor temperature chip that is available in a standard 3-pin transistor-like package, or built into an encapsulated sensor with a long lead. In this project we chose the encapsulated version, but you could also use the 3-pin package version on a breadboard. The chip requires there to be a 4.7kΩ resistor between its data and positive supply pins. The chip itself will work with 5V or 3.3V logic, but you must connect the positive supply to 3.3V when using it with a Raspberry Pi to prevent damage to the Pi GPIO pin that it is connected to.

Temperature sensors are often quite inaccurate, but the DS18B20 is a digital device that is accurate to ±0.5 degrees Celsius.

The IC uses a single GPIO pin on the Raspberry Pi using an interface called the 1-wire. Temperature readings are sent as serial data to the Raspberry Pi.

Building your pipe monitor

As with all projects, it is a good idea to run a test and get everything working while the parts are all out on your workspace. Once you know all is well, you can install the project in its enclosure.

BUILDING THE PROJECT

This is a pretty straightforward project to build. There is no soldering to be done, although if you have a soldering iron, tinning the ends of the wires from the sensor leads to make them a bit thicker makes it easier to catch them in the terminal block.

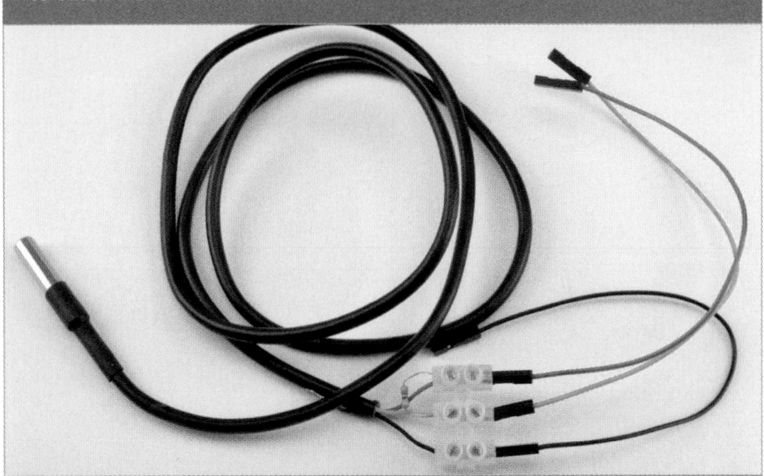

>STEP-01

Connect female header leads

Put the red (positive supply), black (ground), and yellow (data) wires from the temperature probe into the screw terminal, with the leads of the resistor between the red and yellow wires. You may find it helps to wrap the bare ends of the wires around the resistor leads before tightening up the screw terminals.

Fit the male ends of the jumper wires into other half of the terminal block.

Your probe lead may also have a separate bare wire connector to the lead's screening; you do not need to connect this to anything.

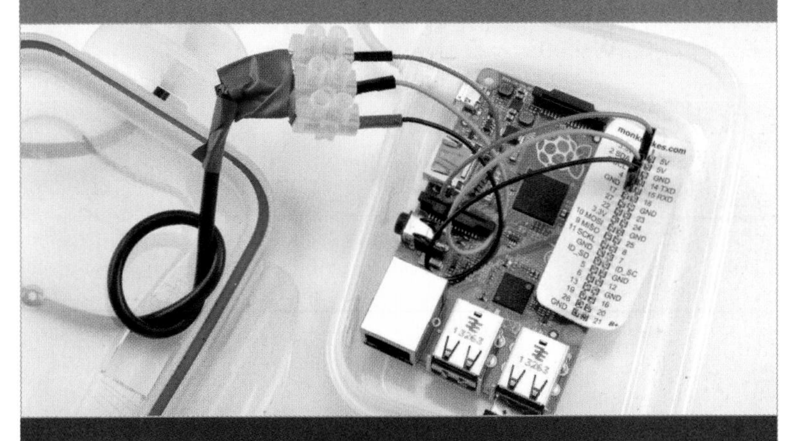

>STEP-02

Connect the temperature sensor

Connect the positive supply lead to the 3.3V GPIO pin, the black ground lead of the sensor to one of the GND pins on the GPIO header, and the data lead to GPIO 4. Using a GPIO pin template such as the Raspberry Leaf makes it much easier to find the right pins.

We used a food container that would hold both the screw terminal and the Raspberry Pi and drilled holes for the USB power and sensor leads. The knot in the sensor lead is to stop the connections being pulled off, and the electrical tape prevents the resistor leads from accidentally shorting anything on the GPIO pins.

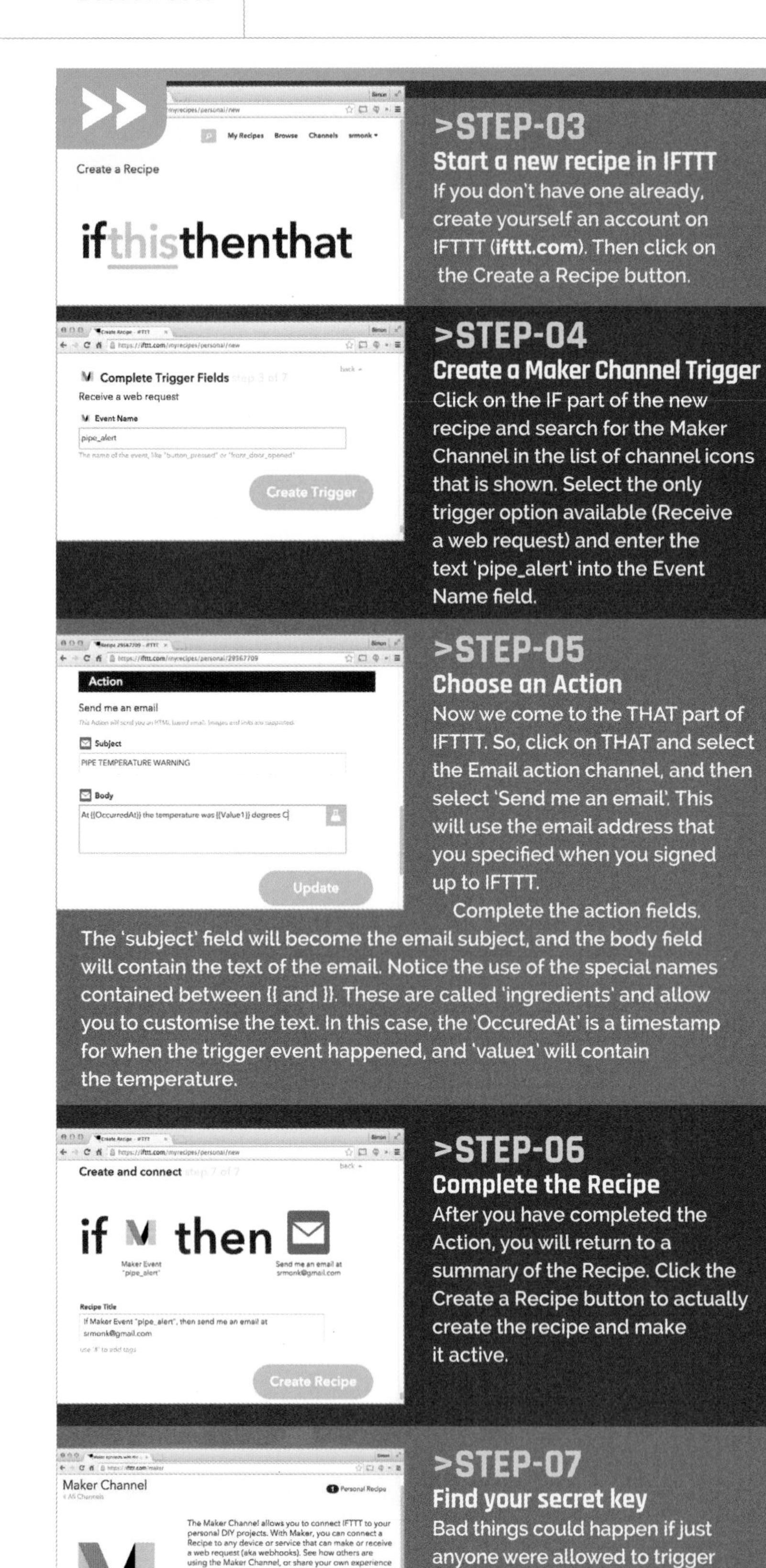

>STEP-03
Start a new recipe in IFTTT
If you don't have one already, create yourself an account on IFTTT (**ifttt.com**). Then click on the Create a Recipe button.

>STEP-04
Create a Maker Channel Trigger
Click on the IF part of the new recipe and search for the Maker Channel in the list of channel icons that is shown. Select the only trigger option available (Receive a web request) and enter the text 'pipe_alert' into the Event Name field.

>STEP-05
Choose an Action
Now we come to the THAT part of IFTTT. So, click on THAT and select the Email action channel, and then select 'Send me an email'. This will use the email address that you specified when you signed up to IFTTT.

Complete the action fields. The 'subject' field will become the email subject, and the body field will contain the text of the email. Notice the use of the special names contained between {{ and }}. These are called 'ingredients' and allow you to customise the text. In this case, the 'OccuredAt' is a timestamp for when the trigger event happened, and 'value1' will contain the temperature.

>STEP-06
Complete the Recipe
After you have completed the Action, you will return to a summary of the Recipe. Click the Create a Recipe button to actually create the recipe and make it active.

>STEP-07
Find your secret key
Bad things could happen if just anyone were allowed to trigger emails to be sent using IFTTT. So when the web request is sent from Python to trigger the email, it must be accompanied by a secret key. To find that key, click on the Channels tab at the top of the IFTTT webpage and then find the Maker channel.

In a little while, you are going to need to paste the secret key into your Python program.

This is the kind of project that you definitely want to use SSH for, so that you can connect to the Raspberry Pi remotely using the WiFi USB dongle. You can find instructions on setting up your Pi to use SSH on the official website: **magpi.cc/1GULmTr**.

Before you can use the DS18B20 temperature sensor, you need to enable the 1-wire interface of the Raspberry Pi. To enable 1-wire, edit the file **/boot/config.txt** using the command:

```
sudo nano /boot/config.txt
```

Add the following line to the end of the file:

```
dtoverlay=w1-gpio
```

Now reboot your Raspberry Pi and 1-wire should be enabled.

You can download the program for this project from your Raspberry Pi command line using:

```
git clone https://github.com/simonmonk/pi_magazine.git
```

Before running the program, open it with the nano editor and change the line:

```
KEY = 'cyR3vPNF1P9K32W4NZB9cd'
```

Change this to the IFTTT key that you found earlier. Run the program as superuser using the command below:

```
sudo python pipes.py
```

When you run the program, you should see the message 'Monitoring' in the terminal, after which temperature readings should start appearing.

How the code works
The Python code for this program is commented. You will probably find it handy to have the code up in an editor while we go through it.

The program starts by importing the libraries that it requires:

`glob` is used to find the device file for the temperature sensor, as the program needs to use wild-card matching because every DS18B20 is given a different device ID during manufacture;

`time` is used for delays;

`urllib` and **`urllib2`** are used to send the web request to IFTTT.

You may well want to change the constants that follow this, especially while you are testing the system. The variable **`ALARM_TEMP`** sets the temperature at which an alarm will be triggered, so set this to a few degrees less than the temperature reported by the program in the terminal and go and get yourself a glass of cold water for testing.

The constant **MIN_T_BETWEEN_WARNINGS** prevents messages being sent more frequently than once every hour. You might want to change this while you are testing the project.

The next set of variables are used to identify the location for the file of your particular temperature sensor. This will be in the folder **/sys/bus/w1/devices/**, but then the folder name after this will be different for every DS18B20.

The function **read_temp** reads the content of the device file. This will be a two-line message from the temperature sensor that looks something like this:

```
28 01 4b 46 7f ff 08 10 4c : crc=4c YES,
28 01 4b 46 7f ff 08 10 4c t=18500
```

The number at the start of both lines is the unique ID for the DS18B20, and the first line ends in YES if the reading was successful, with the temperature being reported at the end of the second line as the number of thousandths of a degree C. In this case, that's 18.5°C. The function **read_temp** extracts the temperature value from the message and returns it.

The **send_notification** function constructs a URL for the IFTTT web service, providing the temperature in the request body.

The main loop repeatedly reads the temperature, to check if it has fallen low enough to trigger an alarm. If so, it calls **send_notification** and then delays until **MIN_T_BETWEEN_WARNINGS** minutes have passed.

Using your pipe monitor

To test the project before you install it, set **ALARM_TEMP** to a couple of degrees lower than the ambient temperature, then put the sensor into some cold water. After a few moments, the temperature readings will start to fall until you get a message:

```
TEMPERATURE WARNING
Congratulations! You've fired the
pipe_alert event
```

If you go and check your email inbox, you should see a notification message.

Even the power-efficient Raspberry Pi generates enough heat to provide a misleading temperature reading. To avoid this, make sure that the DS18B20 is well away from the Raspberry Pi itself, ideally near or even taped to the pipes that you are trying to protect. You will of course also need somewhere to connect a power adaptor, and make sure that your roof space is not out of range of your WiFi router.

This is a project that lends itself to other tasks. You could modify it to just report the temperature at regular intervals, or to check for temperatures getting too hot rather than too cold. You can also pick other actions from IFTTT, such as tweeting or sending a Facebook update.

Pipes.py

Language
>PYTHON

```
import glob
import time
import urllib, urllib2

ALARM_TEMP = 5.0 # degrees C
MIN_T_BETWEEN_WARNINGS = 60 # Minutes
EVENT = 'pipe_alert'
BASE_URL = 'https://maker.ifttt.com/trigger/'
KEY = 'cyR3vPNF1P9K32W4NZB9cd'  # Place your own key here

# These constants used by the 1-wire device
base_dir = '/sys/bus/w1/devices/'
device_folder = glob.glob(base_dir + '28*')[0]
device_file = device_folder + '/w1_slave'

# Read the temperature message from the device file
def read_temp_raw():
    f = open(device_file, 'r')
    lines = f.readlines()
    f.close()
    return lines

# Split the actual temperature out of the message
def read_temp():
    lines = read_temp_raw()
    while lines[0].strip()[-3:] != 'YES':
        time.sleep(0.2)
        lines = read_temp_raw()
    equals_pos = lines[1].find('t=')
    if equals_pos != -1:
        temp_string = lines[1][equals_pos+2:]
        temp_c = float(temp_string) / 1000.0
        return temp_c

# Send an IFTTT pipe_alert event
def send_notification(temp):
    print("TEMPERATURE WARNING")
    data = urllib.urlencode({'value1' : str(temp)})
    url = BASE_URL + EVENT + '/with/key/' + KEY
    response = urllib2.urlopen(url=url, data=data)
    print(response.read())


print("Monitoring")
while True:
    temp = read_temp()
    print(temp)
    if temp < ALARM_TEMP:
        send_notification(temp)
        time.sleep(MIN_T_BETWEEN_WARNINGS * 60)
```

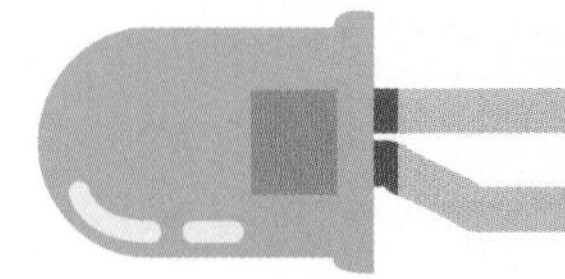

EVERYDAY ENGINEERING PART 11

SIMON MONK

Simon Monk is the author of the *Raspberry Pi Cookbook* and *Programming the Raspberry Pi: Getting Started with Python*, among others.

simonmonk.org

monkmakes.com

PI MI-LIGHT

Solve real-world electronic and engineering problems with your Raspberry Pi and the help of renowned technology hacker and author, **Simon Monk**

You'll Need

- NRF24L01 2.4GHz wireless radio transceiver module (eBay)
- Mi-Light RGB LED light bulb
- Mi-Light 2.4GHz remote control
- 7 × female-to-female jumper wires

Mi-Light light bulbs look just like normal LED light bulbs and are available at a similar price, but they include a 2.4GHz RF radio link. This can be used with an RF remote control to switch lights on and off, with the lights grouped into four zones. The remote control also allows you to vary the brightness and colour of the light. Mi-Light produces a ready-made module that allows you to link the lamps to your WiFi router and then control the lighting with a smartphone app. However, by using a £3 ($5) radio module connected to a Raspberry Pi, you can let your Raspberry Pi take control of Mi-Light bulbs in your home, opening up all sorts of possibilities for home automation.

One possible use is to have the Raspberry Pi operate as a web server, providing you with a web interface that will let you turn lights on and off from the browser of any device connected to your network.

Mi-Light LED bulb

NRF24L radio transceiver

This project is based on an original blog post by Torsten Tränkner that you will find in German here: **torsten-traenkner.de**. The project has only been tested on a Raspberry Pi 2, and may need some adaptation for other models of Pi.

As you'll see from the list of required components, this project does not involve any soldering. The RF module is connected to the Raspberry Pi using female-to-female jumper wires. Even though the Raspberry Pi will eventually take over the operation of the lights, you do need a Mi-Light remote control to set things up in the first place.

Control your home lighting with a Raspberry Pi

BUILDING YOUR PI-MI-LIGHT CONTROLLER

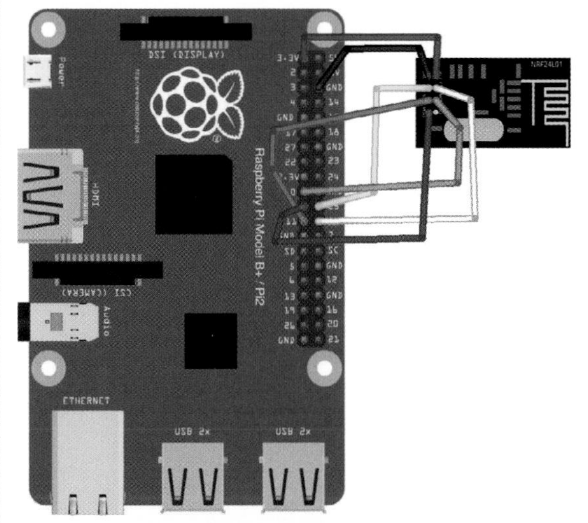

You should wire up the RF module with your Raspberry Pi powered down, and check very carefully that the connections are all correct before you power it back up again. Using a GPIO template like the Raspberry Leaf (by MonkMakes) will help you find the correct connections on the GPIO connector.

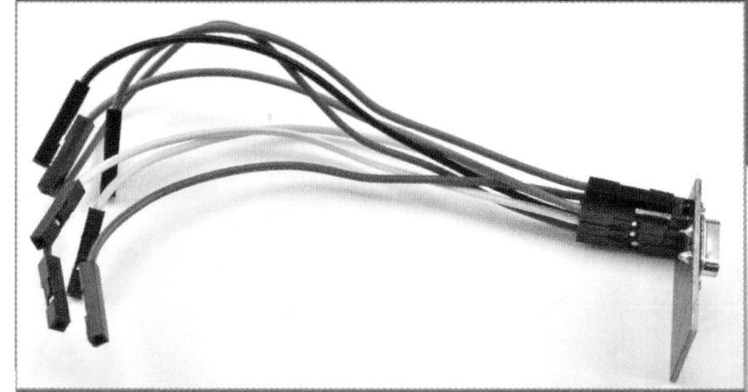

>STEP-01

Attach leads to the RF module

Start by connecting jumper wires to the RF module using the wiring diagram as a reference. You will need connections to every pin except the pin in the bottom right of the connector (pin 8). Using leads of the same colour as the wiring diagram will help you make the correct connections.

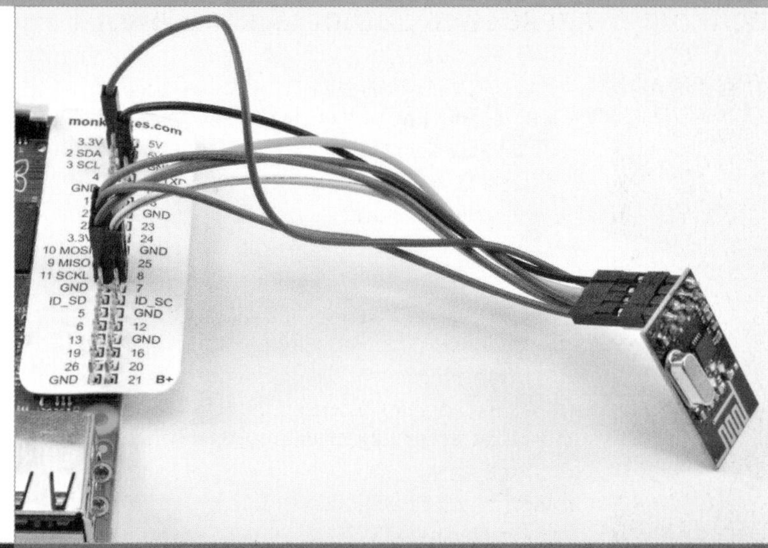

>STEP-02

Connect the RF module

Connect the leads from the RF module to the GPIO header as follows:

Pin 1 (GND) of the RF module to GND on the GPIO header.
Pin 2 (VCC) of the RF module to 3.3V on the GPIO header.
Pin 3 (CE) of the RF module to GPIO 25.
Pin 4 (CSN) of the RF module to GPIO 8.
Pin 5 (CLK) of the RF module to SCLK (GPIO 11) on the GPIO header.
Pin 6 (MOSI) of the RF module to MOSI (GPIO 10) on the GPIO header.
Pin 7 (MISO) of the RF module to MISO (GPIO 9) on the GPIO header.

>STEP-03

Pair the Mi-Light

For this step, you will need to plug your light bulb into an appropriate light socket. Then turn on the normal light switch and immediately press the On button for one of the four light zones on the Mi-Light remote. The lamp will blink three times as confirmation. Once paired, the remote will be able to turn the light on and off and make other adjustments.

This project requires quite a lot of software setup before you can go ahead and use it.

The radio module uses the Raspberry Pi's SPI interface, which needs to be enabled, so run raspi-config using the command:

```
sudo raspi-config
```

Scroll down to the **Advanced** option, select it, and then select **SPI**. Enable it, and when asked if you want the SPI module to load automatically, say Yes.

> This code is all in C++ but can be called from our Python program

Next, you need to install and build the NRF24 library for the RF module by issuing the following commands:

```
git clone https://github.com/TMRh20/RF24
cd RF24
make all
sudo make install
```

After that, you need to download a messaging library that provides a higher-level interface to the basic RF module using the following commands:

```
cd ..
git clone https://github.com/mysensors/Raspberry
cd Raspberry
make
sudo make install
```

Now download the code that Torsten Tränkner wrote using the following commands:

```
cd ..
wget http://torsten-traenkner.de/wissen/smarthome/openmilight_raspberry_pi.tgz
tar xzvf openmilight_raspberry_pi.tgz
```

Below Turn light zones on/off from a phone browser

This code is all in C++ and so that we can make use of it in Python, your expert has written a C++ program called **send_cmd**, which is designed to be called from Python with a command message to be sent to the Mi-Light. Download this program and the Python code for the project from your Pi's command line, using:

```
git clone https://github.com/simonmonk/pi_magazine.git
```

Copy all the files in the project folder **11_mi_light** into the **openmilight** folder, and then compile two of the programs by using the commands:

```
cp pi_magazine/11_mi_light/* openmilight
cd openmilight
sh ./comp.sh
```

You also need to install the Python Bottle library that will be used for the web server, using the command:

```
sudo apt-get install python-bottle
```

Before you can run the main program, you need to find the ID of the Mi-Light remote that you used to pair with the Mi-Light so that your Raspberry Pi can impersonate it.

Run the program **openmilight** using the command below, and then press the On button for Zone 1 on the remote a couple of times. Each time you press the button, you should see a stream of hexadecimal number like the ones in the example below.

```
sudo ./openmilight
in listening mode
B0 A1 56 41 C1 03 72 .
B0 A1 56 41 C1 03 73 .
```

The first three digits (in this case B0, A1, and 56) will be different for your remote, so quit the program using **CTRL+C** and edit the file **lights.py**, changing the value of the **ID** variable at the top of the file to be the three hex digits for your remote.

Finally, you are ready to fire up the web server using the following command:

```
sudo python lights.py
```

Point a convenient web browser at the IP address of your Raspberry Pi and you will see a webpage with On and Off buttons for all four zones. Click the buttons for Zone 1 and you should be able to turn all the lights connected to that zone on and off.

Lights.py

Language
>PYTHON 2.7

DOWNLOAD:
magpi.cc/1NZhcLv

```
from bottle import route, run, template, request
import os

ID = 'B0 A1 56'
MIDDLE = ' 06 C9 '

ZONES = {
    'zone1': {'on': '03', 'off': '04'},
    'zone2': {'on': '05', 'off': '06'},
    'zone3': {'on': '07', 'off': '08'},
    'zone4': {'on': '09', 'off': '0A'}}

def light_on(zone):
    print(zone + "on")
    send(ZONES[zone]['on'])


def light_off(zone):
    print(zone + "off")
    send(ZONES[zone]['off'])

def send(code):
    global ID, MIDDLE
    for i in range(1, 5):
        message = ID + MIDDLE + code +
' 00'
        os.system('./send_cmd "' +
message + '"')

# Handler for the home page
@route('/')
def index():
    zone = request.GET.get('zone', 'zone1')
    state = request.GET.get('state', 'off')
    if state == 'on':
        light_on(zone)
    else:
        light_off(zone)
    return template('home.tpl')

# Start the webserver running on port 80
run(host="0.0.0.0", port=80)
```

How the code works

You will probably find it handy to have the code up in an editor while we go through it.

The program starts by importing the **bottle** and **os** libraries. The **os** library is needed to invoke the **send_cmd** C program from Python.

The constant **ID** needs to be set to the three hex digits for your remote, as described earlier. The codes in **MIDDLE** do not need to change. Note that the spaces in both these constants must be kept as they are, so that when the hex message is constructed, there are spaces between each hex digit.

The Mi-Light remote control allows up to four zones to be defined, and you can attach multiple lights to each zone. There are separate On and Off codes that control each of the zones independently. These are stored in the variable **ZONES**, which is a dictionary or dictionaries, making it easy to look up the appropriate hex code for the command you want.

Two functions (**light_on** and **light_off**) switch all the lights on or off for the zone name specified as their parameter. Both these functions use the **send** function to actually send the command to the RF module via the C program (**send_cmd**). The **send** function first constructs a message string by concatenating the **ID**, **MIDDLE** section, command **code**, and finally **00** into a message string. The C program is then called five times, passing the message as a parameter. Since it can be a little unreliable, sending the message five times makes it almost certain to get through to the light bulb.

Next, there is the web server part of the code, contained in the **index** function. This expects the webpage to provide two request parameters: the zone name (**zone**) and whether it is to be turned on or off (**state**). This information is then used to call either **light_on** or **light_off**. At the end of the index function, the contents of the template **home.tpl** are returned, to provide the browser with the HTML for the web interface.

The final line of code starts the web server running. Switch over to a browser on the Raspberry Pi, or another computer on your network, and type the IP address of your Pi into the address bar. To discover the IP address of your Raspberry Pi, type the command below into LXTerminal:

```
hostname -I
```

It will be at the start of the response as four numbers separated by dots; for example, 192.168.1.22.

Using your PiMi-Light Controller

As well as controlling the lights from the browser on your computer, you can just as easily use the browser on your smartphone, as long as it is connected to the same network as your Raspberry Pi.

You could also adapt the alarm clock program back in issue 33 of *The MagPi* to turn the lights on and off at certain times.

This project simply turns the lighting on and off. Considerable work has been done in reverse-engineering the Mi-Light protocol to figure out what all the codes do. So, if you want to extend this project to adjust the colour and brightness of the lights, then you might want to look at Henryk Plötz's work: **magpi.cc/1NZfcmt**

EVERYDAY ENGINEERING PART 12

SIMON MONK

Simon Monk is the author of the *Raspberry Pi Cookbook* and *Programming the Raspberry Pi: Getting Started with Python*, among others.
simonmonk.org
monkmakes.com

01001010100001011101010011010111010101010100111010 1

BINARY CLOCK

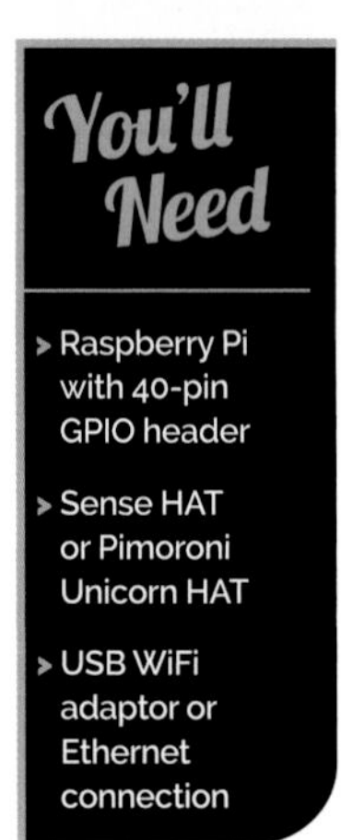

You'll Need

- Raspberry Pi with 40-pin GPIO header
- Sense HAT or Pimoroni Unicorn HAT
- USB WiFi adaptor or Ethernet connection

Solve real-world electronic and engineering problems with your Raspberry Pi and the help of renowned technology hacker and author, **Simon Monk**

This is a very simple project to make. In fact, all you really need to do is plug the Sense or Unicorn HAT onto the Raspberry Pi's GPIO header and install the software.

This project displays the current time in binary. The rows of the display are (from top to bottom) the last two digits of the year (e.g. 15), the month number, the day of the month, the hour (24-hour format), the minute, the second, and finally hundredths of a second.

Reading the binary clock

To read a binary clock, you either need to be good at recognising binary numbers or use a bit of arithmetic to calculate the time, by adding up the binary digit values for the LEDs that are lit on a particular row.

For example, the first row displays the year in two-digit format. So, if LEDs at positions 8, 4, 2, and 1 are all lit, then the year is 8+4+2+1 = 15. In 2016, just the digit position 16 will be lit.

The colours of the LEDs have no significance – they are different to make the display more interesting.

If you're using the Sense HAT, you may need to install the software for the HAT using the following commands:

```
sudo apt-get update
sudo apt-get install sense-hat
sudo pip-3.2 install pillow
```

If you're using a Unicorn HAT, then run the following commands:

```
sudo apt-get install python-pip python-dev
sudo pip install unicornhat
```

There are two versions of the software for this project – one for the Sense HAT and one for the Pimoroni Unicorn HAT – so be sure to use the right version of the program for your hardware. The Sense

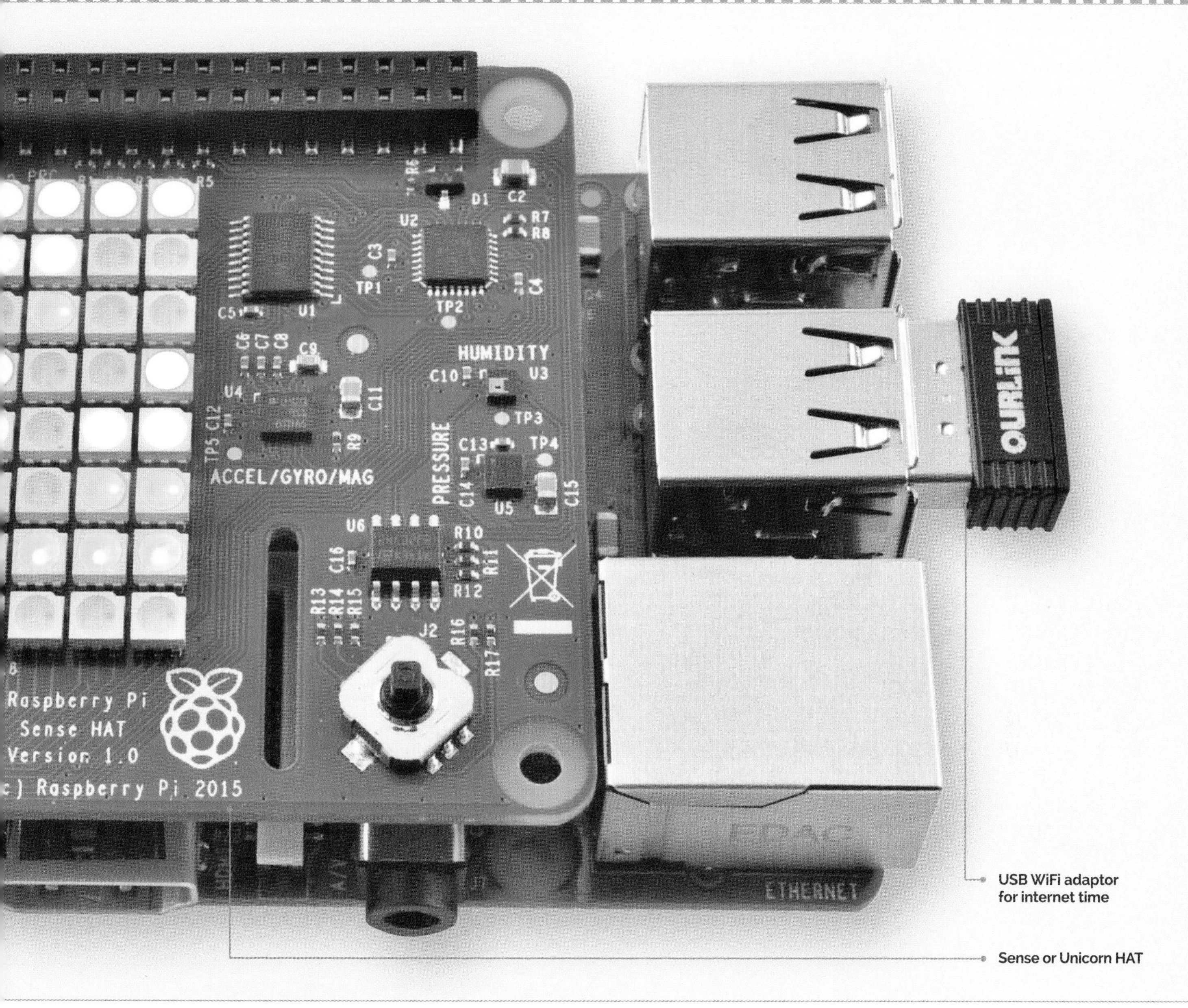

USB WiFi adaptor for internet time

Sense or Unicorn HAT

HAT version is called **binary_clock_sh.py**, and the Unicorn version **binary_clock_uni.py**.

You can download the programs for this project from your Raspberry Pi command line using the command:

```
git clone https://github.com/simonmonk/pi_magazine.git
```

This command will actually bring down the code for all the projects in Simon's *The MagPi* series, so if you've already issued this command for one of the earlier articles, change directory to **pi_magazine** and run the following command to update your directory with this project (**12_binary_clock**):

```
git pull
```

To run the program, change to the directory where the code for this project lives and then run the program using the commands below:

```
cd /home/pi/pi_magazine/12_binary_clock
sudo python binary_clock_sh.py
```

Or, if you are using the Unicorn HAT:

```
sudo python binary_clock_uni.py
```

binary_clock_uni.py

```
#!/usr/bin/env python

import unicornhat as hat
import time, datetime

year_color = (0, 255, 0)
month_color = (0, 0, 255)
day_color = (255, 0, 0)
hour_color = (0, 255, 0)
minute_color = (0, 0, 255)
second_color = (255, 0, 0)
hundrefths_color = (127, 127, 0)
off = (0, 0, 0)

hat.clear()
hat.brightness(0.5)

def display_binary(value, row, color):
        binary_str = "{0:8b}".format(value)
        for x in range(0, 8):
                if binary_str[x] == '1':
                        hat.set_pixel(x, row, color[0], color[1], color[2])
                else:
                        hat.set_pixel(x, row, 0, 0, 0)

while True:
    t = datetime.datetime.now()
    display_binary(t.year % 100, 0, year_color)
    display_binary(t.month, 1, month_color)
    display_binary(t.day, 2, day_color)
    display_binary(t.hour, 3, hour_color)
    display_binary(t.minute, 4, minute_color)
    display_binary(t.second, 5, second_color)
    display_binary(t.microsecond / 10000, 6, hundrefths_color)
    hat.show()
    time.sleep(0.0001)
```

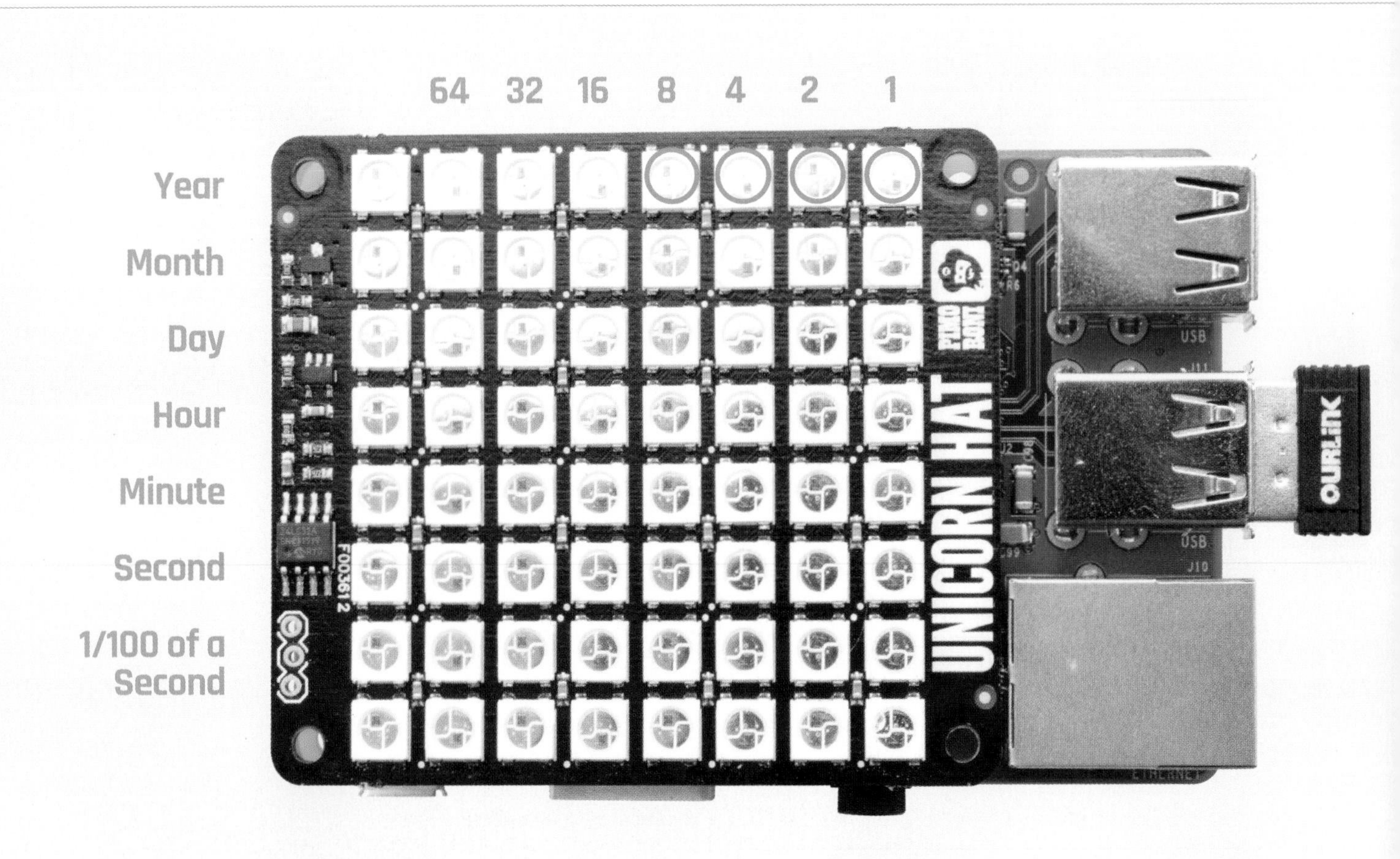

binary_clock_sh.py

Language
>PYTHON

DOWNLOAD:
magpi.cc/1P1182l

```
#!/usr/bin/env python

from sense_hat import SenseHat
import time, datetime

hat = SenseHat()

year_color = (0, 255, 0)
month_color = (0, 0, 255)
day_color = (255, 0, 0)
hour_color = (0, 255, 0)
minute_color = (0, 0, 255)
second_color = (255, 0, 0)
hundrefths_color = (127, 127, 0)
off = (0, 0, 0)

hat.clear()

def display_binary(value, row, color):
    binary_str = "{0:8b}".format(value)
    for x in range(0, 8):
        if binary_str[x] == '1':
            hat.set_pixel(x, row, color)
        else:
            hat.set_pixel(x, row, off)

while True:
    t = datetime.datetime.now()
    display_binary(t.year % 100, 0, year_color)
    display_binary(t.month, 1, month_color)
    display_binary(t.day, 2, day_color)
    display_binary(t.hour, 3, hour_color)
    display_binary(t.minute, 4, minute_color)
    display_binary(t.second, 5, second_color)
    display_binary(t.microsecond / 10000, 6, hundrefths_color)
    time.sleep(0.0001)
```

How the code works

The two versions are actually very similar to each other. Both start by importing the libraries that they need for their displays. They then define a number of colour variables that you can change, if you like, in order to set different colours for each row of the clock.

Most of the action takes place in the **display_binary** function. This takes three parameters. The first is the value to be displayed as binary, the second is the row on which it should be displayed (0 to 7), and the final parameter is the colour to be displayed.

The value is converted into a binary string representation using String's **format** function. The **for** loop then iterates over each column (x value) and if that digit contains a 1, turns on the pixel in that row and column to the colour specified, otherwise the pixel is cleared.

The main loop fetches the current time and then splits it into its component parts, displaying each on a separate row. To display the year in two-digit format, we use modulo 100 (**t.year % 100**), which is the remainder after dividing it by 100.

Using your binary clock

Having a keyboard, mouse and monitor attached to your clock is fine while you are constructing it, but it would be better to have the program start automatically when the Raspberry Pi first boots up. To do this, run the following command to make the program executable:

```
sudo chmod +x binary_clock_*.py
```

Then, edit the file **/etc/rc.local** with the command:

```
sudo nano /etc/rc.local
```

Add the following line after the first block of comment lines that begin with #. Change the line to the **_uni** version if you are using a Unicorn HAT.

```
sudo /home/pi/pi_magazine/12_binary_
clock/binary_clock_sh.py &
```

Restart your Raspberry Pi and this time the program should start up automatically.

Note that you will still need an internet connection for the Pi to pick up the correct time.

"The two versions are actually very similar to each other."

RASPBERRY PI ZERO

A new revolution in computing is upon us

We'd like you to pick up the Raspberry Pi Zero that came with The MagPi 40. You're holding in your hands a fully functional computer that's going on sale for $5 and that you could lose in a small purse. It's quite the amazing feat of engineering and we're very excited to bring it to our readers, along with many pages of content that will take you from a Zero Novice to a Zero Master.

Over the course of our expansive coverage, we talk to the people behind the Raspberry Pi Zero's development, teach you how to hook it up, and also suggest some great uses for your Zero. With its even smaller size, there are some amazing things you'll be able to do with it. Check out the contents at the start of this section to get an idea of what kind of incredible things we're about to do with the Pi Zero.

MicroSD card slot for storing the operating system, files, and documents

30mm

Mini-HDMI port for digital sound and 1080p video

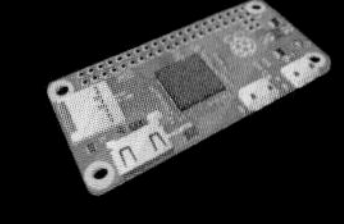

40-pin unpopulated GPIO port for connecting to your electronic circuits

Unpopulated RUN mode pins which can be used to add a reset button to the Pi Zero

Unpopulated RCA composite video out pins so you can connect to an old TV

A smaller camera connector port to connect a Pi Camera Module to

Power and activity LED – this lets you know the Pi Zero is on and working away

Micro-USB port for power – the same kind that charges Android mobile phones

65mm

Broadcom BCM 2835 system-on-a-chip, the same chip that powered the original Raspberry Pi

Micro USB port for connecting to keyboards, mice, WiFi, USB sticks, and more

THE SPECS

CPU: BCM 2835 (same as the original Raspberry Pi), 1GHz single core ARM11

RAM: 512MB

Storage: Via microSD

Power: Micro-USB connector

Video out: Mini-HDMI

Connectivity: 1× micro-USB, unpopulated 40-pin GPIO connector, camera port, unpopulated Composite Video Out

Dimensions: 65mm × 30mm × 5mm **Weight:** 9g

ZER0 UNBOXED

Let's take a closer look at this miniature Raspberry Pi

SD CARD SLOT

You'll need a micro SD card so you can actually give the Raspberry Pi Zero an operating system. Some come with SD adapters so you can plug them into your PC.

MINI HDMI

A mini HDMI-to-HDMI cable is required to hook up a monitor to the Raspberry Pi Zero; a normal HDMI cable won't fit.

MICRO USB

This micro USB port is for data; to actually use it to plug in a mouse, keyboard, or a wireless dongle, you'll need a micro USB-to-USB adapter.

POWER SUPPLY

This is the power jack: don't get it mixed up with the data port! You'll need a mobile phone charger, or one of the official Raspberry Pi power supplies, to turn on the Zero.

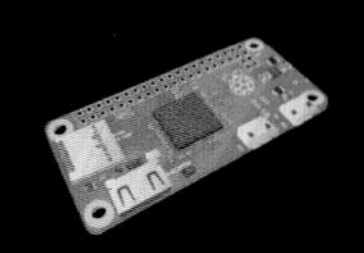

ASSEMBLE YOUR ZERO

It's simple enough to put your Raspberry Pi Zero together: as easy as 1, 2, 3, in fact...

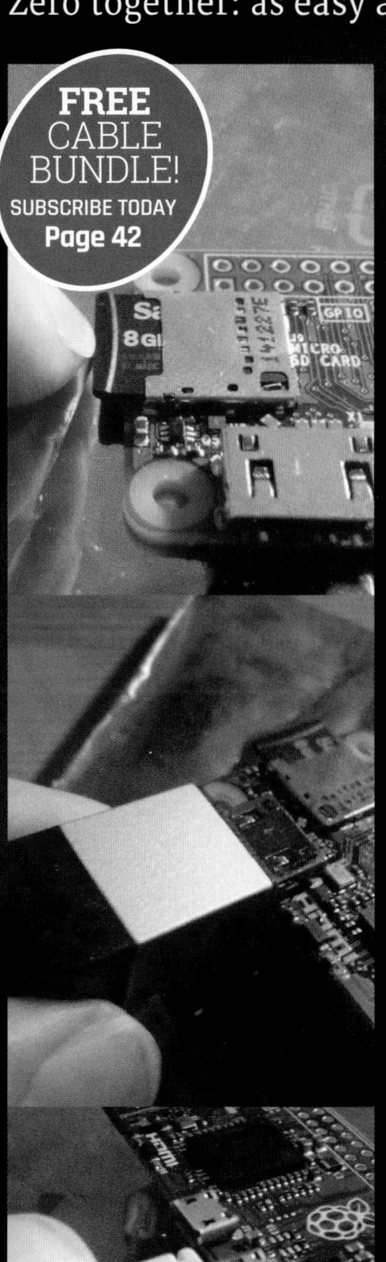

FREE CABLE BUNDLE! SUBSCRIBE TODAY Page 42

> STEP ONE
PLUG IN SD CARD

You'll need to install NOOBS (New Out Of Box Software) on your Raspberry Pi Zero, enabling you to choose an operating system. Plug your micro SD card into another computer and visit the Raspberry Pi download site (**magpi.cc/1MYYTMo**). Download Raspbian and install it via a card writer, as described in our Getting Started guide. Pop it in once it's done.

> STEP TWO
CONNECT CABLES

Plug in the mini HDMI-to-HDMI connector and make sure it's properly connected between the Raspberry Pi Zero and your display. Now plug in your USB adapter, making sure it's in the correct micro USB port, and attach your USB hub. You may not need a hub with external power, but make sure one is handy just in case.

> STEP THREE
POWER IT UP

Plug the power cable into the micro USB power socket, again checking to make sure it's the correct one; at this point it should be the only one left. Plugging the other end of the power supply into a wall socket will immediately turn the Raspberry Pi Zero on. You're now ready to start a new chapter in hacking and making!

GRAB YOUR CABLES

Don't have a mini HDMI or micro USB converter? We've got you covered...

We understand the cables required to get your Raspberry Pi Zero hooked up are not particularly common; although you might have a mini HDMI cable if you bought a really nice camera in the last few years, the micro USB adapters are much less common. With that in mind, Raspberry Pi has put together a cable bundle that will help you get your Zero working in no time. Just head over to the Swag Shop (**swag.raspberrypi.org**) to get a bundle today!

Below These two special cables allow the Pi Zero to be teeny-tiny

RASPBERRY PI ZER0

ESSENTIAL PI ZERO TIPS

HOW TO CONNECT TO WIFI ON THE COMMAND LINE

GIVE YOUR PI ZERO A NETWORK NAME

If you set a static IP as shown in the wireless tutorial on this page, then you'll always be able to access the Raspberry Pi Zero with that IP address from any remote service. However, for those who want the easier automatic way, you can still make it just as easy to connect to the Zero over the network by setting up Zeroconf. From the command line or in the terminal, type the following to make sure it is installed:

```
sudo apt-get install avahi-daemon
```

By default, the Pi will now be accessible via **raspberrypi.local** over the local network.

```
pi@raspberrypi ~ $ sudo apt-get install avahi-daemon
Reading package lists... Done
Building dependency tree
Reading state information... Done
avahi-daemon is already the newest version.
0 upgraded, 0 newly installed, 0 to remove and 1 not upgraded.
pi@raspberrypi ~ $
```

Left On some versions of Raspbian, avahi it may already be installed

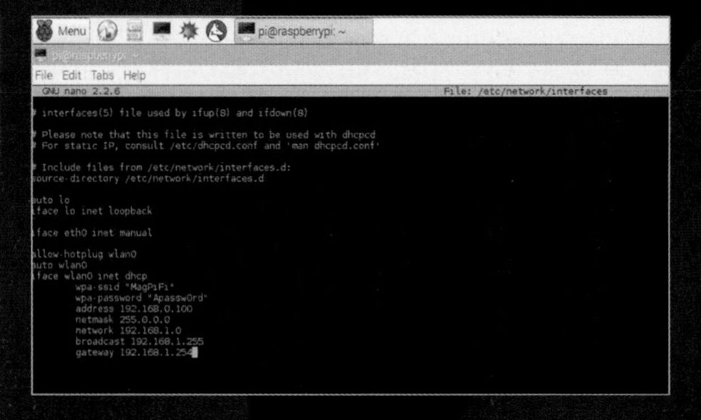

Left To set a static IP on the desktop interface, you'll have to go through the same process

RASPBERRY PI ZERO

While Raspbian makes it dead easy to connect to WiFi on the desktop interface, there's a little more involved in getting it working from the command line. Before we begin, there is one trick you can do: if you set up the WiFi at the desktop, it will still work while in the command line. That isn't always possible, though, so you may need to use the manual way.

First, find out the name of your network and the password. In the Raspbian command line, type: **sudo nano /etc/wpa_supplicant/wpa_supplicant.conf**. There will already be some information but to get the wireless to connect, make sure the file has these lines in it, with your network name (SSID) and its password replacing what's already here:

```
network={
    ssid="YourSSID"
    psk="YourWifiPassword"
}
```

You can also give the Raspberry Pi a static IP. To do this, you first need to do some prep work which requires you to use a computer which is already connected to your wireless network. Open the command line in Windows or the terminal in OS X or Linux. For Windows, type **ipconfig**; for OS X and Linux, use **ifconfig** followed by **netstat -nr**. Note the IP address (inet), the broadcast address, the subnet address, the router IP (Destination), and Gateway address. After that open the DHCPD conf file (sudo nano /etc/dhcpcd.conf) and add:

```
interface wlan0

static ip_address=[address]
static routers=[router IP]
static domain_name_servers=[gateway]
```

USE YOUR RASPBERRY PI FROM ANOTHER COMPUTER

Thanks to a piece of software called RealVNC, you don't even need to plug your Pi Zero into a monitor to use its desktop; you can simply control it from another computer. First of all, go to **magpi.cc/PiVNC** and download RealVNC onto your Raspberry Pi. Also obtain a free licence key (**magpi.cc/1O8Hz4J**), as you'll be needing it.

Once the file is on your Pi, open the terminal, use **cd** to navigate to the file in Downloads (**cd Downloads** should do) and use the following two commands, replacing the square brackets with the appropriate names:

```
tar xvf [VNC file name].tar.gz
sudo dpkg -i [VNC Server package name].deb [VNC Viewer package name].deb
```

Copy the licence key you got and then run **sudo vnclicense -add [License Key]** with your key. Type **vncserver** into the terminal or command line for it to begin, type in your Raspberry Pi's password (it's **raspberry** by default) and make a note of the display number. In our case it was 1, and as Avahi was installed, we can connect using **raspberrypi:1**.

Install a VNC viewer from here: **magpi.cc/1M4uzfG** on your platform of choice, and then connect with: **raspberrypi:[Number]**

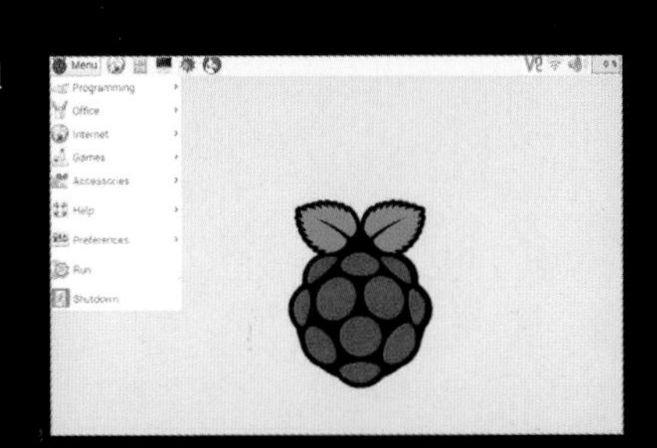

Above On some versions of Raspbian, Avahi may already be installed

ACCESS YOUR PI REMOTELY FROM THE COMMAND LINE

SHARE FILES ON YOUR NETWORK WITH SAMBA

This is especially good if you want to use your Raspberry Pi Zero as a file server. For this, or just generally to be able to access the files on your Zero from anywhere on the network, you'll need to use Samba. First, you need to install it:

```
sudo apt-get install samba samba-common-bin
```

You need to configure Samba to work as intended. Still in the terminal or command line, type:

```
sudo nano /etc/samba/smb.conf
```

First of all, if you have a Windows workgroup with a specific name on your network, find the line starting **workgroup = WORKGROUP** and change the uppercase WORKGROUP to your workgroup's name. If you have no idea what a workgroup is, you can leave this setting alone. Find the line **# wins support = no**, delete the # character, and change the no to yes. Scroll down to the section labelled **Share Definitions** and enter the following chunk of code:

```
[pihome]
    comment= Pi Home
    path=/home/pi
    browseable=Yes
    writeable=Yes
    only guest=no
    create mask=0777
    directory mask=0777
    public=no
```

#PIZERO ACCESSORIES

What you can get for your Raspberry Pi Zero to make using it and creating projects that much easier?

As there's a bit of a Raspberry Pi economy now, when new gear comes out there's a much faster reaction when making new accessories for it. Even though the Raspberry Pi Zero is only a few months old, this means that there are already a few accessories you can get your hands on to improve your Pi Zero experience.

There's also a bit of kit you'll need to make some of the projects in this issue, and even start making your own incredible builds.

ZEBRA ZERO

magpi.cc/2dXqMZ9

A sturdy case made up of two layers of wood along with a thick acrylic centre, the Zebra Zero adds a touch of class to your Raspberry Pi Zero. It also has a massive heatsink, which may be a little superfluous. You can also get a Zebra Zero Plus with a full breadboard attached for easy testing.

ZERO CASES

Keep your Pi Zero in style with these trendy cases

PIBOW ZERO CASE

magpi.cc/1KljtQz

A special Pi Zero version of the classic laser-cut Pibow is already available. With its unique, chip-hugging design, it leaves the ports very open for use with any custom project and even

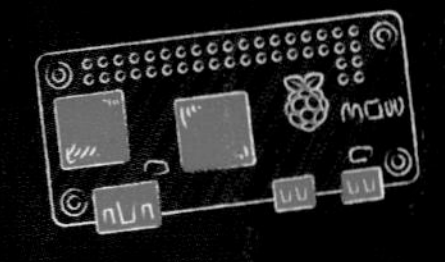

MISCELLANEOUS ADD-ONS

Other bits and pieces to improve your Raspberry Pi Zero

MINI USB OTG ADAPTOR

magpi.cc/1JT9aZc

There are a few of these available – we've had some success with the meZmory brand one, but there are several others. It makes plugging in single USB devices to the Pi Zero much easier – great for projects that just require wireless and nothing else.

RIGHT-ANGLE GPIO HEADER

magpi.cc/1ZF0H31

We've shown you how to solder a standard GPIO header to the Pi Zero, but this cool alternative allows for the GPIO pins to be parallel with the board. This can be ideal for awkward projects or installations where space restrictions are fixed, and it solders in like any other GPIO header.

ESSENTIAL RASPBERRY PI ZERO KIT

magpi.cc/1RSULPN

A nice selection of components that can be used with the Raspberry Pi Zero , including extra adaptors, several GPIO header options, and even little stick-on feet to raise the Pi Zero off the ground. It all comes in a little mint-like tin which can also fit the whole Pi Zero for a makeshift carry case.

SCROLL PHAT

magpi.cc/1JT9cQT

This actually works on other Raspberry Pis as well, but it's designed in the same form factor as the Pi Zero. This board gives you 55 LEDs in a rectangular formation and works similarly to the LED matrix on the Sense HAT. Using a Python script, you can control the LEDs or have it scroll text across the length of the board.

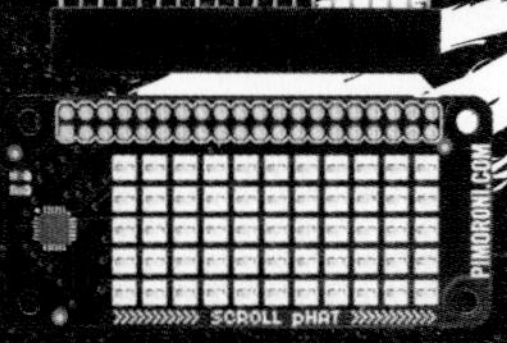

EXPLORER PHAT

magpi.cc/1Pk5SdN

This add-on board for the Zero (and other Pis) allows it to communicate with different objects more easily than wiring them directly to the Pi. This includes motors and sensors – we've seen Explorers used in robots due to this. It allows for analogue inputs as well as other inputs and outputs, and has its own Python library for quick development. Great for tiny projects.

ESSENTIAL KIT

You'll need these basics to create amazing Pi Zero projects

Components

LEDs, wires, resistors, and maybe even some light, heat or motion sensors. All of these are available for very cheap in bundles from a local electronics store, or online from a distributor such as RS Components. You can also get a lot of them in an electronics starter kit, like the one pictured from ModMyPi (**magpi.cc/1RvzWta**). For the tutorials in this issue, we'll make sure you know exactly what sort of components you need before you go out and buy them.

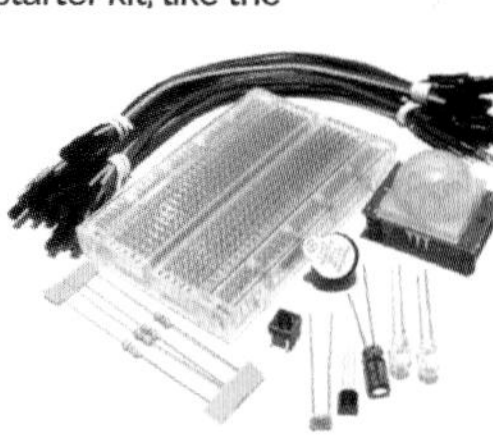

Soldering iron

An important piece of equipment for making more advanced projects, or building some kits available for the Raspberry Pi. As well as the actual soldering iron, you'll need good quality solder to work with. A decent stand for the soldering iron is also ideal – one that you're not likely to burn yourself with, containing a good sponge. Soldering can be dangerous, so make sure to supervise younger makers when they're building.

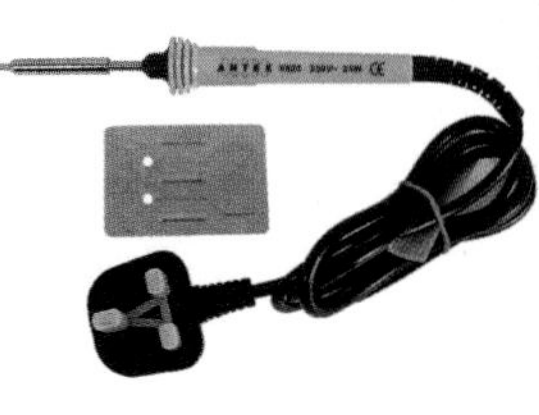

Breadboard

A perfect tool for prototyping and testing your circuits. If you've never used a breadboard, what it does is give you a load of pins that are aligned in columns, acting as connectors so you don't have to solder components together. This means you can quickly change a circuit to get it right, or reuse the breadboard over and over again for new and different circuits. You probably don't need to start with a massive one, but get one with positive and negative rails on each side.

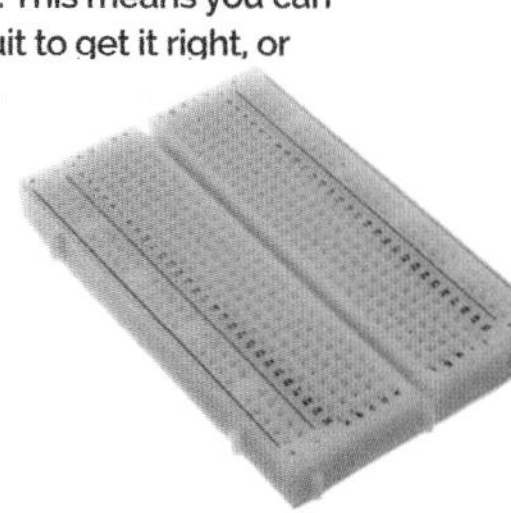

Wire stripper

If you decide to get a spool of wire rather than a load of pre-cut pieces, you'll need a good way of getting wire off the spool. Attacking slowly and carefully with a pair of scissors or a knife gets extremely boring fast, and investing in a decent pair of wire cutters that will also strip the plastic will improve your life by at least 10% (don't quote us on that).

PI ZERO CONSOLLER

The Pi Zero's diminutive stature allows us to make an entire retro gaming console out of a simple USB controller for the first time. Here's how…

You'll Need

- USB SNES controller – eBay
- PowerBoost 500 **makersify.com**
- 3.7V 500mAh LiPo battery – eBay
- RetroPie **magpi.cc/Retro-Pie**
- Mini HDMI-to-HDMI cable (3m) **amazon.com**
- 2× micro USB cables **amazon.com**

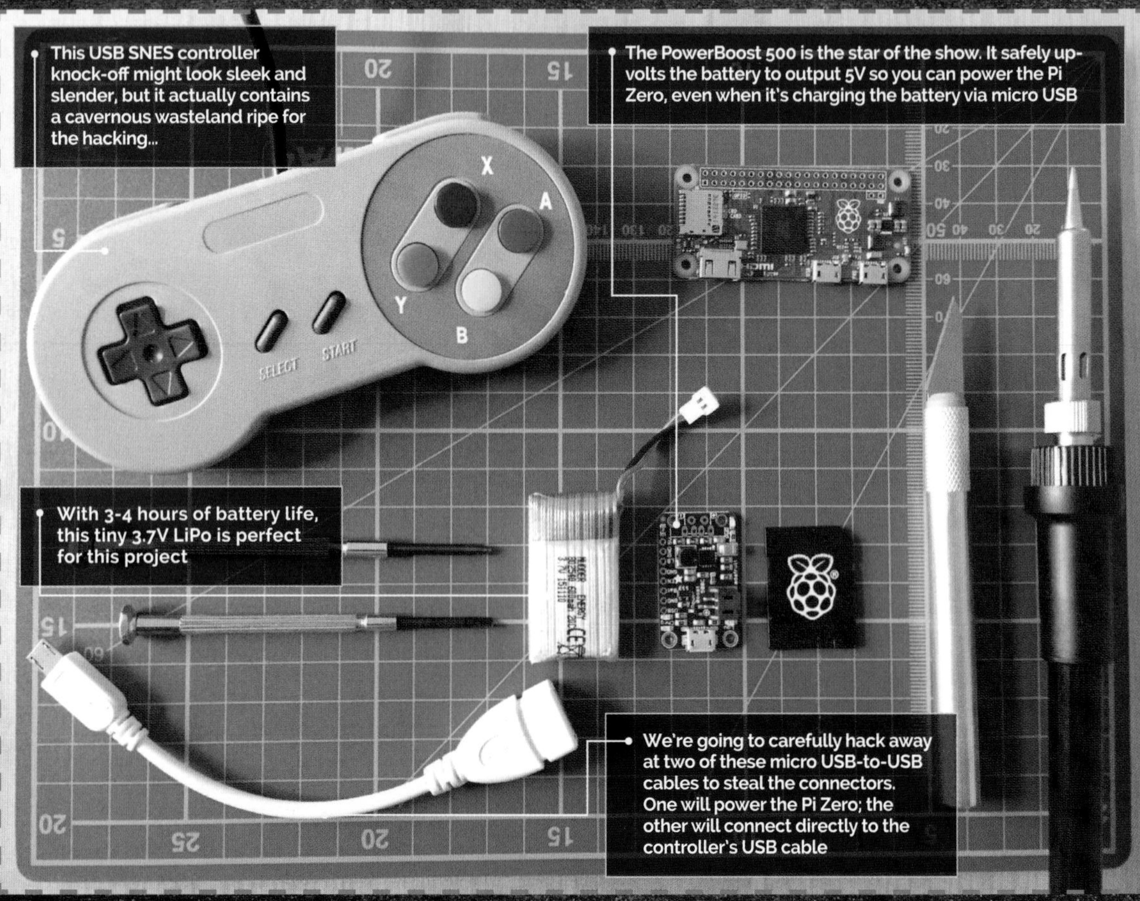

This USB SNES controller knock-off might look sleek and slender, but it actually contains a cavernous wasteland ripe for the hacking...
The PowerBoost 500 is the star of the show. It safely up-volts the battery to output 5V so you can power the Pi Zero, even when it's charging the battery via micro USB
With 3-4 hours of battery life, this tiny 3.7V LiPo is perfect for this project
We're going to carefully hack away at two of these micro USB-to-USB cables to steal the connectors. One will power the Pi Zero; the other will connect directly to the controller's USB cable
X
A
Y
B
SELECT
START

Tip: SNES CONTROLLER

Since they're so cheap, we actually picked up a couple of USB SNES controllers from eBay.

This project was inspired by a similar one undertaken by the magazine's features editor, Rob Zwetsloot, a couple of issues back. Rob took a modern USB version of a retro Nintendo Entertainment System controller, opened it up and put the Pi Zero inside. While it worked perfectly, running classic NES titles via RetroPie, we thought that the project could be taken one step further. Classic controllers don't have two cables coming out of them (in this case HDMI and USB for power), so our new target was to create a completely self-contained console in a controller, with only one cable coming out to connect to the HDMI port on a TV or monitor. Thus the Pi Zero-powered SNES Consoller was born…

There's a surprisingly large amount of technology to squeeze inside the controller for this project to work. Fortunately, most USB controllers are largely empty on the inside, using just four tiny USB colour-coded cables connected to a slender circuit board that deals with the inputs (D-pad and six buttons). How do we take inputs from the controller and get them to the Pi Zero? It actually couldn't be easier – all we're going to do is snip off the controller's USB cable and solder the wires directly to a micro USB connector that will slot straight into the USB port of the Pi Zero. Since USB cabling is entirely universal, it just works.

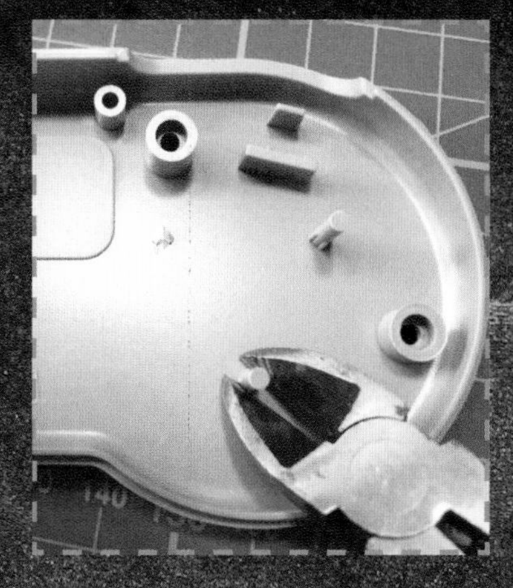

Carving the case

Before we do anything else, though, we need to create some more space in the controller itself. We'll work on the back plate to snip off the support struts first; your mileage may vary depending on which USB controller you buy (there are hundreds), but ours has three supports on each side of the controller. Snip them with some side cutters or chop them with a craft knife, and then sand down any sharp edges so they're flush to the case.

We'll also likely need to remove a couple of the screw hole supports on the controller itself, but don't get carried away yet – you should play it by ear as we try to fit everything inside, so we remove as few of the screw holes as possible.

Once complete, we'll need to snip off the four USB wires connected to the controller's control board, leaving enough play in the cables to ultimately connect the other end to your Pi Zero. To keep things really simple, we're going to connect a slimline mini HDMI-to-HDMI cable to the Zero inside the controller. With our controller, it's actually really easy just to line up the HDMI cable with the USB cable exit on the controller itself, but you'll need to use a craft knife to carve a larger opening and carefully strip back the housing of the mini HDMI connector to get it to fit snugly.

Securing your Pi Zero

The next thing to do is to secure the Pi Zero in place. Its location in the case is decided by the HDMI cable. We want to fix it directly to the controller's control circuit board. There's a good chance there's a couple of raised components on the back, so we're using sticky Velcro Command Strips. This gives us the clearance we need to steer clear of the components, as well as the flexibility to remove or vary the Zero's placement during the build process. Once it's securely Velcroed in place, we can also work on the placement of the battery and the PowerBoost 500, safe in the knowledge everything fits together as it should. We plan to position the PowerBoost board just under the right side of the Pi Zero, so the micro USB power connector on it sits against the bottom-right straight edge at the base of the controller. This allows us to add a power switch in the bottom-centre of the controller and place the battery in the right-hand compartment, which is currently completely vacant.

Since the PowerBoost 500 automatically powers on when you connect a battery to it, we need to fit a power switch to turn our SNES Consoller on and off. We're using a very standard three-pin switch that we got from a basic electronics kit, and three colour-coded male-to-female jumper cables – for power (red), ground (brown), and control (orange) – with snipped-off male ends so they can be soldered to the PowerBoost board later. Next, tape the female ends of the jumper cables together and then simply slot the switch into it. We position

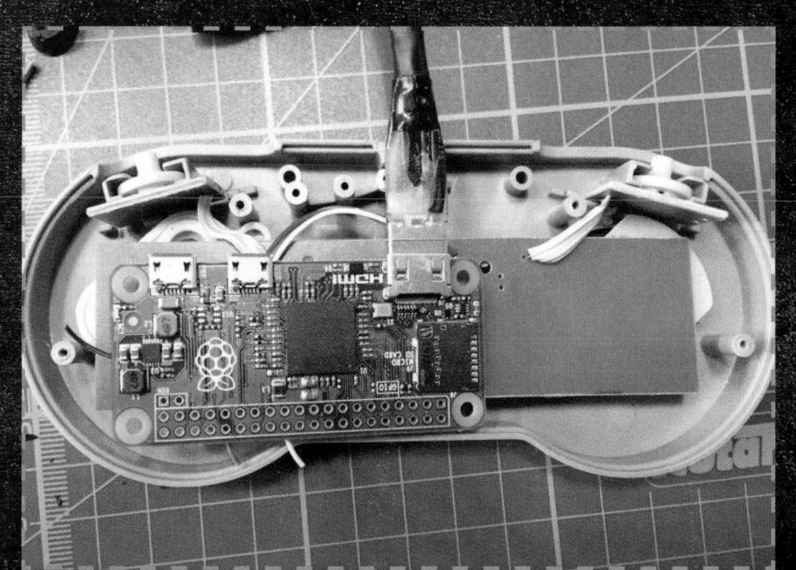

Tip

TOOLS YOU'LL NEED

Make sure you have a very sharp craft knife, a decent soldering iron, and a set of small screwdrivers to hand – you won't get far without them.

SOLDERING THE POWERBOOST 500

Using the PowerBoost 500 to power your project is ridiculously easy and convenient, but we do heartily recommend you refer to Adafruit's excellent guide at **magpi.cc/1PmlDWL**. You'll learn about all its features and capabilities, and also find out how to solder the board correctly. As you can see from the image, we need to solder the three highlighted pins for our power switch to work correctly. Once complete and with the battery connected, you'll find that when you flick the switch from nearest the ground pin (brown) to the power pin (red), the unit will power up and down. You'll also find a handy micro USB port on the PowerBoost board – position this against an outside edge of your Consoller, carve a port out of the plastic, and you'll be able to charge your battery - even while you're playing.

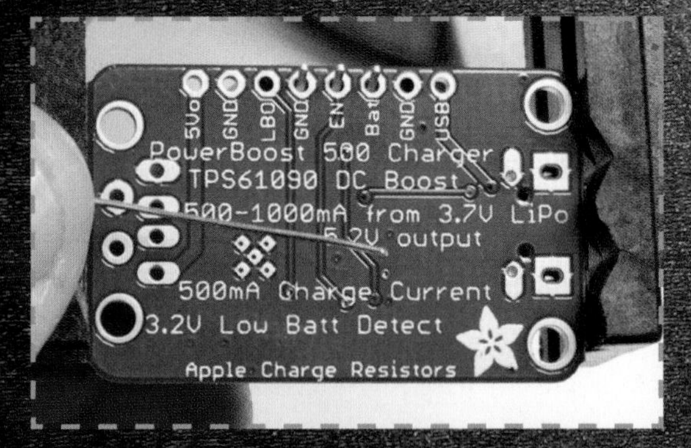

the switch in the middle-bottom of the board (under the Pi Zero and next to where the PowerBoost 500 will go), carve out space for the switch to fit flush, and stick it down to the controller's control board to keep it in place. Refer to the boxout on the left to see how to solder it correctly.

> At this point, it's wise to ensure you can actually still close the case and find any sticking points

Positioning the PowerBoost and battery

With the switch and PowerBoost prepared, we can work on the positioning of both the PowerBoost and the 3.7V 500mAh battery itself. This is probably the trickiest part of the project. Usually, the power cables on these LiPo batteries are quite short, so you might have fun getting it to fit correctly. Also, since we want to utilise the charging capabilities of the PowerBoost board, the micro USB port needs to be facing a clean edge of the controller so you can carve a suitable hole for it.

We've positioned the PowerBoost right next to our reset switch, with the micro USB facing the bottom edge of the board. Helpfully, this means the battery connector is already facing the correct direction to allow the battery to take up the rest of the compartment on the right. Since part of the PowerBoost sits under the right edge of the Pi Zero when it's in the case, we're using two double-sided sticky tabs to connect the PowerBoost to the controller's circuit board so it actually sits lower than the Zero. The battery itself doesn't need fixing in place, since its size means it doesn't move around.

At this point, it's wise to ensure you can actually still close the case

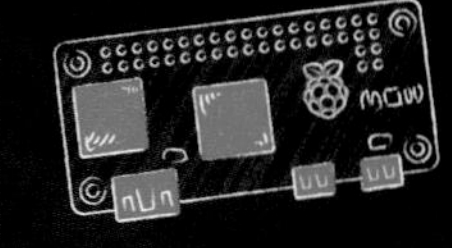

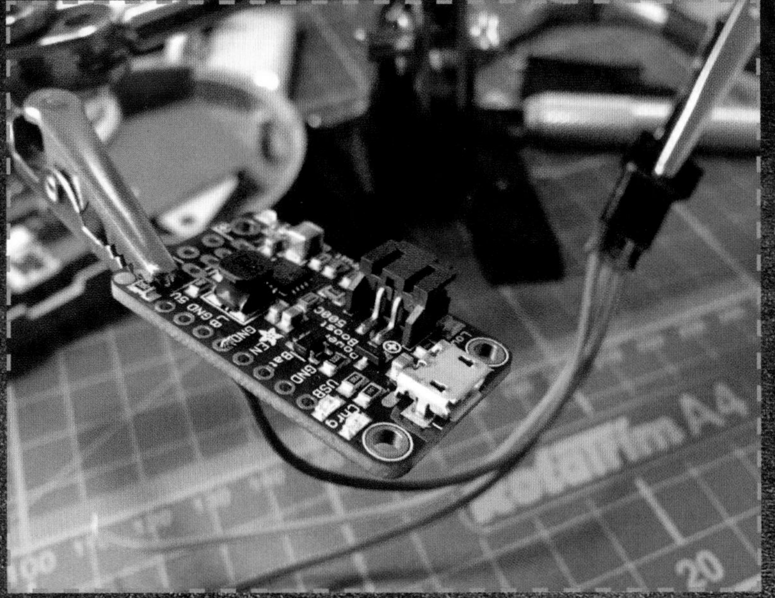

and find any sticking points that need adjustment. We found that we had to remove some of the support struts for the screws, but we made sure at least two (the far left and right ones) were left intact so we could still securely fasten the case.

Soldering the micro USBs

In terms of practical hands-on work left to do, we're nearly there. The final task is to physically connect the Pi Zero to the USB cables and the PowerBoost. With the power, it's perfectly fine to solder the 5V and ground pins from the PowerBoost directly to the 5V and ground pins on your Pi Zero's GPIO, but since you'll likely to want to use your Pi Zero for something else in the future, we've decided to take the less invasive route of ripping up a separate micro USB cable and soldering that to the PowerBoost instead.

The great thing about USB is that the four colour-coded cables are the same, regardless of USB size: two for power and two for control.

> "The great thing about USB is that the four colour-coded cables are the same, regardless of USB size"

To power the Pi Zero, we only need the red and black cables: power and ground, respectively. These go to the two outer connectors on your micro USB cable – with the longest flat edge of the connector facing up and towards you, ground is on the left. Just search for 'micro USB cable connectors' for a handy diagram to refer to. Simply solder the ground and power cables to the 5V and ground pins on your PowerBoost – it's really that easy.

Connect it to your Zero for testing – assuming you have a correctly configured SD card in your Pi Zero, it should light up as normal when the power switch is turned on.

Connecting the controller micro USB is just as easy. With the longest edge of the micro USB header facing up and towards you, the colour-coded USB cables you snipped off earlier are soldered from left to right as black, green, white, and then red. With the micro USB connector soldered, all you need to do now is preconfigure your Pi Zero with RetroPie and you're ready to go!

Setting up RetroPie

That's it – you've done the hard part! Now all you've got to do is follow the instructions at **magpi.cc/Retro-Pie** to set it up on the microSD card to slot into your Pi Zero. It already has a version that supports Pi Zero. Since there's no room for WiFi in your Consoller, we heartily recommend you set it up using a USB hub with keyboard and mouse, making sure you load all the games you want and scraping the internet for synopses and images in advance. We can't help you acquire games for obvious reasons, but search engines are most certainly your friend. Once complete, simply load it in your project Pi Zero, close up the case and power up for some serious retro gaming action!

Tip
RETROPIE

We love RetroPie. It's the Kodi or openELEC (home theatre front-end) of the retro gaming world. Grab it from **magpi.cc/Retro-Pie**

Tip
3.7V 500MAH BATTERY

You'll need to carefully check the dimensions of your case against the dimensions of your chosen battery to make sure it fits correctly. It'll be snug, but it's easily done.

PI ZERO RESET SWITCH

An easy first soldering project, adding a reset switch to your Pi Zero – or full-size Pi – is a great way to prevent crashes and hangs from ruining your day

You'll Need

- Soldering iron & solder
- 2× 2.54mm male header pins
- Recycled PC case reset switch

Or

- Momentary switch, normally open **magpi.cc/2dXrPZ9**
- 2× female jumper wires

A reset switch salvaged from an old PC case is perfect for this project, coming with its wires already attached

Available on any modern Raspberry Pi, the RUN header can be used to recover from a crash or launch a shut-down Pi.

The Pi Zero's diminutive size, low cost, and tiny power requirements mean it's a great fit for embedded projects. There's only one problem: how to quickly get things back up and running if your code hits an infinite loop or otherwise crashes the Pi Zero, especially in projects where the Pi Zero is locked away from prying hands and powered by a hard to interrupt internal battery.

The solution? A reset switch, wired to the RUN header on the Pi Zero, which can restart the Pi in the event of a crash, or power it on from a shut-down state.

>STEP-01

Find the RUN Header

Known as header P6 on early models, the RUN header is linked to a pin in the processor which keeps it in standard running mode – hence the name RUN. When pulled to ground by shorting one contact on the header to the other, the processor leaves the RUN state. To all intents and purposes, this has the same effect as briefly cutting the power to the processor; if the Pi was running, it will reboot, and if the Pi was shut down, it will power on.

The RUN header can be found on the Pi Zero at the right-hand side of the board, sandwiched between the GPIO header and the composite video header (marked 'TV').

>STEP-02

Insert the male headers

The RUN header is unpopulated in all Raspberry Pi models, meaning

With male headers in place, wiring up the switch is as simple as slipping the female headers over the new pins

Pi Zero Tips

it doesn't have any pins inserted. While it's possible to solder a switch directly to the header, doing so will block the GPIO and TV headers; it's better to solder male pins into the header and run wires to the reset switch.

Take two of the pins in a bundle and snap them off by placing your thumbnail into the divot in the plastic between pins and pushing. Insert these into the Pi Zero's RUN header from the top, and secure them with tape or Blu-Tack, ready for soldering.

>STEP-03

Prepare the iron

Make sure your iron is safely in its stand, then plug it into a socket. If you're using a cleaning sponge, wet this under a running tap before wringing it out so it's damp but not sodden; if you're using brass shavings, no water is required.

Give the iron a few minutes to heat up, then wipe the tip on the sponge or brass shavings. When clean, 'tin' the iron by melting a small amount of solder onto the tip, then wiping it on your cleaning material again. The tip should look shiny, with no sign of black residue or discolouration.

>STEP-04

Solder the pins

Turn the Pi Zero over to expose the pins you stuck through the RUN header in step 2. Press the iron against the base of one pin, making sure it's also touching the shiny copper ring or square on the circuit board. Count to three then, with your other hand, push some solder against the base of the pin without touching the iron's tip.

The solder should melt then appear to be 'sucked' into the header's hole. If it doesn't, remove both solder and iron, clean the iron's tip, adjust your positioning, and try again.

>STEP-05

Inspect the joint

With both pins soldered, inspect your handiwork before trying to use the Pi Zero. The solder joints should appear to flow smoothly up from the circuit board to the pin, without any gaps. If you can still see copper on the circuit board or the solder isn't sticking to the leg of the pin, apply the iron again to 'reflow' the solder and, if required, add more.

Make sure you haven't connected the two pins together with excess solder. If you have, use a desoldering pump or braid to remove the excess, otherwise the Pi will fail to boot.

>STEP-06

Wire the switch

If you're using a reset switch from a PC case, the female header can be inserted directly onto the RUN header's new pins in either orientation. Otherwise, use a pair of female-to-female jumper wires to connect the pins to any switch described as 'momentary, normally open'. These can take many forms, from cheap tactile switches to more expensive vandal-proof devices.

Briefly press the switch to reset when the Pi is running, but be warned this can cause SD card corruption if the Pi was writing to it at the time. If the Pi has been shut down, press the switch to power it back on – this is always safe.

QUICK TIPS

KEEP THE TIP CLEAN

A dirty iron tip will make for difficult soldering. Clean the tip regularly while soldering, and re-tin with fresh solder every so often.

A small piece of Blu-Tack or masking tape can help keep a component in position while you flip the board for soldering

EMERGENCY USE ONLY

Just like cutting the power, using the reset switch can cause SD card corruption. Use it only when shutting the Pi down another way is impossible!

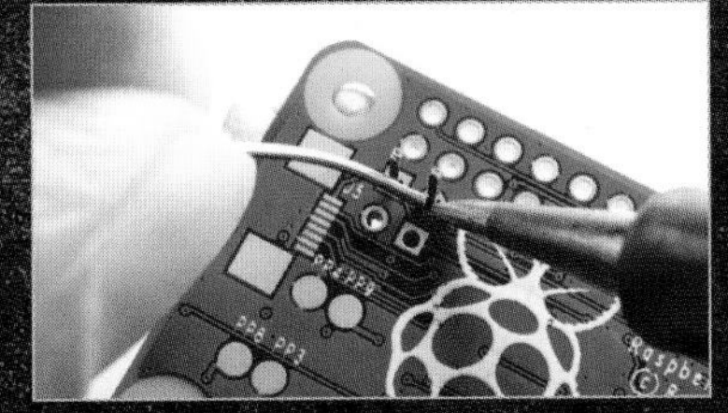

Any momentary-type normally open switch will work fine for this project, including this high-quality metal anti-vandal switch

SLACKTIVITY MONITOR

Track Slack chat activity with this LED display. You'll know at a glance if there's quiet, light chatter, or raucous debate

Use the type of header pins that work best for your desired configuration

The Pi Traffic Light from Low Voltage Labs makes connecting the three LEDs easy

Command Strips are a great way to temporarily mount projects exactly where you want them

To communicate within the Raspberry Pi Foundation we use Slack, the IRC-like chat service. There can be a lot of activity, and it's taken time for people to get their notification settings just right. But we wanted more than what Slack's notifications can provide. We wanted to be able to see at a glance how much chatter was going on among colleagues. Luckily, Slack's API and Python libraries are powerful and easy to work with. Assembly is easy and the materials inexpensive, especially if you use a Pi Zero.

Initial configuration

To set up your own Slacktivity Monitor, start from a fresh install of Raspbian. For the Raspberry Pi Zero, you need to use Raspbian Jessie, which can be found on NOOBS or be written to the SD card using the image found on the Raspberry Pi download page (**raspberrypi.org/downloads**). Like with other Raspberry Pi Zero projects, it's probably easiest to get everything configured and installed with a Raspberry Pi 2 or B+ and then move the microSD card to the Pi Zero when you're ready. Make sure to do the necessary updates by going into the terminal and using:

```
sudo apt-get update
sudo apt-get upgrade
```

You'll need to set some basic configuration options. From the desktop, go to Raspberry Pi Configuration in the Preferences menu. Under the System tab, set your Pi to boot to the CLI

You'll Need

- Pi Traffic Light **magpi.cc/1VamjoL**
- WiFi adaptor
- Right-angle header pins
- Soldering iron and solder
- Blu-Tack or Command Strips

The Slacktivity Monitor is small and light enough to be mounted to a display with Blu-Tack or Command Strips.

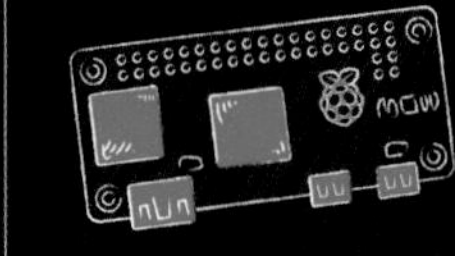

(command line interface) and enable 'Wait for network'. You can also set these options with the command line utility raspi-config. Make sure you've also configured your Pi to connect to your WiFi network. Alternatively, you can use a USB Ethernet adaptor with your Pi Zero.

Software setup

From the command line, download the Python Slack Client library:

```
sudo pip install slackclient
```

Download the project code:

```
git clone https://github.com/mrichardson23/slacktivity-monitor.git
```

You'll need to use your own Slack API token in the project code so that the Slacktivity Monitor can authenticate itself. While logged into Slack, go to **magpi.cc/1Val8OF** and click Create Token for the user and team that you want to monitor. Copy that token code into your code, replacing the text SLACK TOKEN HERE.

The code keeps track of roughly the last minute of activity. If there have been no messages sent within that time period, then the red LED will illuminate. If there have been any messages (but less than 15) within the last minute, then the yellow LED will illuminate. If 15 or more messages have been sent within the last minute, the LED will turn green. You may need to adjust this threshold to match the typical levels of activity in your Slack team.

Set up the script to run at boot. From the command line, execute:

```
sudo nano /etc/rc.local
```

Before the **exit 0** line, add a line to boot your code:

```
python /home/pi/slacktivity-monitor/main.py &
```

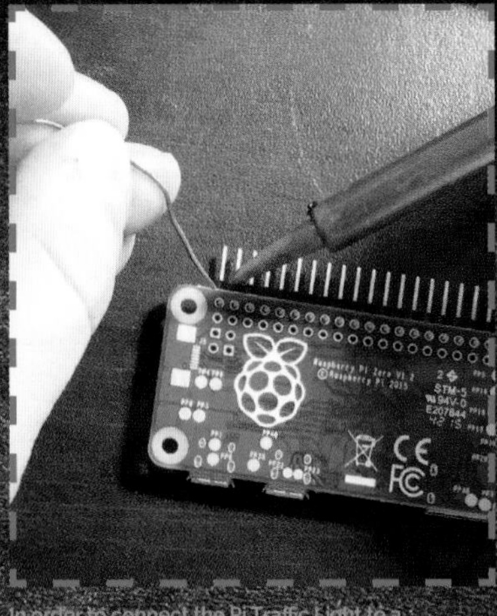

In order to connect the Pi Traffic Light to a Raspberry Pi Zero, you'll need to solder header pins

When you're done, save the file and shut down the Pi so that you can solder the headers, add the Pi Traffic Light, and attach it where you need it.

Physical build

Solder header pins onto the Pi Zero and connect the Pi Traffic Light to those pins. The code uses pin 15 for red, 14 for yellow, and 28 for green. This is because they're all next to each other along with a ground pin, so the Pi Traffic Light will plug right into the header pins and work like a charm. Depending on how you want to arrange your Slacktivity Monitor, you may want to change the pin numbers and colours.

Use Blu-Tack or Command Strips to attach the Slacktivity Monitor to your display.

When you power up the Pi, the script should start automatically and connect to your team's instance of Slack. Even if there's no recent activity, you may see the traffic light turn yellow initially because the Slack API will return the most recent message when a new client connects.

Going further

The code ignores everything except messages, so you could also adjust the Slacktivity Monitor to react to different types of events. For instance, you can use the red light to indicate when your boss is offline, yellow when she's idle, and green when she's active.

Main.py

Language >PYTHON

magpi.cc/2dXrLcb

```
import time
from slackclient import
SlackClient
from gpiozero import LED

token = "SLACK TOKEN HERE" # found at
# https://api.slack.com/web#authentication

red = LED(15)
yellow = LED(14)
green = LED(18)

red.off()
yellow.off()
green.off()

sc = SlackClient(token)

message_counts =[]

if sc.rtm_connect():
    while True:
        message_count = 0
        events = sc.rtm_read()
        for event in events:
            if event['type'] == 'message':
                message_count = message_count + 1
                message_counts.insert(
0, message_count)

            if len(message_counts) > 600:
                message_counts.pop(600)
                total_message_count = 0

            for i in range(
0,len(message_counts)):
                total_message_count =
total_message_count + message_counts[i]

            if total_message_count == 0:
                red.on()
                yellow.off()
                green.off()

            if total_message_count > 0
and total_message_count < 15:
                red.off()
                yellow.on()
                green.off()

            if total_message_count >= 15:
                red.off()
                yellow.off()
                green.on()

            time.sleep(.1)

else:
    print "Error. Invalid token?"
```

The Pi Zero comfortably fits into the handle, so even that can look the part
The pool noodle makes this a much safer and sturdier weapon than some of the toys
As well as a light-up blade, you can have a custom display above your ignition button

You'll Need

- Adafruit bicolour 8×8 LED matrix **magpi.cc/1ZMEBM4**
- A big button **magpi.cc/1ZMEGPM**
- Battery-powered 3v LED Christmas lights
- Adafruit ADXL345 triple-axis accelerometer **magpi.cc/1ZMEMHh**
- A swimming noodle/woggle
- A power bank
- Soldering kit, jumper wires, and stripboard
- Some glue, a craft knife, duct tape, and some Velcro strips

PI-SABER

The Force is strong with the Pi Zero, so how about using one to power your own Pi-Saber?

Recreating your favourite Jedi battles is lots of fun, but many toy lightsabers can be quite delicate. This Pi-Saber should be tough enough to survive some energetic re-enactments. The LEDs that produce the powered-up effect will also fluctuate their brightness as the Pi-Saber is swooshed around, to maximise the excitement.

We're assuming you have a GPIO header attached. However, for a more robust Pi-Saber, you could solder each connection directly onto the Pi Zero.

Padawan's first steps

First, prepare Raspbian on Pi Zero so we can use Python properly:

```
sudo apt-get install git python-pip python-dev python-imaging python-smbus
sudo pip install gpiozero
```

Now install and test the accelerometer. We're assuming you have an ADXL345, but there are plenty of alternatives that will work with some modifications.

First, install the handy Python library:

```
git clone https://github.com/pimoroni/adxl345-python.git
sudo cp adxl345-python/adxl345.py /usr/local/lib/python2.7/dist-packages/
```

The accelerometer uses the I²C bus, so you'll need to activate that by going into the Raspberry Pi Config program and selecting the 'Enable I2C' option from the advanced options. After a reboot, connect the accelerometer to the Pi as shown in **Fig 1**. Change into the **adxl345** directory and run:

```
python example.py
```

Wiggle the accelerometer around and verify that the displayed values for x, y and z change accordingly.

Lights for an apprentice

The Pi-Saber will have a funky display on the handle that also turns on when you press the main button. There are plenty of neat Adafruit 8×8 LED matrix units that come with their own backpack to make

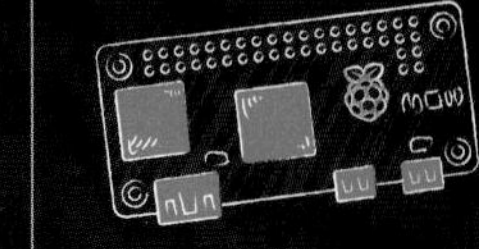

Python control simple. For testing, you can simply connect them via a breadboard, but for the finished product you'll need a more robust method. A simple option is to use a small piece of stripboard and either solder the wires directly or make use of a male header. As usual, there is a great Python library for the LED matrix:

```
git clone https://github.com/adafruit/Adafruit_Python_LED_Backpack.git
```

Then change into that directory and run the installer:

```
sudo python setup.py install
```

There are several example scripts in the repo that you can use for testing.

The other LED components for the Pi-Saber are the ones that will cover the main shaft. There are plenty of options, but Christmas lights are a great and cheap way of getting a string of pre-wired, low-power LEDs. Obviously, the more LEDs you get, the more dramatic the Pi-Saber effect. However, installing each one into the noodle can be quite tedious and time-consuming, so a string of 20 is a good compromise between aesthetics and sanity preservation.

Snip the wires just before the battery holder, strip back the insulation, and add a female jumper housing to the end of each one. Connect them up to the 3V and GND pins on the GPIO and check that they light up. Then switch one wire from the 3V pin to GPIO pin 17.

Jedi Master saber

The final element of the Pi-Saber is a nice big on/off button. Make up some wires with suitable connections, or simply solder directly onto the button's contacts. Then connect it up to the Pi Zero's GPIO pins (26 and one of the GNDs), as shown in **Fig 1**.

Now it's time to put everything together. Check everything is wired up as shown in **Fig 1** and then power

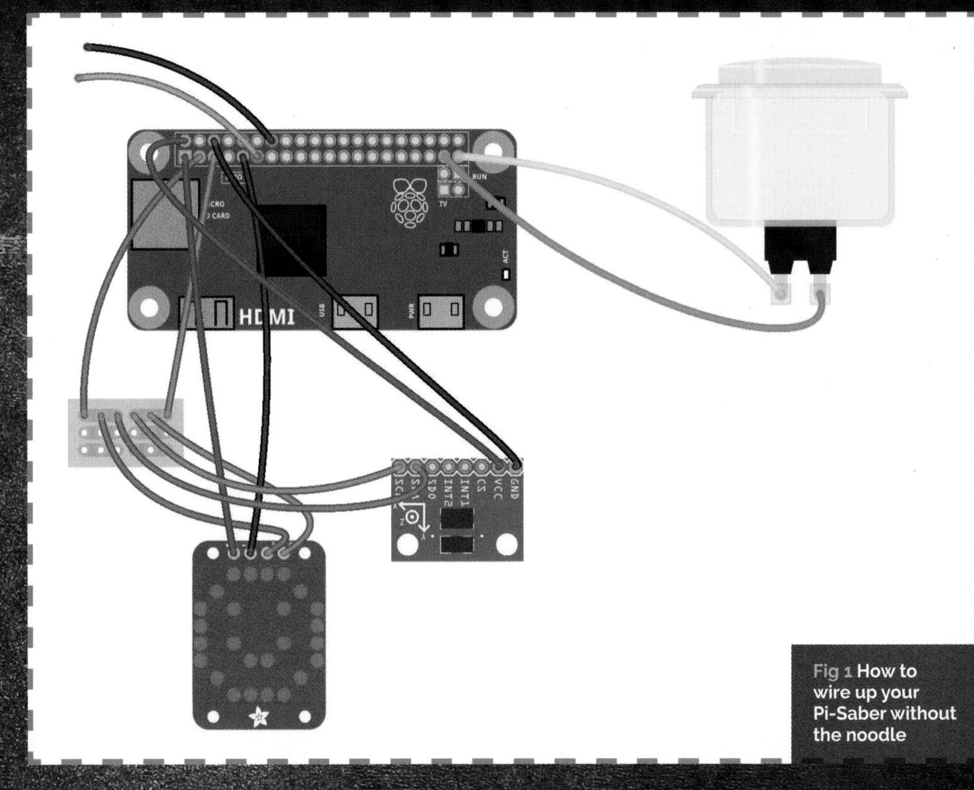

Fig 1 How to wire up your Pi-Saber without the noodle

up the Pi. Download the **PySaber.py** code (**magpi.cc/1ZMFVi3**), or type it into a text editor, and run it.

```
sudo python PiSaber.py
```

Nothing should happen until you press the button: the LED matrix should show a quick pattern and then start 'sparkling'. Meanwhile, the LEDs on the string should all light up. Pick up the accelerometer, jiggle it around, and you should see the brightness of the LEDs fluctuate along the shaft.

Once everything is working, add the line:

```
python /home/pi/PiSaber.py &
```

...to the **/etc/rc.local** file (above the 'exit 0' line) so that the code will run whenever the Pi is booted.

Now chop the noodle in two and then slice one half open lengthways like a hotdog bun – don't cut all the way through. Measure your noodle and make a sketch to work out how your particular power bank and button will fit inside. Once you've got this figured out, completely remove that much of one half of the noodle, leaving a wedge. Then mark out where the components go and cut away those chunks of the noodle. While you're at it, cut out a small trench all the way along the rest of the inner noodle for the LED cable.

"Nothing should happen until you press the button: the LED matrix should show a quick pattern and then start 'sparkling'"

Now calculate how far apart the LEDs should be to give an even spacing all the way round, and then poke them through; make some pilot holes first with a meat skewer or something similar. Once everything is in place and the wires are tidy, glue the slit shaft back together all the way along the length. Cover the handle parts with duct tape and then strap them together with some Velcro.

That should be it – now you're all set for some epic battles.

Language
>PYTHON 2.7

DOWNLOAD:
magpi.cc/1ZMFVi3

You'll Need

- Gaming mouse – eBay
- Mini HDMI cable **amazon.com**
- 2× micro USB-to-USB cables **amazon.com**
- Quake III files (that you own legitimately)

QUAKE III MOUSE

Wouldn't it be great if you could put an entire computer into a gaming mouse? Yes. Yes, it would...

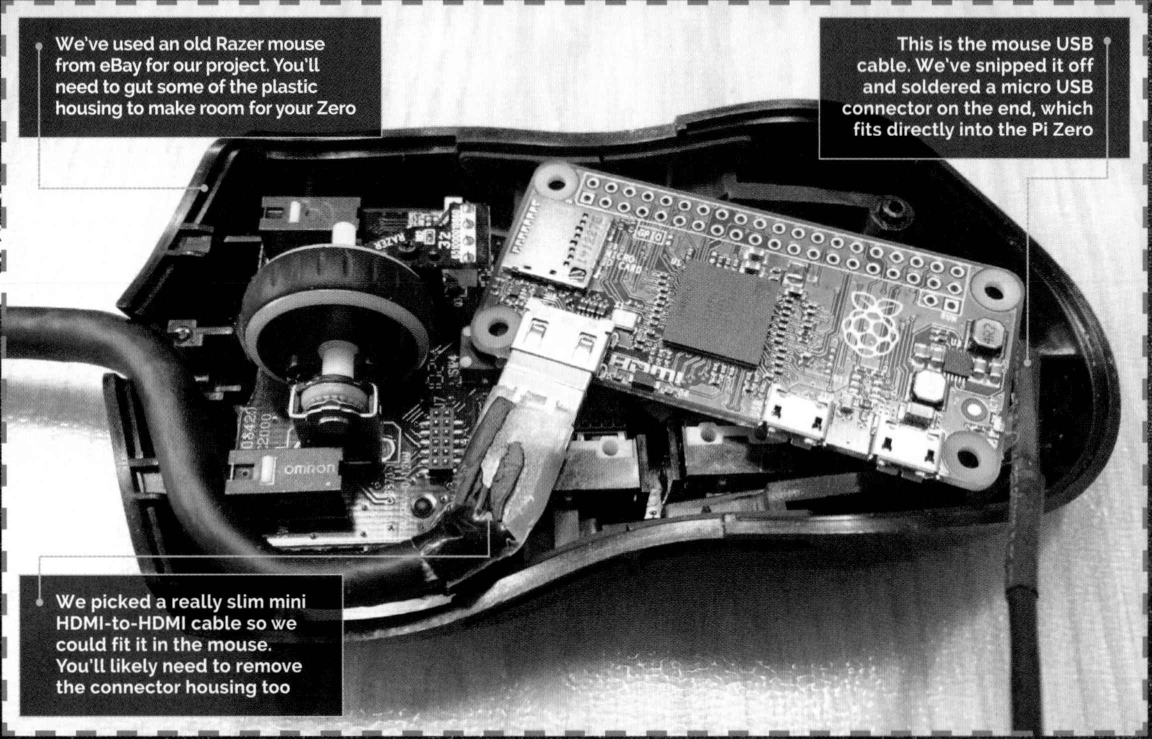

We've used an old Razer mouse from eBay for our project. You'll need to gut some of the plastic housing to make room for your Zero

This is the mouse USB cable. We've snipped it off and soldered a micro USB connector on the end, which fits directly into the Pi Zero

We picked a really slim mini HDMI-to-HDMI cable so we could fit it in the mouse. You'll likely need to remove the connector housing too

#pizero

When the Pi Zero was first announced internally, Raspberry Pi's Eben Upton came up with the idea of putting one in a gaming mouse and installing *Quake III* on it. Our heads exploded. Since modern gaming mice have so many buttons, it's actually pretty trivial to tweak the control settings so that running and jumping can be controlled without the need for a keyboard at all. In essence, a lot of what we're doing with this project is an extension of the SNES Consoller project elsewhere in this feature: gut a gaming mouse (most of it is just empty, ergonomically shaped plastic anyway), connect its USB to the Zero internally, and you're pretty much done and dusted.

Of course, these things are invariably easier said than done, and it did take a few shopping trips on eBay to find a suitable mouse contender. We settled on an old Razer Lachesis from around 2009. It has a scroll wheel, two buttons directly behind said wheel, and two buttons on each side of the mouse. It also has enough dead space inside to fit our Pi Zero and HDMI cable. Perfect.

Since there's a lot more going on inside a gaming mouse than a retro controller, we had to do away with our plan to battery-power the *Quake III* mouse quite early on. The end result means that along with the HDMI cable coming out of the front in place of the original USB connector, we've also got a slimline (but ultra-long) micro USB-to-USB cable. Said cables are easily sleeved or tape-wrapped together, though, and most TVs these days offer USB ports that supply enough power to run the Pi Zero. Ultimately, it's a small compromise.

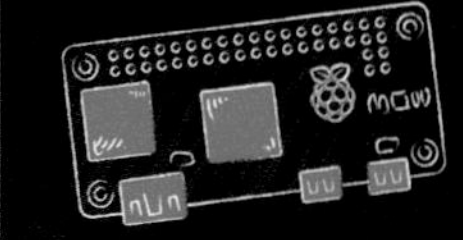

>STEP-01

Gut the mouse

It sounds gruesome, but it's actually easier than you think once you can actually get into the thing. Our Razer Lachesis had a solitary cross-head screw hidden under a sticker on the bottom of the mouse. With that removed, we were able to remove the LED light boards from the roof of the mouse, and trim down some of the support struts and plastic moulding using side cutters. Razer had conveniently used connectors for the LED lights and even for the USB port, so it was trivial to remove everything to create space.

>STEP-02

Soldering the micro-USB

Next, we snipped the USB cable for the mouse, leaving enough play to solder a micro USB connector on the end that fits straight into the Pi Zero. It just works. The cabling is straightforward – with the longest flat edge of the micro USB connector facing up and towards you, the cabling is soldered from left to right – black, green, white, and red. Since USB is entirely universal, there's no way you can get it wrong – just search for 'micro USB cable connector' for example diagrams. It can be fiddly to solder, but with a decent iron and some helping hands to hold it steady, it's pretty straightforward stuff.

>STEP-03

Fitting the Zero and mini HDMI

Now we want to fit the Pi Zero, taking into account that there's going to be a (comparatively) massive HDMI cable attached to it. Our best advice here is to buy the slimmest mini HDMI-to-HDMI cable you can find, but you'll need to use a craft knife to carefully remove the housing without damaging the cable itself. With our Razer mouse, we found that the Zero sat nicely at an angle, with the HDMI cable snaking around the chassis to the front port where the old USB cable was. At this point, it's probably wise to ensure you can seal up the mouse securely, since you might need to carve out a little more of the plastic housing to accommodate it.

>STEP-04

Power your Pi Zero

Sadly, there's just not enough room in the mouse to house a rechargeable battery and accompanying battery controller board. Instead, we're going to run a slimline micro USB cable from the Zero's power port out of the front of the mouse, alongside the HDMI cable. Once the project is complete and working, you can either tape-wrap the two cables together or get some decent heat-shrink sleeving to hold them securely together. You'll need to ensure both cables are long enough so that there's plenty of play at the other end, and both the HDMI and USB cables can be plugged in.

>STEP-05

Installing the software

The next step is to set up a Raspbian Jessie image on your SD card; we advise taking your Zero out of your mouse to do so, and using a USB hub with connected keyboard, mouse, and WiFi dongle. With Raspbian Jessie installed, you need to set up your game (in this case, *Quake III*). Installation isn't exactly a breeze, but you can find full instructions on the process at **magpi.cc/QuakeIII**. You need to recompile the game and acquire the pac files for *Quake III* from a reputable source. Sorry – our lawyers won't let us be more specific than that!

>STEP-06

The ultimate gaming mouse

With power and USB connectivity sorted, and an up-to-date install of Raspbian Jessie and *Quake III* set up, all that's left to do is to pop into the options menu and reassign control to as many of the mouse buttons as you can. We opted to use the wheel to switch weapons, the left two buttons for forward and back, and the opposite two sides for strafing. It takes a while to get used to, but you soon get the hang of it.

QUAKE III

Raspberry Pi Beginners has a really neat YouTube video showing you an alternative method of installing *Quake III* on your Raspberry Pi. **youtu.be/btSGRnXuAAA**

ROB ZWETSLOOT

Tech writer, avid coder, and Raspberry Pi enthusiast with a history of building many things with Raspberry Pi.
magpi.cc

The main indication that something is different about this controller, but it's a small price to pay.

A standard knock-off USB NES controller works perfectly for what we have planned

NES ZERO

We make last month's project idea into reality with a NES controller that's been Zero-charged to be able to run NES games...

You'll Need

- USB NES controller (check eBay!)
- A Raspberry Pi Zero - **raspberrypi.org**
- RetroPie - **magpi.cc/1HVgNba**
- A rotary tool (like a Dremel)
- An old micro USB cable
- A screwdriver, soldering iron and a way to strip wires

Ever since first seeing the Raspberry Pi Zero a few months ago at Pi HQ, we've spent a lot of time since then thinking about the cool ways that the Pi Zero can be used. One of our first ideas was slipping a Pi Zero into a NES controller, taking a bit of inspiration from Ben Heck's great inventions to further miniaturise the NES to its most core component.

We wrote about how you could do this last issue but we have now finally had time to make a proof-of-concept, so we're going to show you how to exactly put a Pi Zero inside an NES controller.

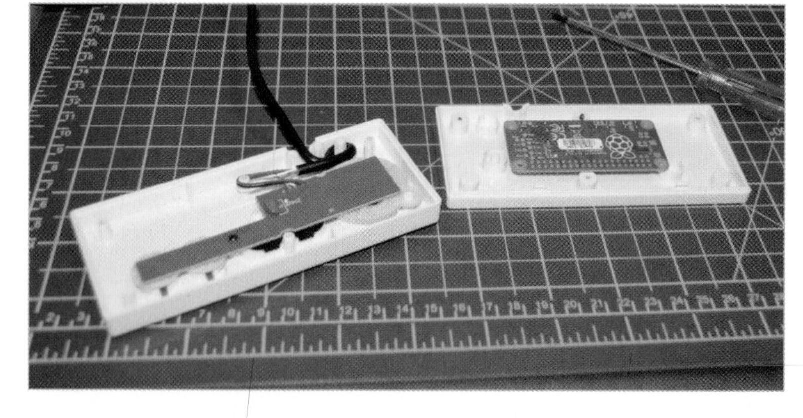

>STEP-01
Set up RetroPie

This is really more for convenience than anything else. Download the RetroPie image and write it to a microSD card using your preferred method (check the Raspberry Pi guide if you've not done this before: **magpi.cc/1XTmymk**). Once it's written, open it up in your file explorer and navigate to home, pi, RetroPie and put your NES ROMs into the nes folder.

Pop the micro SD card into the Pi Zero and hook the USB NES controller up to it before turning it on. You can then do the initial setup and configure the controller.

>STEP-02
Make some space

It seems that many USB NES controllers have roughly the same internal structure (they may be using a mould of the NES controllers, or just a generic one) and it is therefore likely that you'll need to make some space. We used a rotary tool to trim the screw holes and a ring on the edge. We wanted to use the original USB wire port for our HDMI cable, so we suggest that you lay the Pi Zero (with SD card inserted!) inside the back plate and figure out where needs to be trimmed.

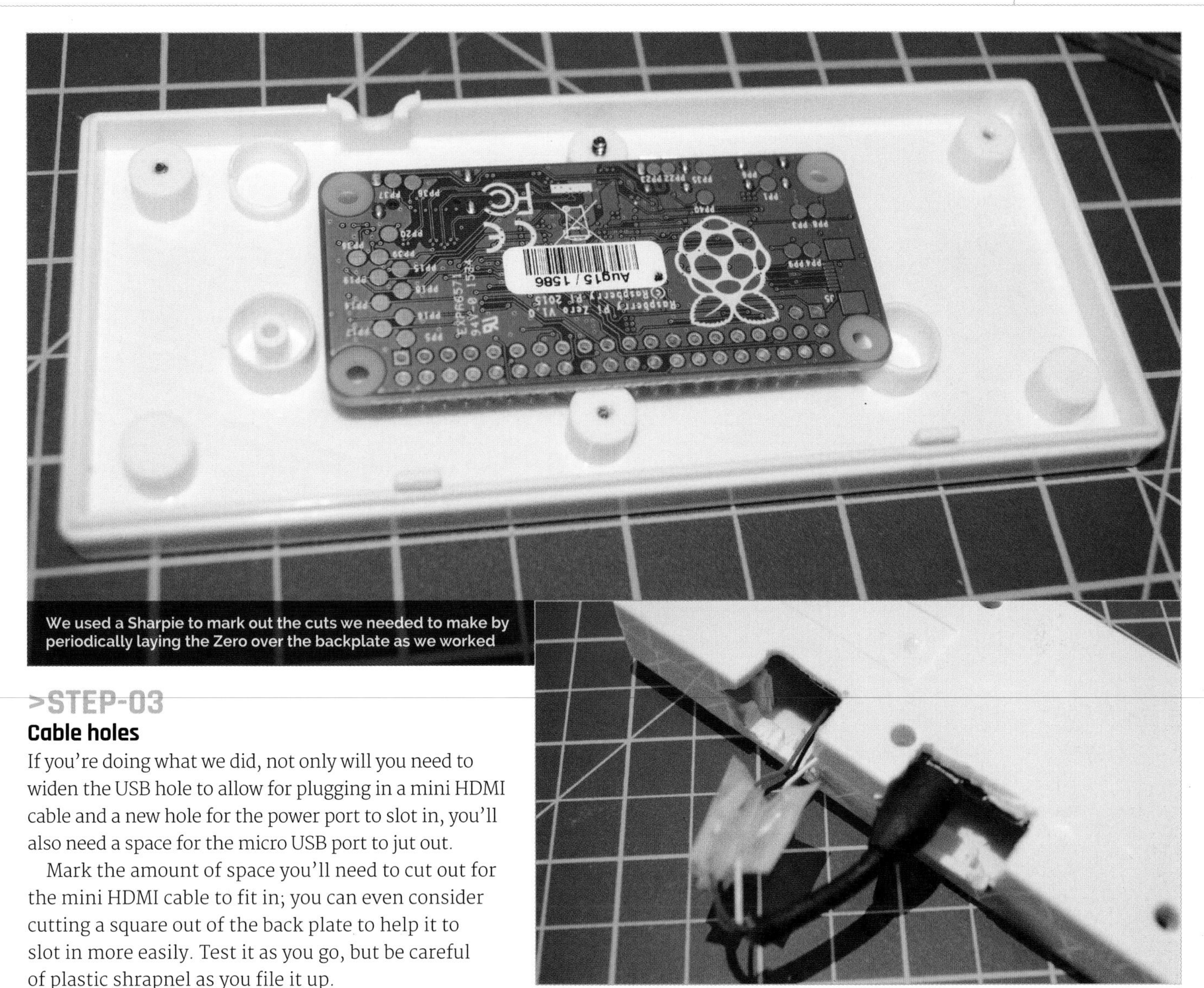

We used a Sharpie to mark out the cuts we needed to make by periodically laying the Zero over the backplate as we worked

Above Our cutting is a little rough in places; you may also need to open up the bottom of the controller to fit the cables in

>STEP-03
Cable holes

If you're doing what we did, not only will you need to widen the USB hole to allow for plugging in a mini HDMI cable and a new hole for the power port to slot in, you'll also need a space for the micro USB port to jut out.

Mark the amount of space you'll need to cut out for the mini HDMI cable to fit in; you can even consider cutting a square out of the back plate to help it to slot in more easily. Test it as you go, but be careful of plastic shrapnel as you file it up.

> "All that's left is to plug it into a TV and power supply..."

>STEP-04
Wire up the controller

USB cables are wired up very simply, with four wires providing power, ground and data. Luckily, the colouring of the wires inside a cable is standard. Snip off the end of the micro USB cable you want to sacrifice and strip off the rubber, the braided wire and the foil surrounding the four individual wires. Strip them to reveal the core. Do the same with the USB cable on the NES board: on ours the wires were accessible before the cable insulated them.

Solder the corresponding wires together and individually insulate them with electrical tape or heat shrink tubing.

>STEP-05
Assemble it

We used a bit of Blu Tack to secure our Pi Zero to the inside of the base plate while carefully making sure the micro USB connector was plugged in and not obscuring any of the screws or clips connecting the controller together. We then carefully screwed it in and checked that the connectors fitted. All that's left is to plug it into a TV and power supply and make sure the whole system works.

>STEP-06
Game on

As we have noted, our version is simply a proof of concept. It did, however, survive a solid six hours of young kids getting very frustrated over old games at Pi Wars, so clearly the controller and Pi Zero are robust enough to handle extended play sessions. You will need to dismantle the device to get to the SD card and load or change ROMs on it. You could, however, probably get it to connect over WiFi and transfer files over SSH.

OTHER CONTROLLERS

You just have to look at the Xbox controller hack from earlier in the magazine to see how this could be done with other controllers

REVIEWS

Find out the best add-ons, operating systems, and books for your Raspberry Pi adventure

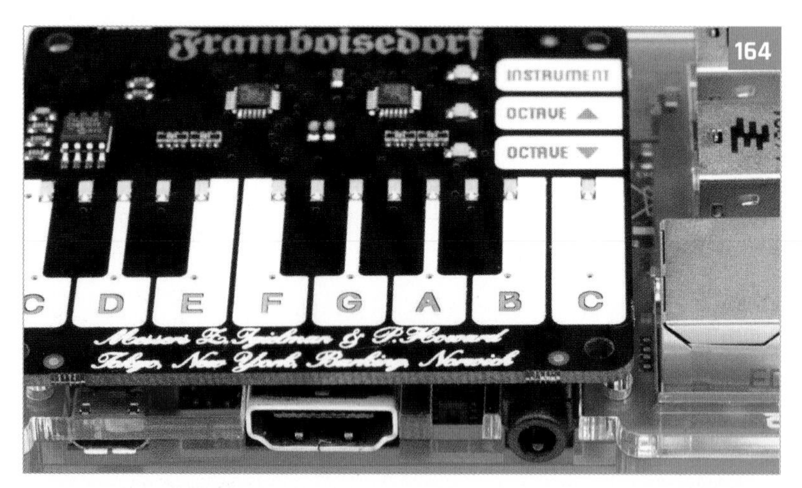

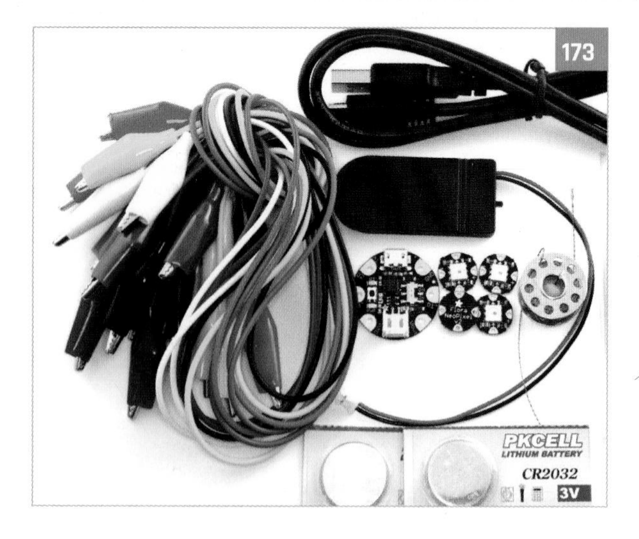

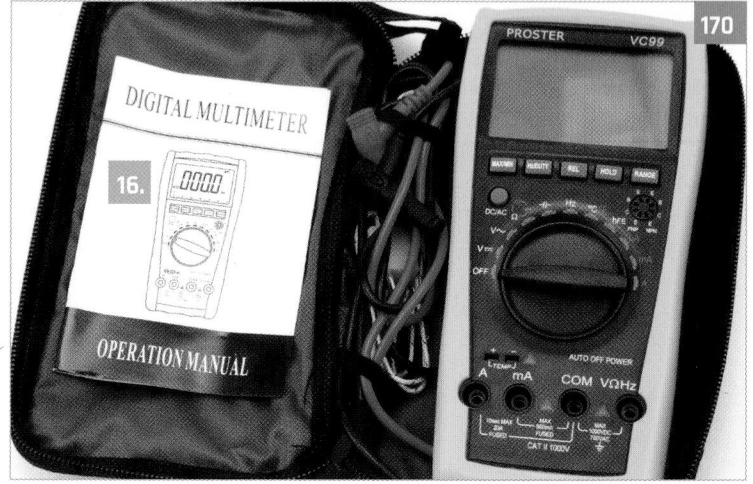

172
GND
D1
PWR
D0
A1

188
RasPiRobot
V3f
MonkMakes.com

178
TENMA
400
Digital
Soldering
Station
ESD SAFE

186

174
MEDIA
PI
PLUS

Reviews

pimoroni.com

£15 / $24

Maker Says

A Pi-based piano, transformed with Pimoroni's signature polish

Pimoroni

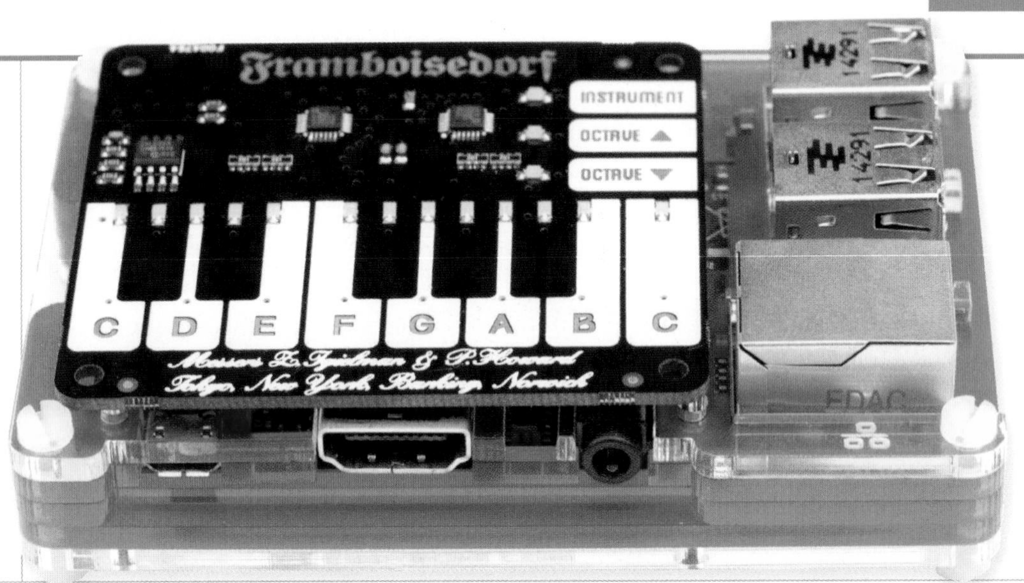

PIANO HAT

Les Pounder looks at a HAT-based piano keyboard which uses capacitive touch keys for input

In 2014, a 14-year-old called Zachary Igielman launched a successful crowdfunding campaign for his Pi Piano. Originally created using a MCP23017 GPIO expander and a series of momentary switches, the Pi Piano used a piezo buzzer to simulate the tone of a note. One of Zachary's advisors was Phil Howard from Pimoroni, who worked with Zachary to create this new and improved version.

Crowdfunded project

The latest incarnation is now known as Piano HAT and uses a capacitive touch-based interface to simulate a portion of a traditional piano keyboard. The board measures 64mm by 56mm and fits neatly on top of the models A+, B+, and Pi 2. Being a HAT board, it also attaches to all 40 of the GPIO pins. As well as the keyboard, we have the ability to raise and lower the octaves and change instruments via three extra inputs on the board.

Hardware is just one part of this project, and the software which supports Piano HAT is all based on Python, which enables existing projects created in this language to easily integrate Piano HAT. Phil Howard has written a series of examples which use the Pygame library to demonstrate how to use Piano HAT as a typical piano via a series of audio samples, which can be swapped for any types of sounds should you wish to build your own input. Piano HAT also comes with a tutorial which demonstrates using the built-in LEDs to teach playing a simple tune, in this case 'Twinkle, twinkle, little star'. So, using this library, we can code our own tutorial for others to learn with.

Powerful MIDI synthesiser

Software is not just limited to simple samples. In fact, Phil has supplied a number of methods to connect the Piano HAT library to a MIDI service running on your Pi. This then turns the Piano HAT into a powerful synthesiser input for software such as Yoshimi and SunVox, although a Raspberry Pi 2 is required for these applications.

The Piano HAT looks like a rather simple board, but thanks to a clear Python library, well-built hardware, and a powerful MIDI control option, we have a board for musical adventures.

Related

MAKEY MAKEY

This versatile board has been used to build a piano from stairs, a camera trigger using water, and a keyboard from pasta.

£40 / $50

makeymakey.com

Last word

Such a simple board, but with limitless applications thanks to Python and MIDI. This is a great platform for musical experimentation and it can easily be used with *Minecraft* and other projects.

iqaudio.com

£30 / $50

Maker Says

"Outstanding sonic performance with variable phono line out and dedicated headphone amplifier"
IQaudIO

IQAUDIO PI-DAC+

Any Raspberry Pi becomes an audiophile music streamer with this high-resolution DAC and headphone amplifier

Even a standalone Pi makes a very decent music streamer, but add a high-quality DAC and it becomes a true audiophile device. The IQaudIO Pi-DAC plus is a HAT-compliant board which uses the I²S interface for optimal transmission of digital audio between the Pi and the DAC. Once fitted, you get analogue output from either two phono sockets, for connection to an amplifier, or a 3.5mm headphone socket, along with additional pinouts for adding optional features.

No soldering required

The board comes without any instructions, but you can find these on the IQaudIO website. No soldering is required, and it works with Raspberry Pi A+, B+, and 2. You need to screw the supplied spacers to the Pi to support the board, then you simply connect it to the Pi's GPIO board, screw it down gently, and that's that.

IQaudIO can also supply a case, an acrylic affair that has suitable cut-outs for the Pi-DAC+ ports.

Once assembled, you can download a number of audio-centric distributions that have Pi-DAC+ drivers built in – including Volumio, RuneAudi, and PiCorePlayer – or follow the directions to add support to an existing installation. There is also a preconfigured Raspbian image on the IQaudIO site. We used Volumio 1.55, which worked perfectly. The music source can be anything from files on a NAS, to a streaming service such as Spotify, or a directly attached USB hard drive.

Excellent sound

The DAC sounds excellent, powered by a Texas Instruments PCM5122 DAC at resolutions up to 24-bit/192kHz. From a sonic point of view, a Pi equipped with a DAC like this can hold its own with far more exotic and expensive company. We were also impressed with the headphone output: tested with a pair of Sennheiser HD600 headphones, the sound was superb, with the clarity and spaciousness that you get from the best audio.

Expansion options at extra cost include attaching a rotary volume control or an IR sensor for remote volume control. The Pi-AMP+ is 2×20W stereo amplifier which attaches to the top of the board. You can also use the supplied optional right-angled header, designed to be soldered underneath the Pi-DAC+ to access the Pi's GPIO signals.

Last word

Great sound and the inclusion of a headphone amplifier make the Pi-DAC+ a recommended accessory for music-loving Pi enthusiasts.

Related

AUDIOPHONICS I-SABRE DAC ES9023

The DAC from Audiophonics is a similar price to the Pi-DAC+, but it lacks a headphone output. It uses the Sabre ES9023 DAC instead of the Texas Instruments/ Burr Brown DAC in the Pi-DAC+, and includes a pass-through GPIO connector so you can stack additional boards.

£30 / $48

magpi.cc/2dr8X2d

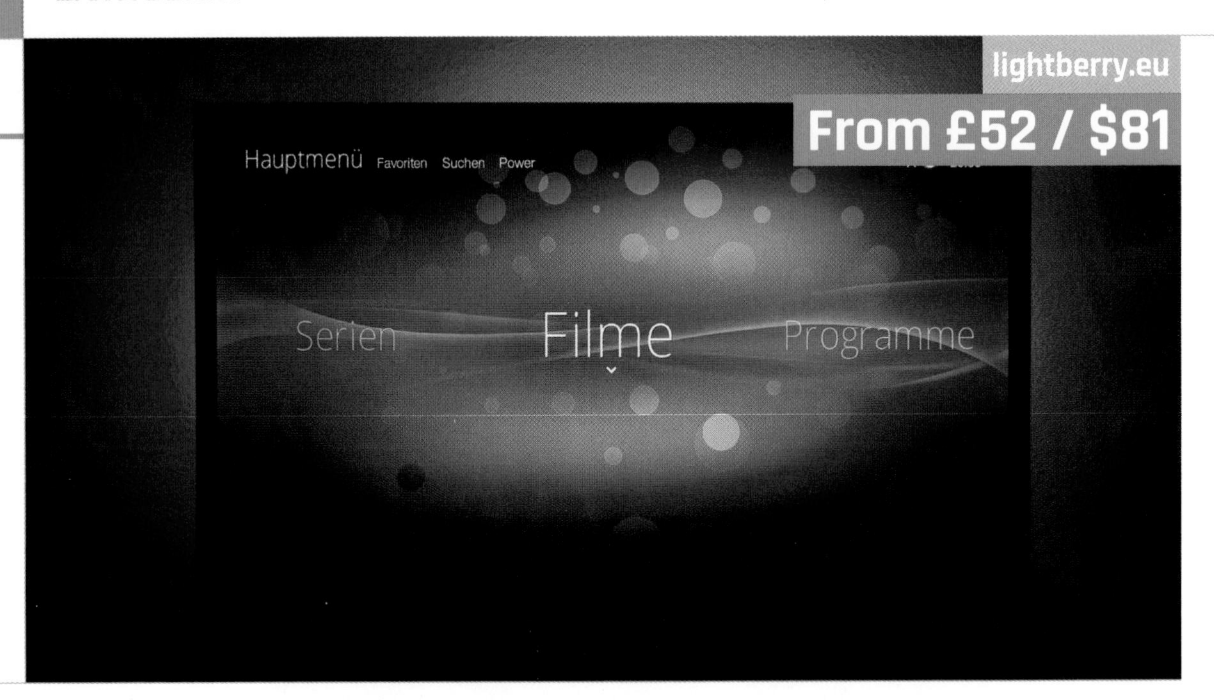

Maker Says

"Easy to install, simple to use, a joy to watch"
Lightberry

LIGHTBERRY

Russell Barnes tests a technology designed to add a new dimension to your home cinema experience

Lightberry is inspired by a TV technology pioneered by Philips called Ambilight. While the tech naturally comes pre-fitted on Ambilight TVs, it's perfectly possible to modify any TV to add its special kind of ambience-enhancing trickery. What does it do? The premise is simple: you affix a ring of colour-switching LED lights to the back of your LCD TV and – assuming your TV is against a wall and the ambient lighting is low – the colours on the LEDs are designed to perfectly sync with the action on screen in colour and intensity, so that light appears to bleed out of the screen and dance against the wall in the background.

As with Philips' creation, Lightberry – which harnesses the power of the Raspberry Pi for computation – is all about adding a little more immersion into your viewing experience. While the idea is simple, the technology behind it certainly isn't, though for most people the results really do speak for themselves.

Sold either as a full kit starting from just over £50 / $80, or as constituent parts available separately, Lightberry is designed to take the pain out of the technical aspects, giving you as close to a plug-and-play experience as you could hope for. Obviously, sampling millions of pixels of onscreen data and converting that to the right LED, colour and brightness at exactly the right moment isn't the simplest project to tackle, but Lightberry manages to make it easy. It's also designed to work perfectly with the best software solutions for this technology, too, including Hyperion and Boblight.

Once you've picked the right length LED strip to fit your particular size of TV and ordered all the kit you need, it all arrives boxed and ready to assemble. While we found no instructions in our box, **magpi.cc/2drsyPG** offers brief but functional step-by-step instructions to get you up and running. Probably the fiddliest part of the process is arranging and affixing the LEDs themselves. Elsewhere it simply requires you to connect the appropriate converter box, download software and install it onto an SD card – a process any Raspberry Pi user should already be intimately aware of.

Related

PHILIPS AMBILIGHT

The real alternative to Lightberry is an actual Ambilight TV. The cheapest we could find (at the time of writing) was £350. Ouch.

From £350 / $550
bit.ly/1JiGm9Y

Last word

While it can take a little trial and error to best position the LEDs, once you've hit the sweet spot we found Lightberry a joy to use. It's not the cheapest Raspberry Pi project, but it's one that is sure to please the movie fans in your household.

magpi.cc/2drsDms

£12.99 / $20

Maker Says

"The security camera solution for the Raspberry Pi"
SB Components

SPI-BOX

A very simple solution to creating a motion-detecting security device that won't break the bank

It's one of those classic tutorials in tech mags with small PCs and microcontrollers: the motion-detecting camera. There are many ways you can do it – some easier than others – and the Raspberry Pi offers many tools to make a project like this quite simple in general.

Enter SB Components with a dedicated motion-detecting camera kit for the Raspberry Pi. Designed as a cheap security system, the features that make up the kit are quite standard: a PIR motion detector, a specialised case for the whole setup, and even a custom version of Raspbian with software for sending security alerts. All for just over £10; throw in the cost of a Raspberry Pi B+ or 2 with a Pi Camera and – on paper – you've got yourself a pretty good security camera for about £50.

Assembly is dead simple. The case splits in two and the Raspberry Pi clips into the bottom part, with full access to all the major ports around the edges. The PIR and Pi Camera can be screwed to the lid, while a set of three wires is used to connect the PIR directly to the GPIO ports. Pop in the supplied SD card and you're all ready to get started.

The case has pretty standard mounting holes on the back for fitting over a couple of screws attached to the wall. You'll need to set up the emailing system on the device, accessed through the config files on the SD card, which you can probably do from another computer; however, all it then needs is a WiFi dongle and power to do its job.

As the code is written in Python, it's quite simple to modify if you need to tweak the sensitivity, or the way it captures photos or video. It all works pretty well, especially for the price, although we wouldn't rely on it for any serious security work.

Really, this is as good as any other Raspberry Pi security camera. It'll be a lot better than one you try to put together yourself, and probably cheaper and neater too, so give it a look if you're interested in a bit of added security.

Related

NATUREBYTES

Although designed for a different use, the Naturebytes Wildlife Cam Kit could be configured for security. It's also weatherproof.

£149.99

magpi.cc/1QnR4k8

Last word

A great little kit that very simply creates a serviceable Pi-powered security camera that's great for any indoor application. It also barely breaks £20 (with camera), making it a cheap way to keep a better eye on something.

★★★★☆

magpi.cc/2drrY4u

£23/$35

Maker Says

Make your own Astro Pi!

Raspberry Pi

SENSE HAT

Space: the final frontier. These are the voyages of the Sense HAT. Its mission: to make sensing the environment really easy for Raspberry Pi users. To boldly go where no Pi has gone before...

Related

ARDUBERRY

While there's nothing quite like the Sense HAT, the Arduberry allows you to connect Arduino boards to the Pi, enabling you to create your own custom sensor suite, albeit at a greater cost.

$29.99/£19.70

magpi.cc/2drt54j

If you've been reading this magazine from cover to cover (which you really should, we have some top-quality content in here. Don't worry, we'll wait here for you to catch up. Done? Good!), you'll have seen our release story for the Sense HAT that starts on page 6. This is the little board that makes the Astro Pi possible, hosting a suite of sensors along with a very simple LED display. The idea is that it sits on top of your Pi's GPIO pins and gives you access to much more data from your surroundings through a few extra packages.

Like all the other hardware produced by the Raspberry Pi Foundation, it is fairly cheap. On the other hand, it'll set you back nearly as much as a Raspberry Pi 2 Model B, so could be viewed as being a little expensive for an add-on board. In the grand scheme of things, though, the Sense HAT represents great value for money considering the functions it grants you. The reason it is so inexpensive is because it was designed to be easily constructed, with a few compromises made to keep the price down.

Cheap as silicon chips

Don't get us wrong, though: the Sense HAT is definitely not a cheap product. It's the same sort of sturdy construction as the Raspberry Pi, and doesn't have any easily broken sticking out capacitors or other components. It's built to be blasted into space, after all, so needs to be pretty robust. We wouldn't start stamping on it to try to test out how tough it is, but it'll survive being man-handled onto and off a Raspberry Pi. It fits very snugly on the GPIO pins (taking up all 40), and can even be used with other GPIO headers or wires to the individual pins. There's no programming issue with this, as long as you're not trying to use the functions of the Sense HAT at exactly the same time, although if you know what pins are used for specific sensors or the LED matrix, you might be able to work around it with a bit of inventive coding.

The specific sensors on the Sense HAT are pretty varied. There's a suite of the usual environmental sensors such as temperature, pressure and humidity, along

> To use the Sense HAT, you can't just open up a graphical interface for it

with a trio of positional sensors which include an accelerometer, a gyroscope, and a magnetometer. They're all pretty accurate and able to sense a wide range in their respective fields, with the outputs instantly modified to be readable with the Sense HAT library.

Put on your coding hat

To use the Sense HAT, you can't just open up a graphical interface for it... at least just yet. It would actually be quite simple to create a general interface or a custom one for your needs, because frankly the coding side of the Sense HAT is very straightforward, making use of Python's basic syntax and some simple command structures of its own. So you can easily get data from the Sense HAT with only a few lines of code, and very easily print out data or images to the screen. Text output is handled by the code, so you don't need to do any ridiculous coding to change individual pictures for it to scroll across the screen.

There's a massive amount of control over the input and output as well, with the full power of the Sense HAT readily available. There are plenty of online resources as well (through the Astro Pi and Raspberry Pi sites) to help you learn exactly how to use it. We like the smiley-face tutorial example; it made us feel happy.

We sense a winner

All in all then, this is an excellent bit of gear. It's well put together with a huge number of functions and it's very easy to program as well, thanks to some great software available for the board. You can use it on its own or in conjunction with other projects (we want to attach it to a robot in the near future), and if it's good enough for the ISS, it should definitely be enough for any crazy ideas you may have for it.

Last word

The Sense HAT is easy to use and doesn't compromise any of its functions to allow that. It's a fantastic board for the price and really expands the amount you can do with the Pi.

Maker Says

Very cost-effective multimeter with analogue bar
Proster

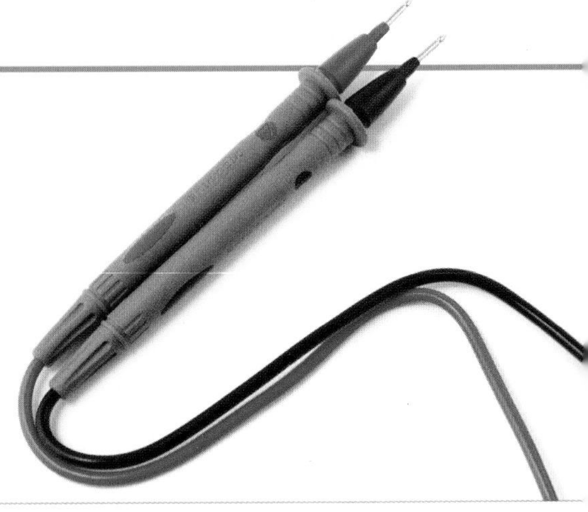

PROSTER VC99 MULTIMETER

With everything a hobbyist could ask for, is the VC family of multimeters the bargain it appears to be?

Related

EXTECH EX330 MULTIMETER

The EX330 has all the features of the Proster VC99, swapping only the transistor test mode for non-contact AC voltage detection, in a more compact package. Sadly, it's also considerably more expensive.

£47 / $60

adafruit.com

For years there was a gulf between affordable multimeters for the hobbyist and professional-grade hardware. Outgrowing a £10 multimeter from a high-street electronics shop typically meant jumping to £100 or more for a pro device. More recently, though, Chinese multimeters have begun to give the big boys a serious run for their money without breaking the bank - devices like the Proster VC99.

Part of the VC family and available from its original design manufacturer (ODM) under different brands, the Proster VC99 is designed to give the hobbyist a wider range of functionality than your average pocket multimeter. The usual features are, of course, present and correct – there's AC voltage sensing up to 1,000V and DC up to 700V, current measurement up to 20A for a maximum of ten seconds, capacitance measurement, and resistance measurement with visual and audible continuity test modes. But the VC99 really packs out the extras list: there's a frequency counter mode suitable for measuring up to 60MHz with a ±0.5% accuracy, a temperature sensing mode with bundled K-type temperature probe, and a current gain test (hFE) for PNP and NPN transistors through a built-in multi-pole socket. For anyone who has ever bought a multimeter with an hFE mode plug-in adapter, only to lose said adapter shortly after purchase, that feature alone is worth the asking price.

Paying for quality

Naturally, there are reasons why the Proster VC99 doesn't cost twice the price. Chief among these is its accuracy: while the base accuracy of ±0.5% compares well with even expensive multimeters, the ±3.5% accuracy rating for capacitance measurement is decidedly less impressive. The screen, while large and easy to read in most conditions, is not back-lit, and the kickstand to the rear of the chassis is only capable of holding the multimeter at one rather shallow angle.

Surprisingly, the VC99 doesn't cut every corner. Included with the multimeter is a handy zipped storage bag, while the anti-shock rubber around the outside of the chassis includes storage mounts for the probes. These are worth mentioning, too: compared to similarly priced rivals, the probes included with the VC99 are of a surprisingly high quality. Unless you need something specific, like probes ending in test hooks, you're unlikely to be looking to upgrade any time soon.

amazon.co.uk

£25 / $28

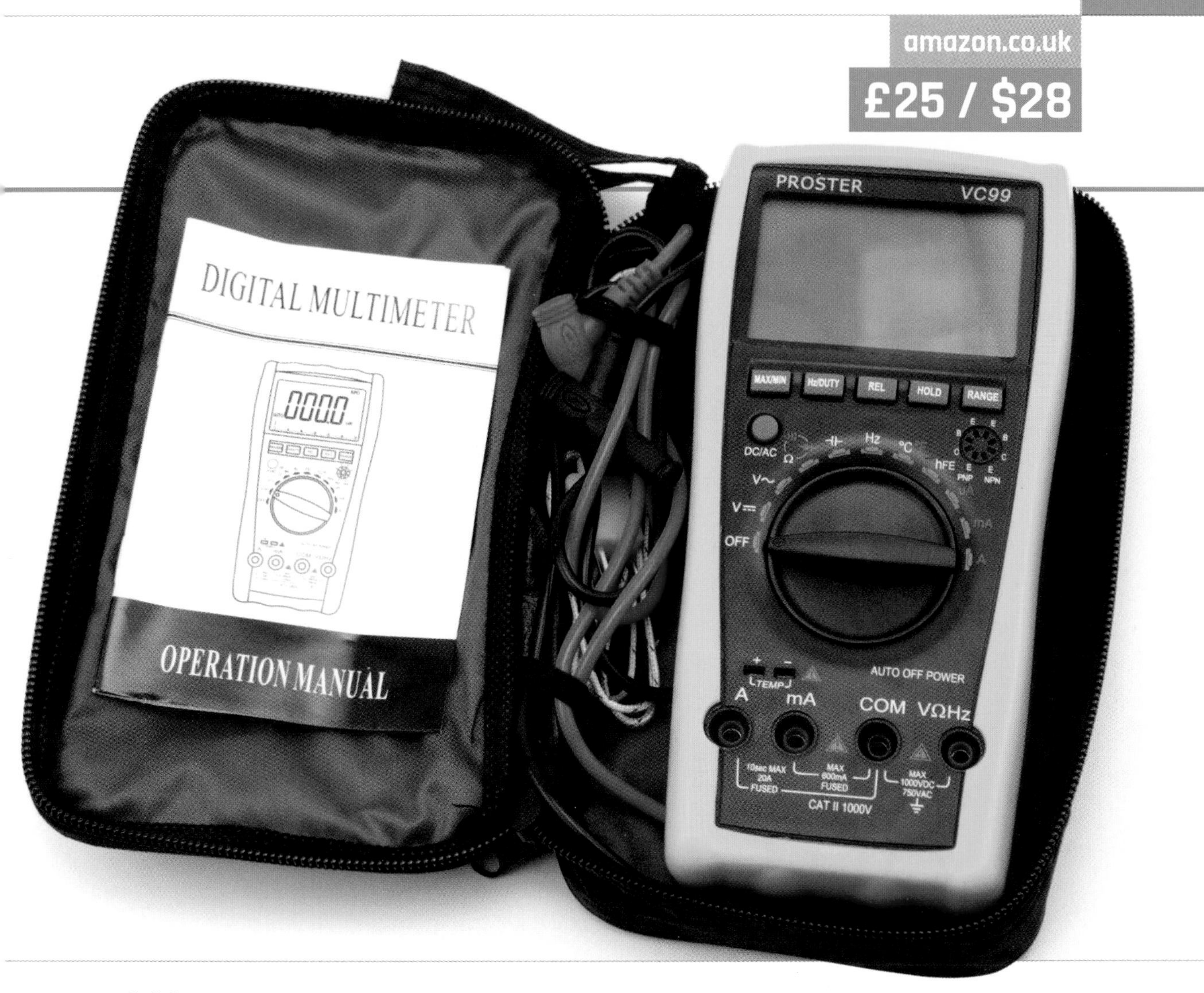

Essential features

When setting the VC99 up for measurement, it's easy to forget that it's a budget multimeter. The probes sit securely in their ports, and the mode dial switches with a pleasingly tactile click. Buttons are included just below the display for various functions, including the ability to switch between frequency and duty cycle measurement – handy for testing Pi projects which use software-driven pulse-width modulation – and for enabling recording of maximum and minimum readings. There's also a button to enable relative measurements to be taken: when measuring resistance, for example, this can be used to automatically subtract the resistance of the test probes themselves from the displayed figure.

What you don't get for the low purchase price is any sign of a calibration certificate. While the measurements on our test unit proved accurate against calibrated hardware, there's no guarantee the next model off the production line will be as well-calibrated. It's possible to remove the casing from the multimeter and calibrate manually by adjusting on-board potentiometers, should you have access to calibrated hardware against which to compare measurements, but doing so will invalidate any warranty you may have had.

A tough read

The only other bone of contention with the Proster VC99 is the bundled manual. Small and confusingly written, it provides most of the information you could need to get the best from the device, but not in the most accessible manner. Signs of poor translation are also present, including on the face of the multimeter where its ability to power off automatically after 15 minutes of inactivity is proudly emblazoned as 'AUTO OFF POWER'.

These are minor niggles. While not every hobbyist will need anything more feature-packed than your average pocket multimeter, those who do will find the VC99 more than up to the job. Anyone working in an ill-lit environment, though, would do well to spend any money saved on a lamp to make up for the lack of illumination on the multimeter's display.

Last word

While its accuracy is definitely more suited to the hobbyist than the professional, the Proster VC99 multimeter offers a wealth of functionality at a pocket-friendly price.

Maker Says

"A tiny wearable platform board with a lot of might"
Adafruit

ADAFRUIT GEMMA STARTER PACK

As an introduction to programming wearable electronics, has Adafruit put together the perfect kit?

Related

KITRONIK ELECTRO FASHION E-TEXTILES DELUXE KITA

Reviewed in issue 37, the Kitronik kit offers less programmability than Adafruit's, but can be had at a cheaper price in the UK.

£15 / $35
cpc.farnell.com

With wearable computing proving a burgeoning business, it's no surprise to find companies helping makers to get started in the field. The majority of the resulting kits are based around conductive thread which can be sewn into fabric to link components electrically. It's easy, then, to see the LEDs and conductive thread bobbin included in Adafruit's Gemma Starter Pack and dismiss it as just another me-too product. Doing so, though, ignores the titular star of the show: the Gemma.

Designed and built in collaboration with the Arduino company, the Gemma is a smart break-out board for the ultra-compact ATtiny85 microcontroller from Atmel. A cut-down version of the ATmega chips which power the full-size Arduino boards, ATtiny microcontrollers are a great choice when low power draw and a small footprint are more important than the number of pins you can access. This makes them an obvious choice for wearable projects.

The two biggest hurdles to using an ATtiny with conductive thread – the need for special programming equipment and its package type – are solved by the Gemma. The chip is placed on a tiny 28mm diameter disc which features connectors for three programmable I/O pins, a 3.3V supply and ground, and a voltage input. A JST connector allows batteries to be easily connected, while a USB connector coupled with a specially written bootloader means the Gemma can be programmed from any PC using the standard Arduino IDE and the bundled cable.

The Gemma is the star, but there are plenty of other parts to the starter kit. A bundle of colourful crocodile leads makes it easy to prototype your design before sewing it down with the conductive thread, needles for which are also provided. There are four of Adafruit's famous programmable RGB NeoPixel LEDs, in wearable-friendly Flora guise, and a battery holder for the bundled CR2032 batteries with integrated power switch.

The thread itself is of great quality with a generous 23-metre length provided. A thin, two-ply formulation made from stainless steel, it's easier to work with than the thicker thread used in the rival Kitronik Electro Fashion range, but comes with a warning that it is ill-suited for projects in which your components will draw more than around 50mA. A three-ply alternative is available separately, and is good up to 100mA; both are provided on pre-wound bobbins suitable for any heavy-thread sewing machine.

cpc.farnell.com

£23 / $30

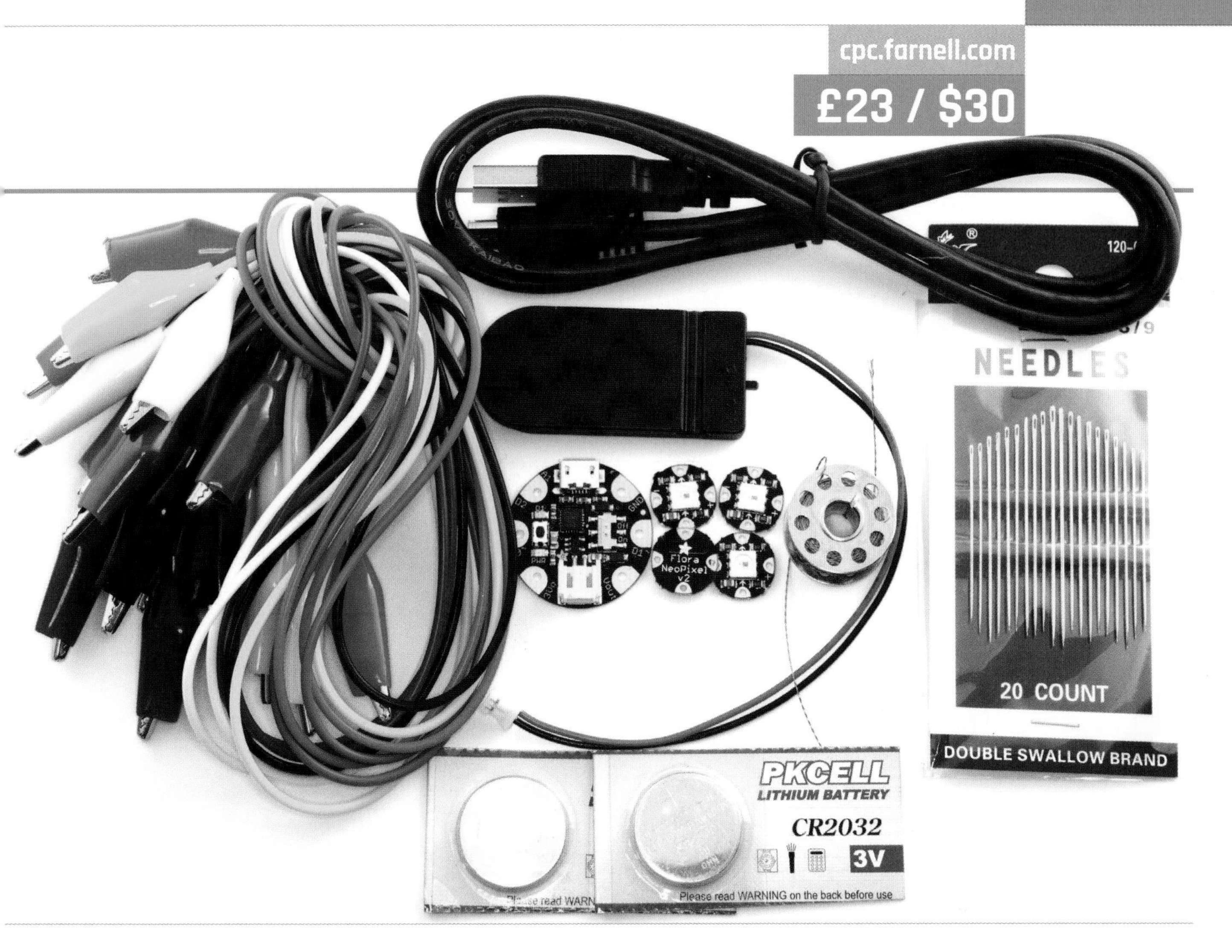

Above The kit has everything you need to get started

> The Gemma is the star, but there are plenty of other parts

As with most electronic textile starter kits, there's an undeniable focus on LED projects. Once you've amused yourself adding RGB glowing eyes to kids' toys, though, you can begin to experiment with the power of the Gemma. Although three input-output pins feels limited, they offer surprising flexibility: two of the three offer pulse-width modulation (PWM) support for dimming LEDs or driving small servos, while one can also be used as an analogue input to read a variety of optional sensors. These, however, must be compatible with the 3.3V logic used by the Gemma, in contrast to the 5V logic more common in the Arduino world.

There are some disappointments, too, for Arduino fans who were hoping that their projects would be directly transferable. Aside from the limited number of pins, the Gemma has no accessible serial port. This means it can't be combined with, for example, a serial-connected Bluetooth or Wi-Fi adaptor to easily make connected clothing.

To focus on what it can't do is to ignore the kit's true goal, however. Adafruit bills the Gemma kit as the perfect way for beginners to get started with programmable wearable and electronic textile projects, and the obvious next step from its non-programmable LED-based kit. The use of RGB LEDs, which can be cycled through your choice of millions of colours, keeps things interesting and the low cost of the kit makes it accessible to those with even a passing curiosity in electronic textiles projects, as well as Arduino users keen to try something a little different in their next build.

The only real negative is the lack of printed documentation. While there's a wealth of supporting information, tutorials, and projects on Adafruit's website, a small booklet like that provided with the rival Kitronik kit would have been welcomed and helped to make this bundle a truly standalone product.

Last word

If you have experience with the Arduino platform and want to get into wearable electronics, the Gemma is the way to go and this kit a perfect way to get started.

★★★★★

magpi.cc/2dVKN2t

£39.99 / $60

Maker Says

"The new MEDIAPI+ augmented case for Raspberry Pi 2"

SB-Components

MEDIA PI PLUS

A media centre case and remote for your Raspberry Pi: is it a necessity for a TV-connected Pi, though?

We all know at least one person who just has a Raspberry Pi for a media centre, running their TV on Kodi or even an ancient version of XBMC that does the job. One of the things that has been lacking from this equation for the longest time is a suitable case for a Pi hooked up to your television – a case that can slip in unnoticed under your TV, next to a Sky+ box and that Wii you haven't touched in years.

While the Media Pi Plus isn't the first one, or even the first Media Pi product, they're rare enough to highlight and discuss. In the Media Pi Plus's case, it's a re-release to fit the form factor of the Raspberry Pi B+ and the Pi 2. In aesthetic terms, it absolutely looks like something you'd put under your TV, specifically something like a Freeview box: it's unassuming, black, and with very little branding.

There is some construction required with the case, as a Raspberry Pi is not included. Popping the case open, you can see exactly how it works: it extends out and relocates a number of the Raspberry Pi's ports throughout a largely empty box. While this may seem slightly redundant, it does provide extra power to the USB ports, allowing for hubs to be connected. You can also connect an IR receiver directly to the GPIO ports, which works well with the media remote included, even if you have the ability to turn the Pi off but not on again with it.

It's really designed to be used with Kodi, which is why our version came with OpenELEC on a pre-formatted SD card, although other Kodi versions and offshoots (we're looking at you, OSMC) will work just fine. You may need to tweak some of the remote settings, but it will be fine nonetheless.

The best thing about the Media Pi Plus is that it's very cheap. Even if you factor in a Pi 2, it's just south of £70 for the whole thing, which is pretty great value for a media centre that will reliably serve you 1080p for a long time to come. Construction is a bit tricky and the case can feel a little flimsy, though if you aren't planning on flinging it around or otherwise treating it roughly, it's a perfectly serviceable way to make your Pi media centre just that bit easier to use.

Related

MODMYPI MODULAR CASE

The modular case can be modified to fit in better with your lounge, revealing only the ports you need to connect to a TV.

£5.99 / $9

bit.ly/1M4gQTi

Last word

The box is a bit bulky in relation to the Pi's size, but it does a good job of making the small jump needed to get the Pi better suited for powering a TV.

pimoroni.com

£12 / $15

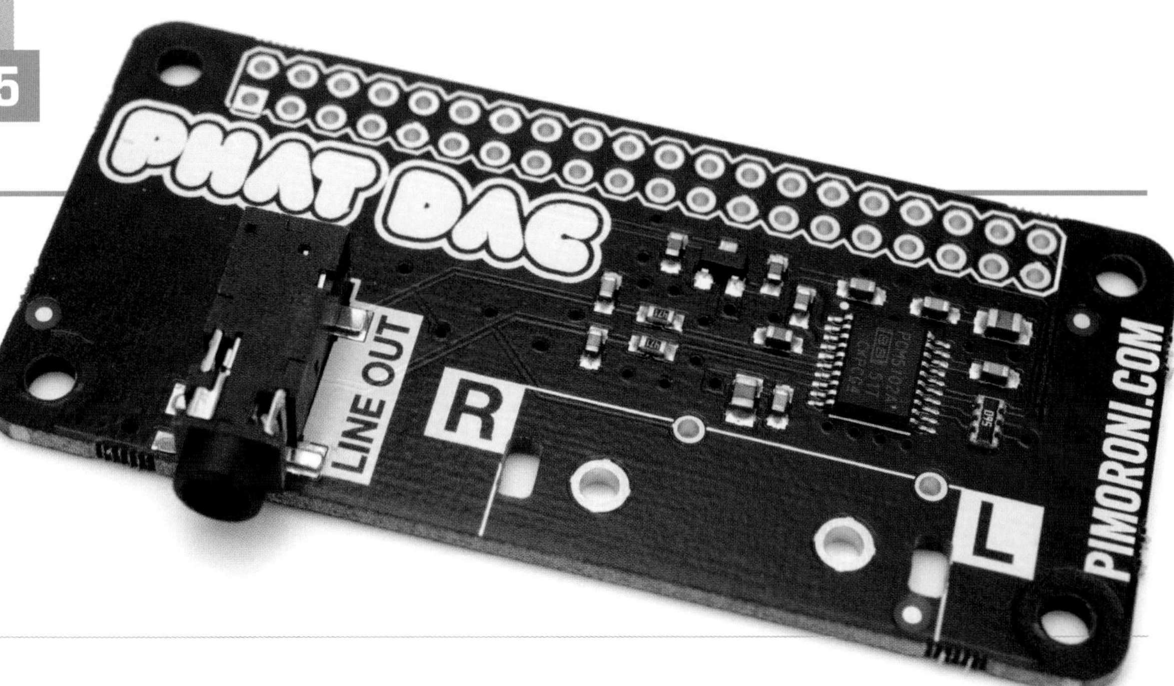

Maker Says

A super affordable high-quality DAC for the Raspberry Pi

Pimoroni

PIMORONI PHAT DAC

If you're disappointed by the Pi Zero's lack of analogue audio output, the pHAT DAC may be just the add-on you need

The Pi Zero's minuscule dimensions make it well-suited to a variety of tasks, except for one omission from its feature list: analogue audio. For anyone trying to embed a Pi Zero into an old radio or speaker system, that's a loss too far. Fortunately, the clever people at Pimoroni have a solution in the form of the pHAT DAC.

Part of the pHAT family - a range of Hardware Attached on Top (HAT) boards built with the Pi Zero form factor in mind - the pHAT DAC adds a high-quality digital-to-analogue converter (DAC) to the board, allowing any Pi Zero to output line-level audio, ready for external amplification.

The output of the pHAT DAC shouldn't be confused with that of the analogue output of the full-size Raspberry Pi family, either: the pHAT's Texas Instruments PCM5102A DAC is a cut above, offering noise-free 192kHz 24-bit line-level audio.

The pHAT DAC is supplied with a 40-pin female header which needs to be soldered onto the board before it can be connected to the Pi Zero, to which you'll need to have soldered a 40-pin male header. There's method in Pimoroni's madness here: if you're building a permanent project, you can drop the female header and solder the pHAT DAC directly to the Pi Zero's pins to create an ultra-thin circuit board sandwich. You can also add a pair of RCA connectors, available separately for £1.50, to complement the 3.5mm jack.

With the soldering out of the way, installation isn't as straightforward as it could be. Step-by-step instructions are provided, but are unsuitable for the latest Raspbian release – and while a community member has stepped up and provided an installation script to make things easier, this isn't yet linked from the product page.

There's another fly in the ointment once installation is complete: there's no easy way to switch between the pHAT DAC and HDMI outputs. For most uses this isn't a problem, but if you were planning to turn a Zero into a multi-function portable music player, it may cause a headache.

When you're up and running, there's plenty to like about the pHAT, though – in particular, the superb audio quality when paired with a good-quality amplifier and decent set of speakers.

Related

HIFIBERRY DAC+ STANDARD RCA

The HiFiBerry uses top-quality components and has RCA jacks pre-soldered, but its size makes it less suitable for Pi Zero use.

£23 / $40

hifiberry.com

Last word

While the installation experience needs work, the pHAT DAC certainly fills a hole. If you need analogue audio from your Pi Zero, it can't be beaten – but paying three times the cost of the Zero itself may sting a little.

pi-top.com

£195 / $300

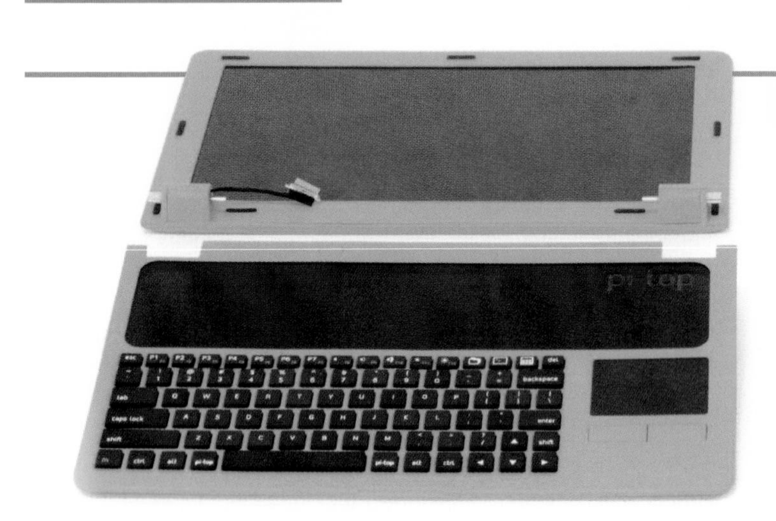

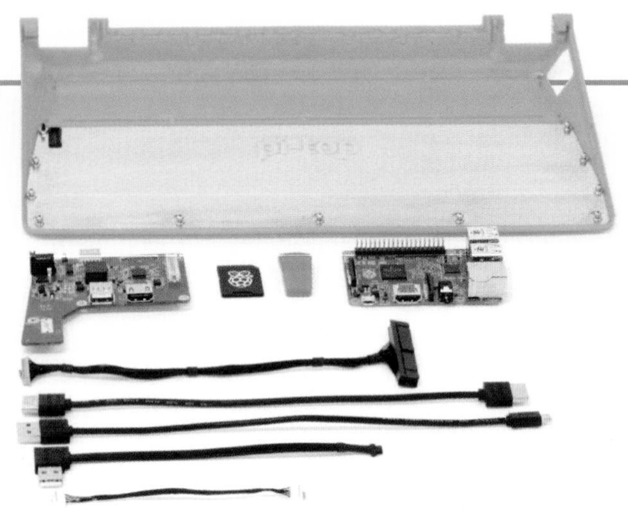

PI-TOP

A laptop built from a Raspberry Pi and crafted yourself. Is it too limited by the Pi, or is it a great little portable teaching tool?

It's really not that old, but do you remember the One Laptop Per Child (OLPC) project? It was a cheap laptop with yesteryear's components, created specifically to try to make getting computing into the poorest of developing nations as easy as possible. It was also very green, and we don't mean ecologically - although it was also quite low-powered, so it technically is 'green' in that sense. When we got the pi-top out of its box, that was the first thing that came into our minds, but definitely not in a bad way!

The elevator pitch for the pi-top is that it's a crowdfunded laptop kit that the user needs to assemble, which is powered by an included Raspberry Pi. There's a lot more to it, though, and we'll get into that shortly, but already this gives you a basic impression of what we're dealing with.

Brush away those first impressions

The pi-top has a big educational focus built into it. Each pi-top user has to create a cloud account before logging in, which then syncs settings and such to this account. It also syncs data from CEED Universe, the gamified learning software that is custom-made to meet the new GCSE curriculum. This, on top of the usual Raspberry Pi teaching resources, gives it an edge in the classroom, as students can use whatever pi-top they want without having to carry too much in the way of data around with them.

It sounds great in theory. Let's first go back to the box opening, though, before we start discussing its other merits. The box itself is lovely, with the first thing you see being the detached laptop screen's bright green back with the pi-top logo in it. All the parts are stored in layers, carefully packed with a soft foam. You'll have to look carefully to find the laser-cut removable circuit cover and the selection of required screws and cables, but they're all there.

The instructions, and indeed the assembly, are quite simple. There are three main parts of the laptop chassis, and only two pieces of circuit board including the Raspberry Pi, so the majority of the process is preparing and fitting the parts together. While the instructions are generally good, they don't distinguish very well between the two types of screws.Hint: the screws that look like motherboard spaces need to be affixed to the PCBs; they have a thread running down the centre of the head. Also, one of the connection orientations is not completely clear. We found ourselves having to take it apart a bit so we could construct it properly at one point.

Related

KANO

Similar in terms of gamifying programming education and building, although it's not the all-in-one product pi-top is.

£120

uk.kano.me

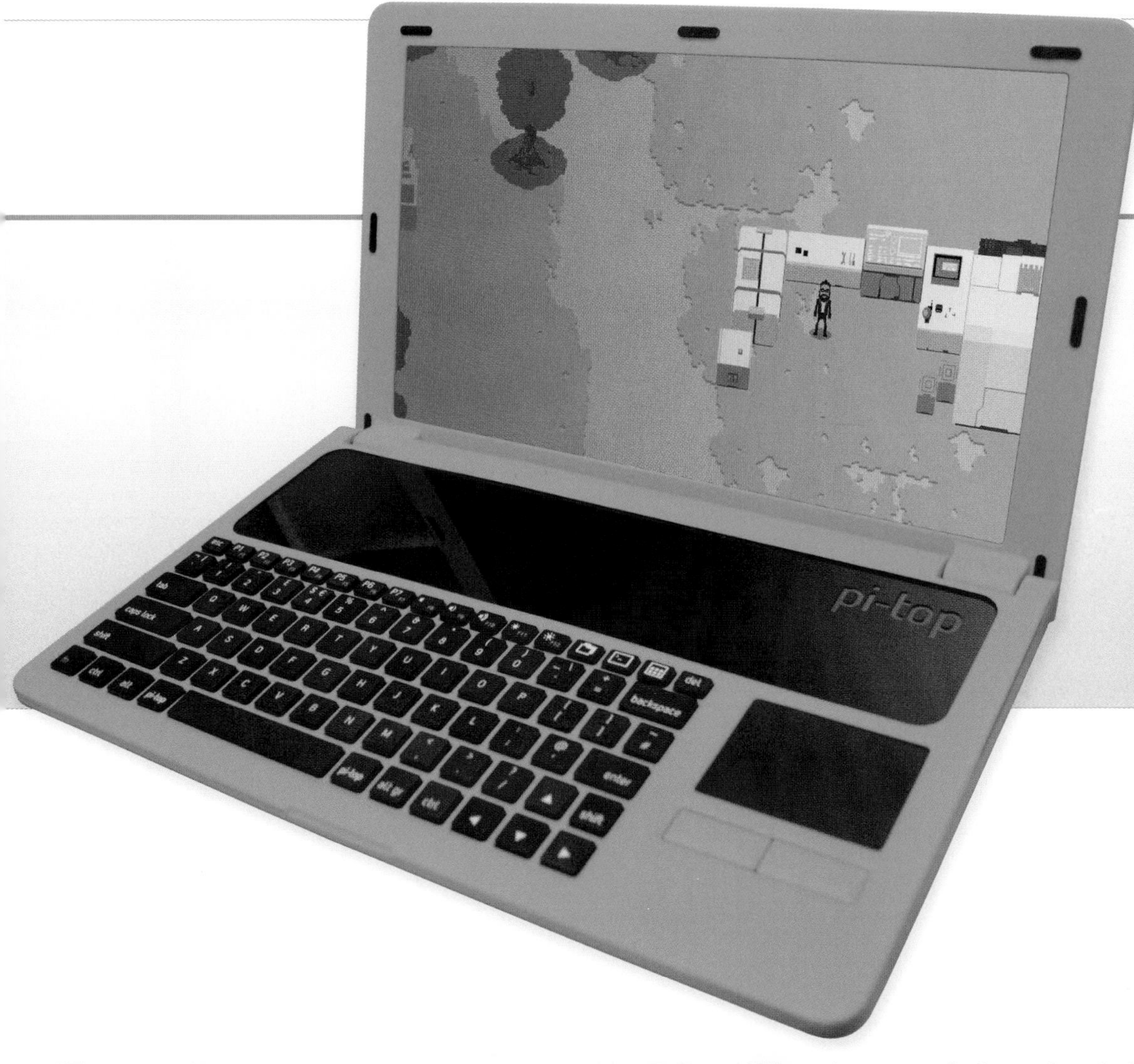

Maker Says

"Use me to play, learn, and create!"

Pi-Top

> It looks great and works absolutely fine, thanks to the extra oomph of the Pi 2's processor

Otherwise, assembly was quite quick. We stuck on Netflix and after a couple of episodes of *BoJack Horseman* it was ready to boot up, so less than an hour and probably quicker without giggling every minute. Make sure all the ports and cables are properly connected and you can turn it on for the first time.

It's quick and easy to set up an account the first time, and you get some choices as to what software you want to be able to quick-launch from the panel. The pi-topOS is a custom interface built on top of Raspbian Wheezy that has a different offering of default software, albeit with full access to the standard packages you can get on Raspbian anyway.

The interface is roughly the same as normal Raspbian's, but with the panel down at the bottom and a bit more of an OS X vibe with some of the display characteristics. It looks great and works absolutely fine, thanks to the extra oomph of the Pi 2's processor; the only issue we had was that the Chromium browser selected by default is still a little too slow.

The CEED Universe, currently in early alpha at the time of writing, is quite interesting. Taking the resource-gathering and building elements from *Minecraft*, and applying them to a top-down aesthetic from early nineties PC games as a way to teach coding and physical computing, is fairly unique. Players are asked to perform Python coding tasks as part of the game, starting off with something akin to Hello World. It's very gamified, and the final version could be really something if done right.

The pi-top, then, is a great piece of kit. While it's probably not going to replace a normal laptop in a similar price range, it's an excellent educational tool. It's also a portable Raspberry Pi with a ten-hour lifespan, which is pretty great on its own. Hopefully, it will make its way into classrooms or into the hands of budding young coders.

Last word

Makes great use of the Raspberry Pi to create a fully functional laptop that you build with your own hands – the entire system is a great experience for those wanting to learn.

Maker Says

"Provides almost instant working temperatures"
Tenma

TENMA 60W DIGITAL SOLDERING STATION

Gareth Halfacree sees if degree-accurate temperature control has a place in the hobbyist soldering toolkit...

Breadboards are all well and good for prototyping, but there comes a time in every electronics hobbyist's life when it's time to melt some metal and start soldering something together. Whether it's fixing something that's broken or building something new, soldering is an important skill, and one which can be made easier or harder depending on the tools you choose.

The Tenma 60W Digital Soldering Station is designed to bridge the gap between ultra-cheap fixed-temperature irons which are the mainstay of hobbyist solders, and the high-end, finely tuned tools you'd find at a professional engineer's workstation. Selling for sub-£50/$70, the feature list is nevertheless impressive: the hefty base unit provides control of the iron temperature between a minimum of 150°C and a maximum of 450°C, either by flipping between three preset temperature levels or by setting your own, and it boasts a stability of ±1°C with 60W of power to back it up.

To get something out of the way early on in this review: no, you almost certainly don't need a highly accurate, temperature-controlled soldering station. It can, however, make life easier. If you've ever tried soldering and found that sometimes the solder just doesn't want to flow – in particular when making large connections – then you've experienced the frustration of using an underpowered iron that couldn't supply the heat fast enough. If you've watched an LED or other heat-sensitive component go up in smoke during soldering, then you've experienced the flip side: an iron which delivered too much heat.

Temperature-controlled

A temperature-controlled iron solves all that. You can set the temperature just right for the solder you're using, and it will be tracked and adjusted by the on-board controller. If a large joint is drawing heat away from the tip too quickly, the output is increased; if the tip gets too hot, the output is decreased. The aim is temperature stability of a single degree. It's a powerful feature, and a definite step up from cheaper variable-temperature irons which don't adjust their output automatically.

As an entry-level example, though, you'd expect to see some corners cut in Tenma's build. Looking at the base unit, they're not obvious: the unit is solidly built and includes a physical power switch, while the large backlit LCD display at the front is clear and easy to see while

Related

WELLER SP25N

For small soldering jobs, a good quality fixed-temperature iron like this Weller SP25N is a cheaper alternative to a bulky soldering station.

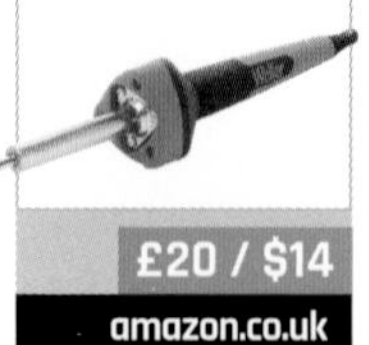

£20 / $14
amazon.co.uk

cpc.farnell.com

£47 / $79

The iron itself is lightweight, since the electronics are located in the base unit

soldering. A multi-pole connector provides power to and feedback from the iron, which is a small and lightweight unit thanks to the bulk of the electronics being located in the base unit. The only real negative here is that the unit is fixed to the power network of the country of purchase – either 220V or 110V – and its power lead is integrated rather than removable.

Saving pennies

It's not until you look to the bundled stand that you begin to see where Tenma has been saving its pennies. While the stand itself is a sturdy metal housing, it fails to grip the iron adequately, largely thanks to the lack of weight in the iron and the relatively heavy lead which connects it to the base unit. It's functional, but care is needed to make sure the iron doesn't drop out. The bundled cleaning sponge, meanwhile, is barely adequate, and should be replaced with something thicker – or an alternative tip-cleaning system – as soon as possible.

These points aside, though, the Tenma soldering station is a joy to use. Its 60W output and dual heating coils mean the iron's tip – which is easily replaceable through a quick twist of a retaining nut, with various shapes and sizes available – comes up to temperature rapidly. Plus, the live temperature readout on the base unit means there's no guesswork when it comes to seeing whether it's ready for use or not.

Another feature is Tenma's claim to electrostatic discharge (ESD) safety. This is the promise that – unlike extremely cheap irons often found in starter kits and from bargain-basement shops – there's no risk that a blast of static electricity will fry any sensitive components as you touch the metal tip of the iron to one of their contacts. It's a problem unlikely to have affected most hobbyists, but the reassurance it won't bother you in the future is undeniably nice.

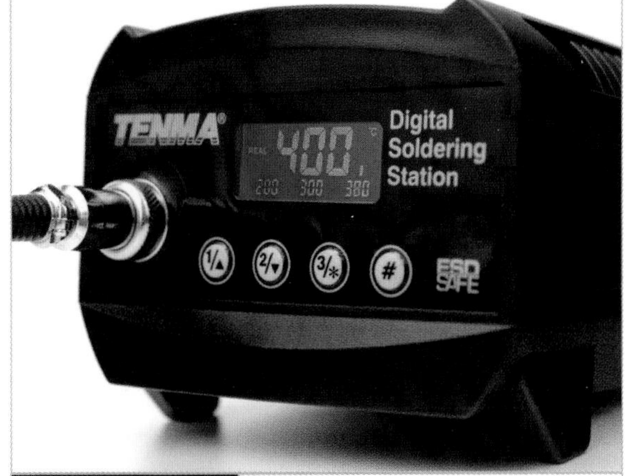

Above The cleaning sponge isn't great

Above top The large LCD is clear and easy to read

Last word

With such a small cost premium over a quality fixed-temperature iron and a fair list of advantages, if you fancy treating yourself to an iron upgrade, you could do a lot worse than the Tenma.

Maker Says

All you need to start transforming the world around you

Bare Conductive

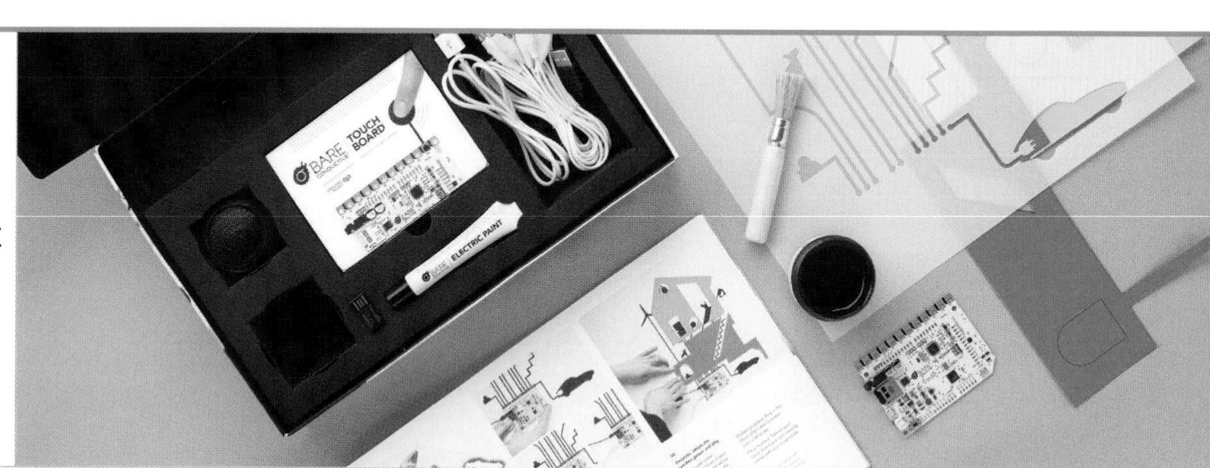

BARE CONDUCTIVE TOUCH BOARD STARTER KIT

With slick presentation, is the Touch Board the conductive marvel Bare Conductive has promised?

The first thing to discuss about the Bare Conductive Touch Board Starter Kit has to be its price. At just a shade below £100 in the UK and $150 in the US, it's certainly no impulse buy for the maker on a budget. At the same time, though, it's hard to call it bad value for money when you see the care and attention that has gone into its creation.

The box, a sizeable affair that has no hope of slipping through a letter box while you're out, contains an impressive selection of parts. The highlight, naturally, is the Touch Board itself, which is joined by a generous pot of conductive paint with a thick brush, a tube of the same paint with a fine-tipped nozzle for more precise application, a self-powered rechargeable speaker, USB cables, a microSD card reader, and banana clip cables. This is in addition to a rolled-up stencil set (about which more later) and an impressive, oversize, full-colour guidebook covering the kit's three primary projects.

The guidebook is far from an afterthought, but it's hardly required to get started. The packaging of the Touch Board itself, a box within a box, doubles as a quickstart guide and reveals a very clever feature: pre-recorded instructional messages already loaded onto the bundled 128MB microSD card.

The Touch Board, for those unfamiliar, is an Arduino-compatible device designed to make working with conductive paint, thread, and even Play-Doh as simple as possible. It arrives preconfigured to play MP3 files from the SD card each time one of its 12 electrode inputs is touched. This is then used to drive the user's introduction: connect the micro-USB cable and the bundled speaker or a pair of headphones, touch input E0 with your finger, and you'll hear a congratulatory message; press E1 and you'll learn about the board's inputs. This process continues through to E11, which sends you off to the Bare Conductive website to learn more.

With the Starter Kit, though, you have offline support too. The aforementioned guidebook does a fantastic job of walking you through three example projects in a step-by-step fashion. With full-colour pictures at every step, it's hard to get lost or confused.

The first suggested project is the biggest: learning how to make graphical sensors. This involves the rolled-up stencil and overlays, which come with handy sticky tabs.

Related

MAKEY MAKEY

The device that brought the banana piano to the masses, the Makey Makey is a cheaper way to get started with conductive materials.

£40 / $50

makeymakey.com

bareconductive.com

£95 / $150

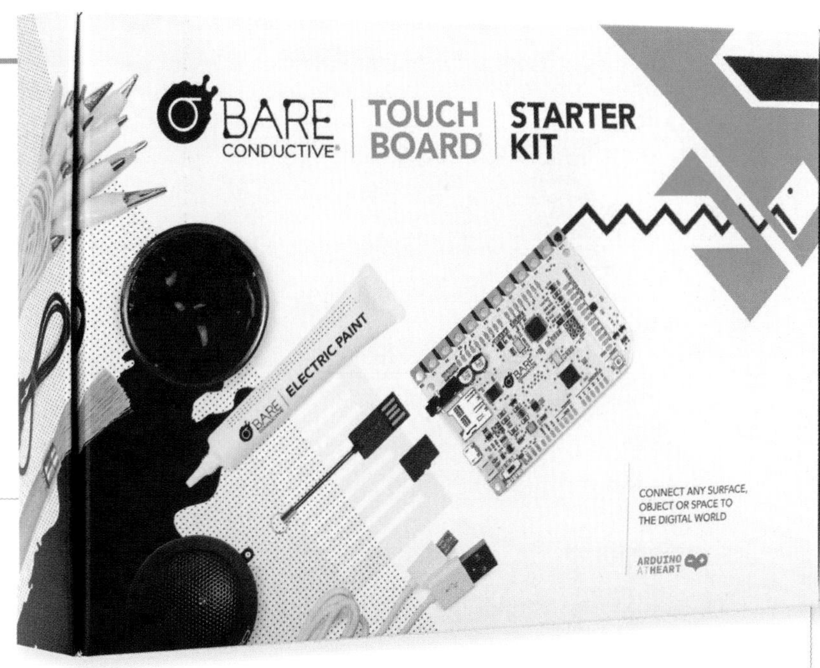

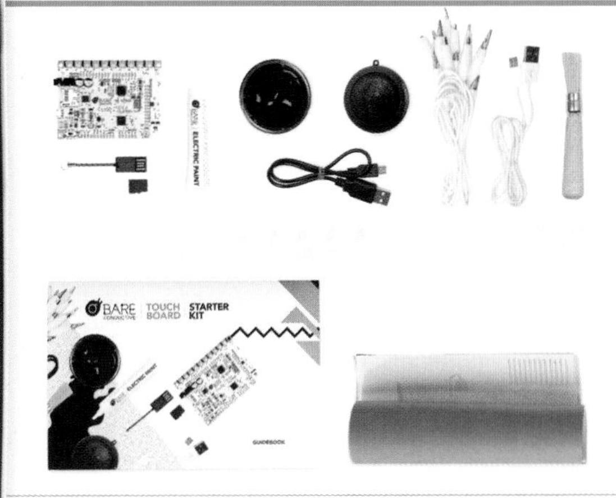

> The guidebook does a fantastic job of walking you through three example projects

Attach the stencil to a wall - or, if you're not sure about the somewhat permanent nature of the paint becoming a fixture of your house, a large sheet of paper or card - and brush on the paint. Decorate with the coloured overlays, use the thinner paint tube to draw wires leading to the Touch Board, copy the MP3s to the microSD, and voila: an interactive house.

The remaining two projects are variations on a theme. The first adds touch-sensitivity to everyday objects, such as a pill bottle which reminds you of dosages, or a photo frame that describes its own scene. The final project has you brushing the paint onto the floor to create an intruder alarm, albeit one which only works if said intruder is barefoot.

The three projects detail some, but not all, of the Touch Board's capabilities. A page of extended projects at the back of the guidebook points you towards the website to learn about the board's more advanced capabilities, such as reprogramming it to operate as a non-contact distance sensor or a Makey Makey-style musical instrument.

At this point, the Touch Board is likely to have entranced children but potentially turned more advanced hobbyists off. Towards the back of the guide, it's revealed that the Touch Board is more powerful than it would first appear: it's a fully functional Arduino, compatible with various Shields and add-ons to provide everything from Bluetooth connectivity to motor control.

A glance at the board itself reveals the familiar Arduino headers, albeit without pins, with full access to these for more advanced creations. This, combined with an Atmel ATmega microcontroller, gives the board the ability to do anything an Arduino can do, including interfacing with external hardware, such as motors, servos, sensors, or even the Raspberry Pi itself. Combined with the flexibility of Bare Conductive's clever paint, this gives the kit considerable legs when the three bundled projects are finished.

Last word

It's not cheap, but for anyone looking to get started with conductive paint or touch-based projects, this kit is easy to recommend and very well put together, with considerable attention to detail.

★★★★★

magpi.cc/1NFn0iv

£132 / $200

Maker Says

"Great for experienced users and novices alike"
Magzor

MAGZOR MECHATRONICS STARTER PACK

A modular robot that can be built to your specification, without even having to write any code. Is it too good to be true?

At a time when Raspberry Pi robotics kits are branching out in all directions – whether they be simple, easy and cheap, or more advanced – it's nice to see something that is trying to bridge the gap from beginner to intermediate level.

The Magzor system starts with a kit of parts that can interact with each other in any combination, and hook up to the Raspberry Pi to create your own robot or mechatronic project.

The kit works by having you input what you want to use on a web interface, a bit like the blocks of a puzzle. The interface then creates a custom recipe of how the parts should fit together, and even offers some basic code to get them all working. It's quite intuitive, although we didn't get one of the more universal parts in the starter kit we received. This meant that we had to figure out what other bits of information it would need before giving us a build that was possible with our equipment.

The instructions themselves are good, but we did find ourselves slightly confused at times; at one point we were looking for a port which wasn't really labelled on the PCB in the way the instructions described. By the time we had finished an initial build, though, we had basically figured out the language that the instructions were trying to use.

In a large departure from how Raspberry Pi-centric devices work, the kit is programmed in C++. A basic script is generated that gets everything activated, which you can modify yourself to get it to your exact specifications. It's a weird jump in skill level from the construction phase to the programming phase, though, requiring you to manually compile your code rather than being able to run it live and make changes as you go.

While this level of programming is a good thing to learn, it does seem at slight odds with the nature of the quickly iterable and rebuildable robot. With the tutorials the way they are now, there's no easy step-by-step guide for creating the code and moving it to a Pi to then compile and run it; a bit more intuition and knowledge is required than some robotics beginners might possess. With some more focus on that side of the system, it will be a lot better, but for now it's maybe outside the range of the beginner-level folks.

Related

CAMJAM EDUKIT #3

Also reviewed in this issue, the CamJam kit allows you to build a robot and then fairly simply program it to perform various tasks. Much simpler and aimed towards a very beginner level of robotics, though.

£17/$26

magpi.cc/105UEOh

Last word

There are some great ideas here, but some parts of the building and programming are a bit obtuse. It's quite good for people doing slightly more advanced mechatronics than simple robots, though.

magpi.cc/1SWEq9s

£17 / $26

Maker Says

"Create your very own Raspberry Pi-powered robot"

CamJam

CAMJAM EDUKIT #3 ROBOTICS

A low-cost robot kit that can teach you how to put together a Raspberry Pi robot, as well as how to program it

If you cast your mind back a few issues, you may remember that we did a cover feature on how to create a £50 Pi-powered robot. The only real problem with the robot was that there were a lot of different components you'd have to buy from many different places to keep the price down. We didn't quite have the time to put together a kit for people to buy; it doesn't look like that matters too much any more, however, as the latest CamJam EduKit is incredibly close to what we would have created.

A box full of very standard robotics components – and a custom board – make up the third CamJam kit. While it does have these standard components, it's not like a Lego or IKEA kit that some of these robot kits resemble. As they're components without a chassis (although the box it comes in will do in a pinch), the CamJam EduKit #3 is designed to give you more freedom in what you create and actually make you think about what you're constructing.

A breadboard is also supplied with the kit. While on its own you might just think it's another breadboard and reduces the soldering you need to do, it also gives you lots of ways to actually expand beyond the limits of the original robot, with extra sensors, components, and suchlike. This makes it very good for extracurricular learning beyond the scope of the original robot.

The online worksheets for the robot are very comprehensive, teaching you how to put it together and code it. As the release of the EduKit #3 is somewhat tied to Pi Wars, there are also tips on how to program it for some of the styles of challenges that were involved in that event. Indeed, we saw a few robots powered by this kit trundling around at Pi Wars, and one of them did extremely well on the line-follower course that others were failing with.

It's a great beginner's kit then, or at least a kit for people wanting to take a step further than some of the very simple kits. It teaches you a bit more about how the Raspberry Pi can actually control a robot, and gives you room to grow.

Related

PI2GO

A little more pricey. However, this is also a great little starter kit that can teach you about robotics with the Pi.

£55 / $83

magpi.cc/1SWFHxi

Last word

A great kit for beginners looking to be a bit more hands-on with the robots they create. There's plenty of excellent documentation to get them properly started, as well.

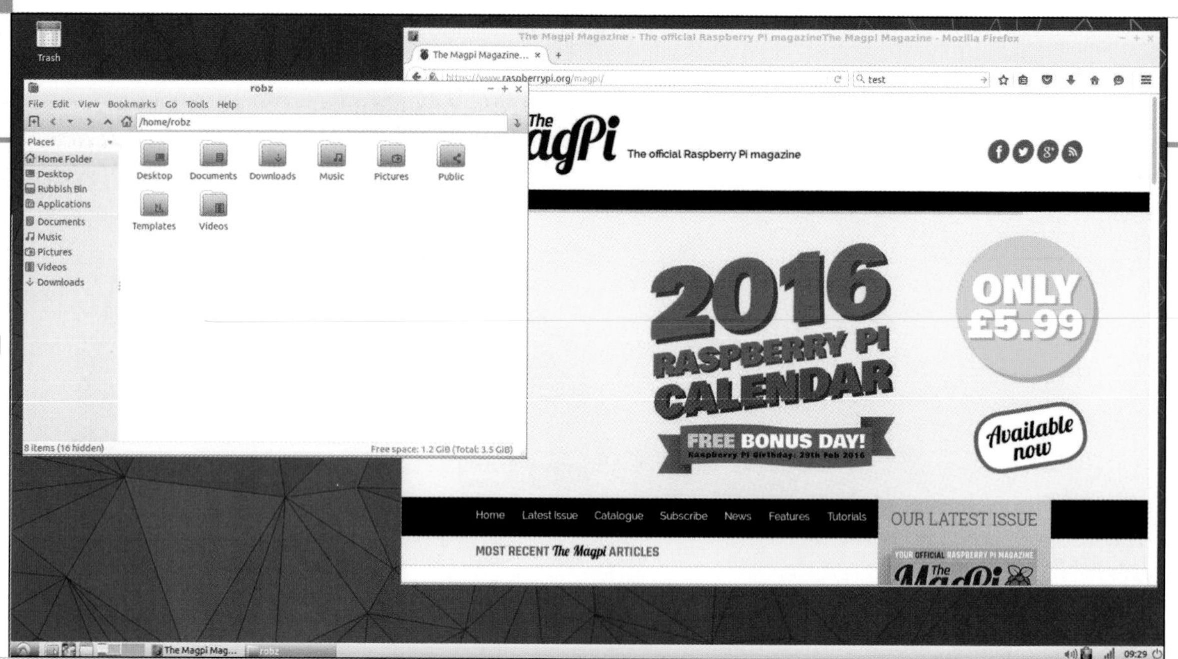

Maker Says

Make as many Ubuntu flavours for the Pi as you can think of

Ubuntu Pi Flavour Makers

UBUNTU PI FLAVOUR MAKER

More flavours of Ubuntu for your Raspberry Pi. Does the Pi provide enough power for them, though?

If you've been following Raspberry Pi long enough, you may know that early on in its life there was a call for Ubuntu to be used as an operating system for it. As one of, if not the most popular, version of Linux for home users, this distro was wanted by many seeking something familiar for their new tiny computer. It never came to be. However, as Ubuntu is based on Debian, Raspbian was basically the next best thing.

When the Raspberry Pi 2 came out, this changed with the release of Ubuntu MATE for the Pi, and this opened the door to more 'versions' of Ubuntu – or, at least, different desktop environments running on Ubuntu. Ubuntu Pi Flavour Maker is one of the results of this.

At its core, Flavour Maker is a series of scripts that allow you to build a slightly custom version of Ubuntu for the Raspberry Pi. It uses the all-important armhf build of Ubuntu that's optimised for the type of chip running on the Pi 2, giving you options for different software and desktops, and even the choice between server and desktop versions depending on your needs.

That may sound a little complicated for some more novice users, but don't worry – the kind folk who make the software have created a series of images you can install to an SD card, much like any Raspberry Pi operating system. On tap are two versions of Ubuntu Server: one a very minimal install for maximum speed, and a regular install if you need more software. There are also three 'spins' that use different desktops: LXDE, Xfce, and MATE. LXDE and Xfce are common lightweight desktop interfaces used on low-powered PCs; Raspbian has used LXDE, or at least a version of it, since it came out.

Booting up

How do they actually run, then? Much like the normal Ubuntu, there are a few setup steps on your first boot, although the main installation has already occurred so it's a little truncated. Settings such as locale and keyboard are sorted before booting you into the desktop, although this does take a few minutes to actually occur. Each successive boot is much faster, though, albeit nowhere near the speed of booting into Raspbian.

The OS is presented in a very different way from Raspbian. Whereas much of Raspbian is optimised for the Raspberry Pi, with a lot of educational tools in there as well, the Ubuntu spins

Related

UBUNTU MATE

When the Raspberry Pi 2 came out, Ubuntu was finally able to come to the Pi, starting with a version of Ubuntu MATE.

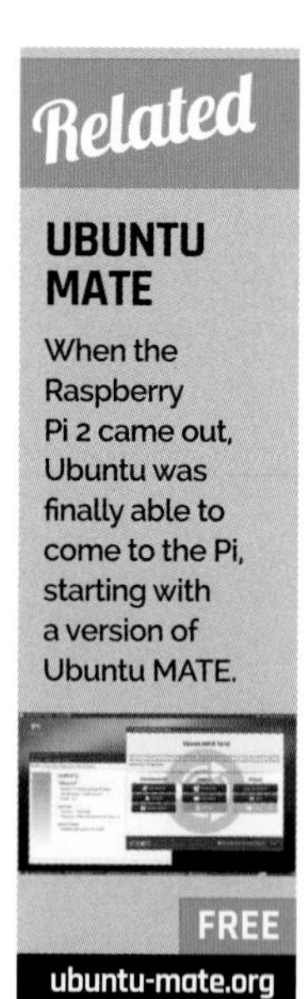

FREE

ubuntu-mate.org

magpi.cc/1StOfyK

Free

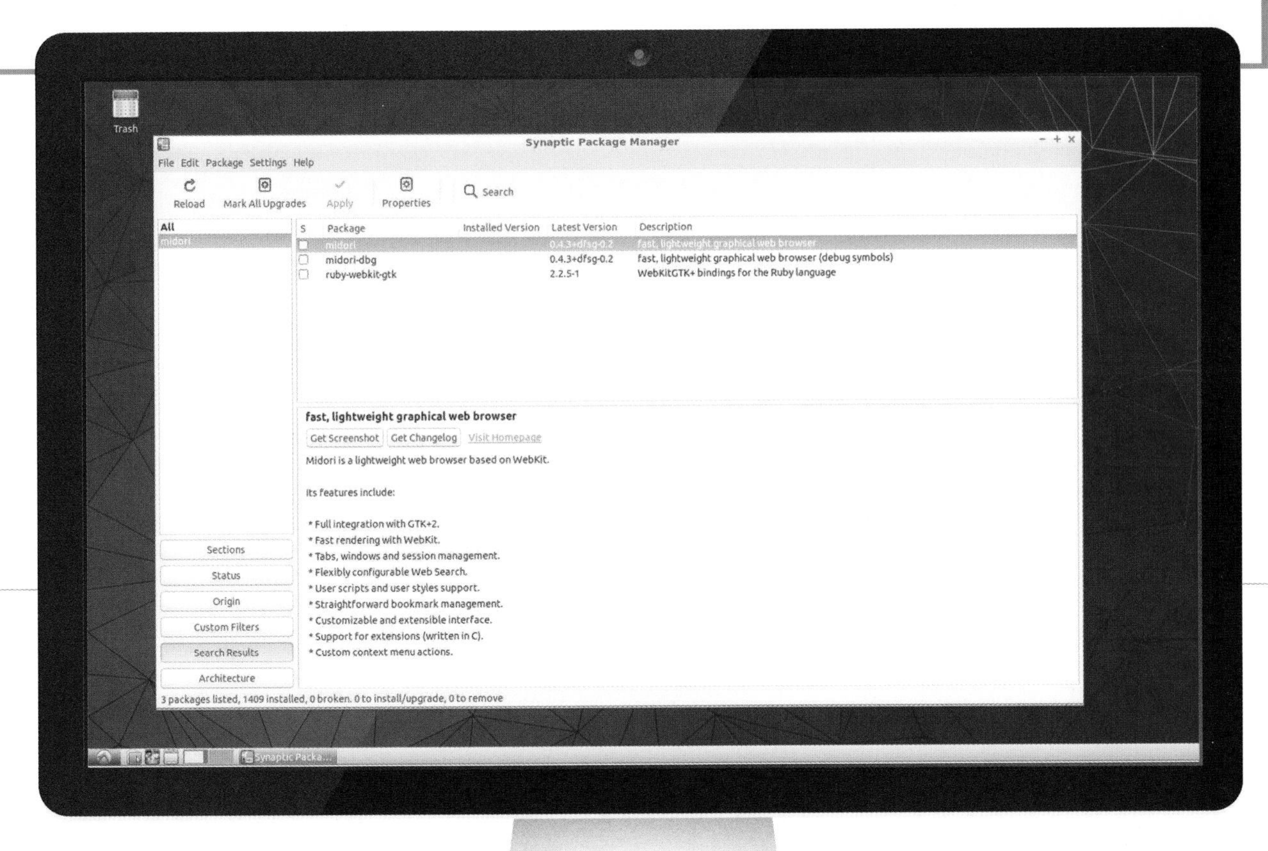

Above A selection of graphical package managers makes installation much easier

are more a traditional desktop – no programming tools installed as standard, and using normal programs as well.

A novelty compared to Raspbian is the addition of a graphical package manager. Both Software Centres and classic Synaptic are available, giving users a way to search for software they may want, which Raspbian currently doesn't let you do easily. As this is based on Ubuntu armhf, the selection isn't as broad as in the full version of Ubuntu, but it's still very good. A lot of major software is available, with the only real limit being the power and performance of the Raspberry Pi 2 running Ubuntu.

Due to its use of more standard software, Ubuntu can lag a bit on the Raspberry Pi 2. Firefox is the default browser, and while a lightweight alternative like Midori is available, it's not always fast and responsive. It feels like how the browser used to be on the original Raspberry Pi – functional, but a little frustrating to use after a while. Video on YouTube seems right out as well, if you want to watch anything larger than 360p.

It's not all slow, though. With the right selection of packages and the right use case, it can be just fine. Ubuntu is a slightly more resource-heavy base than Debian as it is, so for anything requiring the extra power, it was never going to be the operating system or distro of choice. The Xfce version does run the best out of the three, but Raspbian is still better in terms of performance.

As a desktop system, though, it's better. With a few modifications to the default apps, it's perfectly usable as one, and looks a bit more the part than Raspbian as well. For projects and more niche uses, however, it looks like Raspbian is still king.

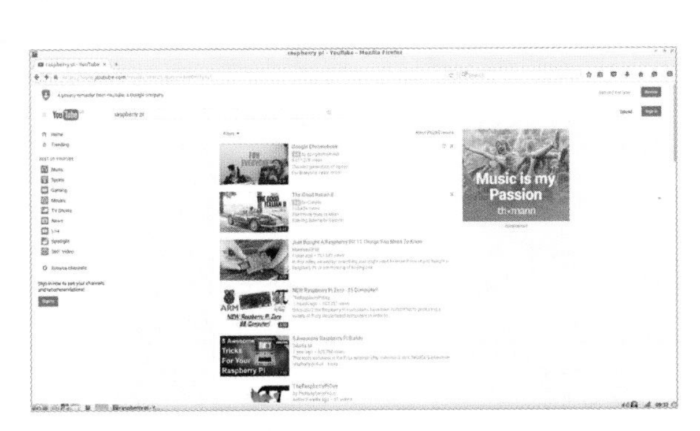

Above YouTube is hit-and-miss, especially on a more resource-heavy browser like Firefox

Last word

It was never going to be as quick as Raspbian, but it's a fantastic effort that adds some more variety to the operating systems available for the Raspberry Pi.

★★★★★

magpi.cc/2drADnu

£7 / $10

Maker Says

Touch-sensitive screen gives you finger-tip control

SB Components

LCD CONTROL CASE

A simple case for mini-LCD Raspberry Pi screens - how does it hold up under proper use?

Last issue we reviewed the SPI-Box from SB Components, a custom case for the Raspberry Pi 2 (and B+) that allows for a motion sensor and a Pi Camera Module to poke out of the case. With the bundled software, this means you have a functional and cheap security camera, with plenty of software bells and whistles to make it genuinely useful. Using a similar design ethos, SB Components has also created a special case for using a 3.2″ LCD touchscreen with the Pi in a proper enclosure. It's very inexpensive as well.

The case comes in three parts: a base that's near enough identical to the SPI-Box's design, along with an interstitial layer to protect some of the Pi components from the screen, and finally a top part that fits snugly over the Pi and screen. Like the SPI-Box, the base has the Pi snapped very firmly in place; possibly a little too firmly, as removing it again can be a little bit of an undertaking.

Putting an LCD screen over the interstitial layer and then enclosing it with the top is very easy – a lot of Pi mini TFT screens only use the first 26 GPIO pins, a legacy from the original Raspberry Pi design. The interstitial layer only opens up these pins, meaning there's no confusion. The entire screen is then accessible through the case, and even the usual array of microswitches (like on the Adafruit screen) can be accessed via little pinprick holes. Think a reset switch on an old piece of electronics – just try to avoid using something sharp.

With the case alone, you have an excellent addition to a Raspberry Pi you're using with a touch LCD screen. It's sturdy, very easy to construct, and microswitch access is quite neat as well – normally those sort of switches are forgotten in these cases. Crucially, there's also more than enough room to use the full screen. In addition, it has mounts to fix to the wall, much like the SPI-Box does. As it technically only needs power and maybe a wireless dongle, it can be a great portable Pi or a cheap home automation controller on the wall – the only thing really hampering that is the depth of the full unit, although that's not the case's fault.

If you like the idea of the screen and case but are baulking at the idea of buying a screen, assembling it, and then making the whole setup work on your Raspberry Pi, then SB Components also offers a bundle kit (**magpi.cc/2drz490**). At only £29.99 ($43) on top of the Raspberry Pi, you basically get the kit to create a portable Pi for just over £50 in total.

Related

PIBOW PITFT+

The updated PiTFT Pibow allows for the slightly larger second version of Adafruit's PiTFT screen on the Pi Model 2 and B+.

£13.50 / $19.95

magpi.cc/10AI31M

The bundle comes with a compatible mini touchscreen that works with the Pi and the case, a power supply, a WiFi dongle, and a pre-prepared SD card. As it's the exact same case, construction is the same; the real treat, however, is the SD card.

> The bundle comes with a compatible mini-touchscreen that works with the Pi

In the past, preparing Raspbian to work with these touchscreens was not a quick process. It's slightly easier now, thanks to more readily available images. Even so, it's nice to have one that just works out of the box. It still runs modern Raspbian, which includes the interface update from just over a year ago. It's a little tricky to use on this size of touchscreen, but it's not completely unusable. At the very least, it leaves it open for you to create your own custom interface and it can also access the SPI-Box, which is a nice little addition.

Both versions of the LCD case are great value for money, especially as they fill a slightly niche market for people using or wanting to use this type of screen. It's easy to modify the microswitch holes to be slightly more usable as well, so you can improve it with the right know-how. Whether you want the beginnings of a portable Pi or a touchscreen remote, you can't go far wrong with this.

Above Much of the Pi is accessible with the screen off, although it concentrates on the first 26 pins of the GPIO

Last word

A sturdy and well-presented box that is as good as any other for using one of the small touchscreen displays, opening up a world of possibilities for other projects and uses.

monkmakes.com/rrb3

£18/$30

Maker Says

"Turn your Raspberry Pi into a robot controller!"

MonkMakes

RASPIROBOT V3 BOARD

Get a head start in making a Raspberry Pi robot with this board: it handles all the basics you need

If you've ever made a Raspberry Pi robot, you'll know there are some basic essentials to bear in mind: running the motors of your automaton via the Raspberry Pi, and the ability to power the Pi and motors independently without using a trailing power cord. Then there are other, less-necessary bits such as wiring the robot up properly, and the ability to add sensors. These are still important and something you'd have to learn, but there are different layers to cover.

There are some products that try to encompass it all, and RasPiRobot is one of these. It's a HAT (a board that attaches on top of the Raspberry Pi) offering access to two motor controllers, and will also power the Pi from a battery pack attached to it. This covers several of the issues faced when creating a robot; add I²C and ultrasonic sensor connectors on top of this, as well as full access to the GPIO pins the board covers, and you have quite the complete package.

The board is nice and compact, fitting neatly on top of the standard Raspberry Pi B+/2/3 form-factor, and is even smaller than the A+. The board only requires the first 26 GPIO pins, making it functional on the original Model A and B too, in case you have one lying around waiting to be used for something. Everything comes pre-soldered and, honestly, for the price it's a bit of a steal. Even if it may be slightly more targeted towards novices, it leaves plenty of room to grow.

The board comes with its own Python library, with plenty of examples to figure out how it works. It's fairly simple, requiring you to make sure the motors and main sensors are plugged into their intended slots, and you can definitely program any robot you create with it very efficiently.

RasPiRobot V3 does what it sets out to do well, at a very good price. If you're looking to start out in Pi robotics or want to take a step beyond beginners' kits, you could do a lot worse than this board.

Related

ULTRABORG

A different yet still very competent way to add motorboard and robot control to the Raspberry Pi. You can get it in many different kit versions.

£16 / £23

magpi.cc/1RJjeWC

Last word

An easy-to-use kit that offers a lot of functionality for Raspberry Pi robot makers, with very little fuss or hassle. It's also very cheap for what you get, making custom robots a more attractive and affordable prospect.

thepihut.com

£5 / $6

Maker Says

"The ultimate protection for your new little friend!"
C4 Labs

ZEBRA ZERO CASE

A case for the Raspberry Pi Zero that you can also get with a wooden finish. Is it practical or more for the aesthetics?

Cases for the Raspberry Pi Zero have been fairly quick to market: by the time *The MagPi* issue 41 was released, there was already at least one to get your hands on, and more have been popping up since. This may be because of the popularity of the laser-cut acrylic sheets that Pimoroni has promoted – either way, it has created a small market of cases made with a more interesting material: wood.

One of the first of these was C4 Labs with its Zebra Zero case. It comes in both a wood-finish version and a normal clear acrylic one, so you have your choice of style. However, even the wood-finish case isn't fully wooden: a pair of ABS-plastic spacers separate the two wooden plates at either end. This is much more cost-effective while still achieving the overall effect. The wood is also laser-cut, so it's nice and smooth. Each important port is uncovered and labelled via etching into the wood panel. It's simple, neat, and it works well. The GPIO is completely uncovered, which, while making the Pi Zero seem a little naked at first, does make a lot more sense when a GPIO header is soldered on. Unfortunately, there don't seem to be any Pi Zero cases that cover up this part of the board, and while there are definitely arguments for having it open, the option to have it closed off if needed would be nice.

Like the wooden case, the acrylic one has the same etchings, precision cuts, and smoothness. Both are supplied with very sturdy screws that interlock over each other, rather than a nut and bolt. These same holes grab the Pi Zero as well, so they could be used for mounting purposes with the right equipment.

Both versions of the case are great and sturdy. The heatsink seems a little like overkill, but it's a nice little touch and it looks good aesthetically with the wooden case. If you really like the Zebra Zero case, there's also a much larger one available that incorporates a breadboard, perfect for prototyping.

Related

NUCLEUS ZERO CASE

Another wooden case: this one has more wooden layers and a more abstract design. It also covers the GPIO pins.

£5 / $7

magpi.cc/1KWsFAF

Last word

A great case with a fairly unusual look. It allows for full access to the ports on the Pi Zero – although if you're not using the GPIO, it makes it seem a little exposed.

★★★★☆

RASPBERRY PI BESTSELLERS TAB ELECTRONICS

McGraw Hill's little maker-oriented offshoot has turned out several popular titles for hobbyists...

PROGRAMMING THE RASPBERRY PI

Author: Simon Monk
Publisher: Tab Electronics
Price: £9.99
ISBN: 978-0071807838
magpi.cc/2dXcZlC

A brilliant Python introduction which plays to the Pi's strengths. Buy this one now (but read the online errata), then pass on to a friend when you buy the updated edition in November.

PRACTICAL ELECTRONICS FOR INVENTORS

Authors: Paul Scherz & Simon Monk
Publisher: Tab Electronics
Price: £24.99
ISBN: 978-0071771337
magpi.cc/2dXbX9o

How to use and understand electronic components, with updated chapters on sensors, microcontrollers, modular electronics, and the latest software tools. Worth the price for the theory chapter alone.

RASPBERRY PI PROJECTS FOR THE EVIL GENIUS

Authors: Donald Norris
Publisher: Tab Electronics
Price: £15.99
ISBN: 978-0071821582
bit.ly/1GBAHJx

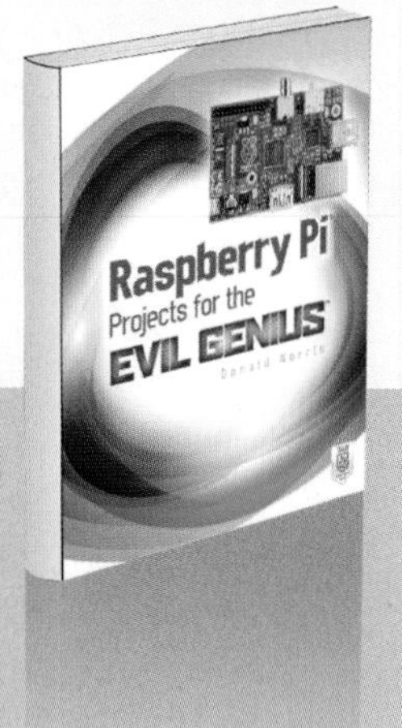

Quirkily written beginner's introduction to building hardware projects with the Pi (based on the older B model, but little change needed on most projects for current models), from a Bluetooth-controlled robot to a weather station.

TEACH YOUR KIDS TO CODE

Author: Bryson Payne
Publisher: No Starch
Price: £19.99
ISBN: 978-1593276140
nostarch.com/teachkids

Dr Payne promises "programming so easy a parent can do it!" Starting with turtle graphics, the reader is drawn in, and Python seems natural, easy, yet still a thing of wonder. Learners are encouraged to experiment, rather than overloaded with details of how and why - but where details are necessary, such as number types and operators, they are introduced.

As concepts are introduced, we feed them into turtle graphics - so conditionals lead to fractal spirals, and user input selects the shape drawn. Programming challenges at the end of each chapter - turning the High Card game into War, or adding sound effects to the Pong game - steer further learning.

Aimed at children aged nine and up, there's enough here for everyone - parents can take younger children through some of the projects, and teens shouldn't feel talked down to. Payne has the balance right beween giving enough in plentiful, fun projects to keep interest, and introducing programming concepts to build real understanding almost by osmosis. Python and Pygame installation are banished to an appendix, where you'll also find instructions on creating your own modules! And once more, delightful illustrations by Miran Lipovača lift an already excellent No Starch book to another level. Strongly recommended for learners of all ages.

JAVASCRIPT ROBOTICS

Author: Edited by Rick Waldron
Publisher: Maker Media
Price: £19.99
ISBN: 978-1457186950
oreil.ly/1Gv23Rv

The Raspberry Pi is a great little board, but it doesn't move around very much - unless you put it inside a robot, of course. The Johnny-Five robotic library offers the chance to easily program robots on various platforms with JavaScript - in this book's case, "robots that rove, swim, type, walk, dance, send alerts, make music" and more.
Of the projects, only the PiDuino5 Mobile Robot Platform demands a Raspberry Pi (combining the Arduino's extensive peripheral range with the Pi's high performance software) - in an excellent project by Jonathan Beri that includes useful tips for hardware newbies, such as connecting to the Pi without hooking your robot up to a network, as well as offering challenges to build into the project, such as computer vision.

The other chapters all feature different boards, and vastly different costs. Some have ready-made parts available and some involve a lot of great DIY - particularly the chapter on Delta Bots, the kind of industrial robot that built your car (unless you're driving a Morgan). This chapter also offers a lot of flexibility for dropping in another Pi and extending the interface. All feature clear colour pictures to help construction. Plenty of fun, plenty of learning, and a great introduction to practical robotics.

MACHINE LEARNING WITH SPARK

Author: Nick Pentreath
Publisher: Packt
Price: £30.99
ISBN: 978-1783288519
bit.ly/1GnnQdE

With its four cores and 1GB of RAM, the Raspberry Pi 2 is just the thing for a small cheap cluster to run Apache Spark – the cluster computing framework that excels with machine learning algorithms. Enter Pentreath with an example-led book on machine learning with Apache Spark.

Clustering framework MapReduce has too high an overhead for the Pi 2; however, Spark's easy-to-understand API, and design optimised for keeping intermediate tasks and data in memory – yet still fitting in the Hadoop ecosystem – is a great platform for studying and developing machine learning algorithms. This work starts with setting up on Amazon EC2, but there's plenty of online help for getting a Spark cluster running on the Pi, then you're ready for the remaining chapters.

These chapters cover real-life use cases for machine learning which will take anyone with basic or no knowledge of the subject a long way, and help those with some machine learning experience gain a strong understanding of using Spark, from text mining to dimensionality reduction. Examples are nearly all in Scala and Python – the latter a welcome plus point for the book from the Pi user's perspective. Recommended for all aspiring data scientists.

DATA SCIENCE FROM SCRATCH

Author: Joel Grus
Publisher: O'Reilly
Price: £26.50
ISBN: 978-1491901427
oreil.ly/1awOcy7

There are some great titles that steer you through frameworks and libraries to build data science projects, but Grus takes a different approach to educate the data curious: building tools and implementing algorithms from scratch, to illuminate particular points that will enable you to take better advantage of the frameworks when you finish the book.

After introducing data science, we start with a fast-paced intro or refresher in Python programming that does the job well, but highlights this book's one flaw – data science libraries still depend, for the most part, upon Python 2.7, and thus there's no Python 3 here. However, the Python 2 is very good and worth sticking with for the other early lessons in maths.

The chapters on statistics, probability, and linear algebra are an excellent refresher for those of us who are rusty, and form a strong basis for what comes next.

Having covered the maths and the programming – "the raw materials to do data science", as Grus puts it – the author turns to both the science and the art of working with data, showing how to explore what you've got before getting to modelling and machine learning. Grus looks into details where necessary, but trusts the reader to follow up references herself in other cases. In all cases, this book should make better data scientists.

ESSENTIAL READING: SECURITY

Security is not a checkbox, but a continual process. These five recent titles should keep you thinking

The Book of PF

Author: Peter N.M. Hansteen
Publisher: No Starch
Price: £23.50
ISBN: 978-1593275891
nostarch.com/pf3

OpenBSD's stateful packet filter, pf, helps you build flexible and powerful firewalls – from traffic shaping to blocking policy.

Network and System Security

Author: John Vacca
Publisher: Syngress
Price: £37.99
ISBN: 978-0124166899
magpi.cc/2dXdzQ8

Useful overview for the challenges of organisations' complex networks – from LANs to RFID, via cloud security and intrusion detection.

Penetration Testing

Author: Georgia Weidman
Publisher: No Starch
Price: £33.50
ISBN: 978-1593275648
nostarch.com/pentesting

Great introduction to finding vulnerabilities in your system – penetration testing made accessible, and well illustrated too.

Blockchain: Blueprint for a New Economy

Author: Melanie Swan
Publisher: O'Reilly
Price: £16.50
ISBN: 978-1491920497
oreil.ly/1L2AFMq

Blockchain is more than just bitcoin, and information security and digital liberties will become more dependent upon this technology.

Bruce Schneier on Trust Set

Author: Bruce Schneier
Publisher: Wiley
Price: £26.99
ISBN: 978-1118906835
oreil.ly/1JfnR7G

Bargain pairing of Liars & Outliers (how trust works – and fails – and what we need to rethink) and Carry On (155 "thought-provoking" essays).

RASPBERRY PI BESTSELLERS

APRESS

Apress has several practical books for Pi users. Here's our pick from the most popular

LEARN RASPBERRY PI PROGRAMMING WITH PYTHON

Author: Wolfram Donat
Publisher: Apress
Price: £17.50
ISBN: 978-1430264248
bit.ly/1LeM9N6

Project-based Python intro for the Pi: make a web spider, a weather station, a media server, a home security system, an underwater photography system, and a near-space weather balloon with a camera.

RASPBERRY PI HARDWARE REFERENCE

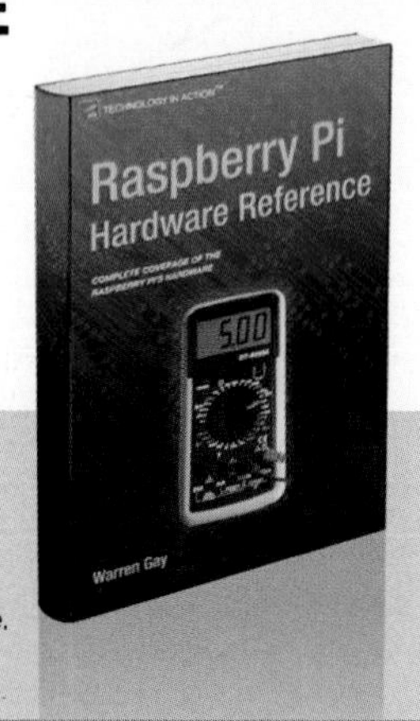

Authors: Warren Gay
Publisher: Apress
Price: £11.50
ISBN: 978-1484208007
bit.ly/1KWUipn

Delve deep into the Pi's workings for your sensor project: power, memory, USB, Ethernet, SD cards, I²C, GPIO, and the UART (serial) interface. With test code in C.

BEGINNING SENSOR NETWORKS WITH ARDUINO AND RASPBERRY PI

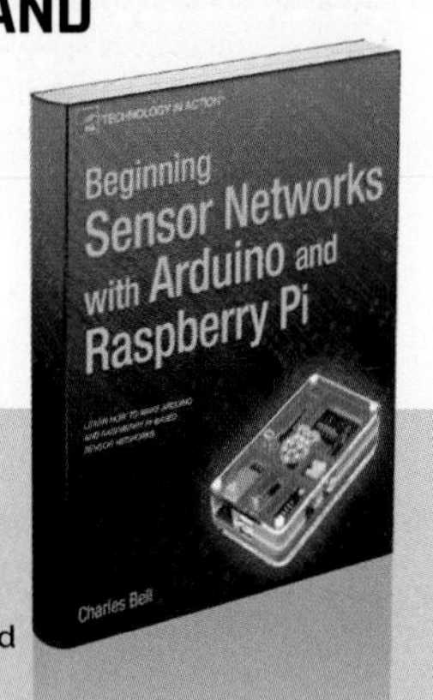

Authors: Charles Bell
Publisher: Apress
Price: £23.50
ISBN: 978-1430258247
bit.ly/1uu1HaB

Build a Raspberry Pi-based sensor node, then connect Arduino sensor nodes and XBee radio modules to the Pi, and collect data on a Pi-hosted MySQL database server.

RASPBERRY PI FOR KIDS

Author: Richard Wentk
Publisher: Wiley
Price: £21.99
ISBN: 978-111904951-7
bit.ly/1K7C41E

A well-paced introduction that goes from setting up to programming and debugging, embracing command line skills along the way. Fun software projects – like Turtles and *Minecraft* (controlling both with Python), simple and dynamic websites, and using a webcam – introduce many useful computing skills. Remembering the intended target audience, the inevitable setting-up chapters are both necessary and well judged, with details on cables and other information to enable younger makers to get going without adult help.

Ignoring the 'For Kids' branding, this book would be a valuable start for any nervous adult computer user keen to gain Pi enlightenment. From command line and nano, to Python, choosing a web server and learning programming skills, Wentk introduces and teaches using Raspbian. He does so in a clear style with gentle humour and an ability to make each learning challenge approachable.

PHP may be losing its lustre but it gives the quickest start in working with data, and is subsequently used for running shell and Python commands. Running webcam.py within PHP then leads on to debugging web problems, fixing Unix file permissions, and testing your software – all essential skills for growing your knowledge after finishing the book.

FUNCTIONAL PROGRAMMING IN PYTHON

Author: David Mertz
Publisher: O'Reilly
Price: Free PDF download
oreil.ly/1Kclhgo

Functional programming "worries about what is to be computed rather than how it is to be computed," preferring the evaluation of expressions over statements, and treating functions as first-class objects (you can pass a function to another function as if it were a piece of data). Python, despite not being a functional programming language, is "a multiparadigm language that makes functional programming easy to do when desired, and easy to mix with other programming styles."

Right from the first chapter, '(Avoiding) Flow Control', the author (a Python Software Foundation director and sometime philosopher) brings you code that is subtly altered from imperative samples, with changes that won't alarm you but will work softly on your brain, cumulatively helping to shift focus from the 'how' to the 'what'.

"Simply changing the form of expression can often make a surprisingly large difference in how we reason about code and how easy it is to understand," says Mertz, as he uses list comprehensions, generators, and dictionaries and sets to abstract the 'how' and reorder our thinking on data, working up to lazy evaluation and higher-order functions (those that call or generate other functions). A good, quick introduction for all Pythonistas looking beyond OOP.

THE HARDWARE STARTUP

Author: Renee DiResta, Brady Forrest & Ryan Vinyard
Publisher: O'Reilly
Price: £23.50
ISBN: 978-1449371036
oreil.ly/1LRSDmb

The hardware startup company of today is a very different beast from its antecedents, thanks to the very low cost of prototyping with boards like the Pi and Arduino, a new ecosystem for hardware manufacturing, including small manufacturing runs and 3D-printed parts, and the transfer of lean techniques from software to hardware businesses.

In *The Hardware Startup*, DiResta, Forrest and Vinyard provide a roadmap for anyone enticed by the lower cost of entry to transform their side project into a hardware business. From prototyping and manufacturing, to community engagement and legal concerns, and every aspect of developing and producing a product then getting it to customers, is considered in appropriate depth for those thinking seriously of turning a product idea into a business.

Open-source hardware is only touched on briefly, and selling your users' data is almost taken for granted, but the focus on a narrow, Silicon Valley view of what a startup is all about is unsurprising, given the smaller number of community and cooperative ventures in hardware than in software. However, the Raspberry Pi itself stands as a shining example of a social enterprise approach to running a successful hardware business.

RASPBERRY PI COMPUTER VISION PROGRAMMING

Author: Ashwin Pajankar
Publisher: Packt
Price: £16.99
ISBN: 978-1784398286
bit.ly/1Pdzlbf

Learning computer vision is best tackled with a practical approach: using the BSD-licensed OpenCV library, which enables image and video processing in C/C++, Java, and Python. Pajankar introduces OpenCV in a specific Pi/Python context but assumes no previous Raspberry Pi knowledge - fortunately, his Pi introduction is admirably brief. However, the OpenCV installation section is strangely lacking in refinement.

Python knowledge is assumed, but only the basics: NumPy is introduced early, for the mathematical functions needed in using OpenCV. Practical examples on images and webcam, using the Pi Camera Module, carry the less mathematical reader through. Noise removal and edge detection, useful tasks for your own Pi camera projects, are followed by motion detection and barcode reading. More real-life computer vision techniques are covered; there is a longer final chapter on the SimpleCV library, a framework to make computer vision tasks easier.

While many OpenCV books are now available, others focus on C++, Java, and cross-platform Python programming. We could be picky about the coding style but overall, for a Pi user with a little Python experience looking to get started with OpenCV and learn the basics of computer vision, this curate's egg of a book has much to teach.

ESSENTIAL READING: APPLIED PYTHON

Not just for teaching & Pi projects, Python's a great language for real-world tasks of all sorts

Python Data Science Essentials

Author: Alberto Boschetti & Luca Massaron
Publisher: Packt
Price: £26.99
ISBN: 978-1785280429
bit.ly/1bCAZEA

Direct and practical introduction to data analysis with Python, with good code examples and a problem-solving focus.

Web Scraping with Python

Author: Ryan Mitchell
Publisher: O'Reilly
Price: £21.50
ISBN: 978-1491910290
oreil.ly/1NkXYBu

Thorough grounding in the basics of web scraping, with balanced and concise coverage of a topic that continues to grow.

Mastering Python for Finance

Author: James Ma Weiming
Publisher: Packt
Price: £32.99
ISBN: 978-1784394516
bit.ly/1f32g4U

Comprehensive collection of financial theory and mathematical models applied to lucrative problems, with OOP and FP. Educational and interesting.

Black Hat Python

Author: Justin Seitz
Publisher: No Starch
Price: £23.50
ISBN: 978-1593275907
nostarch.com/blackhatpython

Penetration testing and security analysis, writing network sniffers, manipulating packets, infecting virtual machines, and creating stealthy Trojans in Python.

Learning Robotics Using Python

Author: Lentin Joseph
Publisher: Packt
Price: £29.99
ISBN: 978-1783287536
bit.ly/1lrlaeZ

"Robotics is an art." Python, ROS, and OpenCV, for building interactive autonomous mobile robots from scratch.

RASPBERRY PI BESTSELLERS

C PROGRAMMING

For reliable embedded programming on your Pi, nothing gets you closer to bare metal than the C programming language

HEAD FIRST C

Author: David Griffiths & Dawn Griffiths
Publisher: O'Reilly
Price: £33.50
ISBN: 978-1449399917
oreil.ly/1heoaQR

Approachable intro for coders wanting to learn C, with useful self-study projects.. Not a definitive reference, but a friendly start on the path to understanding C.

THE C PROGRAMMING LANGUAGE

Authors: Brian W Kernighan & Dennis Ritchie
Publisher: Prentice Hall
Price: £41.99
ISBN: 978-0131103627
bit.ly/1F2D4bq

K&R, as it's known, is a work so concise as to almost be a Zen kōan, yet all C is there: it will make you a better programmer, and deepen your understanding of C.

C PROGRAMMING: A MODERN APPROACH

Authors: K N King
Publisher: W W Norton
Price: £52.50
ISBN: 978-0393979503
magpi.cc/2dXdPin

Fast becoming the best-loved book for C learners – comprehensive, very correct in its approach to C standards, and repays hard work with C enlightenment.

NUMPY COOKBOOK

Author: Ivan Idris
Publisher: Packt
Price: £29.99
ISBN: 978-1784390945
bit.ly/1MrED5c

Python's libraries are a terrific asset, and NumPy's fast precompiled functions for numerical routines – complemented by SciPy, Matplotlib, IPython, and Scikits – provide not just MATLAB-like functionality, but a scientific software ecosystem with applications you may not even have considered. Idris surveys all of examples you'd expect for scientists, engineers, programmers, and analysts, as well as unexpected uses like audio and image processing.

"We NumPy users live in exciting times," says Idris, referring to new and future NumPy developments around cloud, concurrency, and online analytical processing (OLAP) for multi-dimensional analytical (MDA) queries. But sticking with the present, NumPy Cookbook introduces the powerful IPython environment and gets you started with NumPy's basic building blocks: arrays and universal functions – where it gets onto some Fancy Indexing, and starts working on WAV files.

Audio, and images, yes, either side of which is more on arrays and functions, as well as speeding up code. All this is done in a broad context of the SciPy ecosystem, and speaking to the wider world – whether MATLAB and Octave, or R and JPype (for JVM languages). Profiling, debugging, testing, and behaviour-driven development follow, making this a useful book for anyone looking at writing practical Python code that has life beyond their own computer. Recommended.

THE SMART GIRL'S GUIDE TO PRIVACY

Author: Violet Blue
Publisher: No Starch
Price: £11.99
ISBN: 978-1-59327-648-5
magpi.cc/2dXeikt

The difference in being logged onto a site as a female and as a male has to be experienced to be believed: the author recommends getting a throwaway account on a social media site just to try it. Women are targets online, and privacy is at risk from threats including friends with good intentions, greedy companies, and people from whom we all need to take steps to protect ourselves. The book comes with privacy stickers, to prevent people using your device's camera to record you without your knowledge.

Eight "privacy tips to use right now" provide a ready guide to tipping the balance hugely in your favour, as does taking the privacy check-up. That done, Blue shows what information not to share in order to stay safe. If you think this is paranoia, read here about (male) *Wired* journalist Mat Honan, whose digital devices were wiped and Twitter account offensively defaced – all from the attacker finding Honan's address (a simple whois lookup) and using it to get Amazon account data, then move on to Apple.

Blue provides practical steps to deal with all the horrors and harassment, recover from identity theft, and still be able to pursue romance online. Sadly, a very necessary book.

HOW SOFTWARE WORKS

Author: V Anton Spraul
Publisher: No Starch
Price: £19.99
ISBN: 978-1593276669
magpi.cc/2dXeMH6

"We live in an age of magic," writes V Anton Spraul in the introduction, referencing Arthur C Clarke's famous dictum on advanced technology. After all, many of us work with technology but lack a real understanding of what's going on inside the computer. From security topics, like password hashing and encryption, to other underpinnings of modern life like search, and map routes, this book shows what is happening inside programs, what the limitations are, and what may develop in the future.

Encryption lies at the heart of so many daily tasks, from shopping to checking your bank balance. Spraul takes us back to pre-computer encryption, with a lucid explanation which will help even non-technical users understand the process. Particularly important is Spraul's discussion of potential flaws and weaknesses in each technology, which will put in perspective for the reader various news stories on security scares.

The insights into game graphics, computer animation, and image compression are fascinating. Explanations of techniques used in search – from quicksort algorithm to hashing – and in concurrency programming, will help beginner programmers on the Pi as they gain understanding to really support the methods they're learning. Map routes is another informative chapter, particularly if you're working on a robotics project.

RASPBERRY PI ROBOTICS PROJECTS

Author: Richard Grimmett
Publisher: Packt
Price: £29.99
ISBN: 978-1-78528-014-6
bit.ly/1U6oOVD

Right from the set-up chapter, with remote access via SSH and VNC, and nmap to locate your Pi on the network, Dr Grimmett assumes no knowledge, but introduces important topics – the second chapter, on programming with Python, covers some OOP features, using Emacs, and briefly examines C and C++.

The first robotics topic is speech, with Espeak and PocketSphinx to handle input and output – "what self-respecting robot wants to carry around a keyboard?" – and your brief acquaintance with C used to edit and rebuild the controlling program. In the vision chapter, the basics of installation and use of OpenCV are well explained. For robot mobility, the GPIO controls a motor (no soldering necessary), driving wheels, and voice commands control movement. Then, with a choice of ready-assembled legs, and a little Python to interpret voice commands, your robot is ready to tackle uneven ground, or even stairs.

Obstacle-avoidance sensors stop your robot blundering into walls; wireless and GPS find the robot. Finally, Robot Operating System (ROS) manages system control. Then, using model kits that can be controlled by the Pi, take your robot on or under water, or up in the air. Beginner to roboteer in just 276 pages!

ESSENTIAL READING: 3D PRINTING

3D printing is within reach of everyone, by building your own, or sharing at a local makerspace

Make: 3D Printing

Author: Anna Kaziunas France
Publisher: Maker
Price: £13.50
ISBN: 978-1457182938
oreil.ly/1KliLGq

Arms you with everything you need to know to understand the exciting but often confusing world of 3D printing.

3D Printing Blueprints

Author: Joe Larson
Publisher: Packt
Price: £30.99
ISBN: 9781849697088
bit.ly/1Ige22Z

Makerbot-focused, project-based guide to preparing designs for 3D printing, using the free and open -source Blender program.

3D Printing For Dummies

Author: Kalani Kirk Hausman
Publisher: Wiley
Price: £21.99
ISBN: 978-1118660751
bit.ly/1WT7lJD

Puts 3D printing in context, and shows you how to build your own RepRap.

Open-Source Lab

Author: Joshua M. Pearce
Publisher: Elsevier
Price: £33.99
ISBN: 9780124104624
bit.ly/1JyYNas

Academic guide to building a RepRap, then 3D-printing a complete laboratory of scientific instruments.

Eventorbot!

Author: eventorbot
Publisher: Instructables
Price: FREE
bit.ly/1PUix9w

Fewer materials and a stronger structure give a cheaper, easier, and very stable, well-designed 3D printer. 100% open source.

RASPBERRY PI BESTSELLERS

SEVEN WEEKS

Pragmatics' Seven Weeks series compares solutions in hot topics for programmers

SEVEN DATABASES IN SEVEN WEEKS

Author: Eric Redmond & Jim R Wilson
Publisher: Pragmatic Bookshelf
Price: £23.50
ISBN: 978-1934356920
bit.ly/1eLiCzB

A practical dip into NoSQL databases: Redis, Neo4J, CouchDB, MongoDB, HBase, Riak (after PostgreSQL for comparison). The easiest way to quickly gain enough experience to make hands-on comparisons.

SEVEN CONCURRENCY MODELS IN SEVEN WEEKS

Authors: Paul Butcher
Publisher: Pragmatic Bookshelf
Price: £25.50
ISBN: 978-1937785659
bit.ly/1L5FltS

As multiple cores proliferate in the GPU as well as the CPU, Butcher tackles the competing techniques for parallelism and concurrency. Well written, and strongly grounded in Clojure.

SEVEN WEB FRAMEWORKS IN SEVEN WEEKS

Authors: Jack Moffitt & Frederic Daoud
Publisher: Pragmatic Bookshelf
Price: £25.50
ISBN: 978-1937785635
bit.ly/1VEahMc

A fascinating and enjoyable journey: explore minimalism, composition, static typing, state machines, declarative syntax, and other approaches to web programming, using Sinatra, CanJS, AngularJS, Ring, Webmachine, Yesod, and Immutant.

GETTING STARTED WITH PYTHON & RASPBERRY PI

Author: Dan Nixon
Publisher: Packt
Price: £25.99
ISBN: 978-1783551590
bit.ly/1KZemHZ

We get to review many good and interesting Python tutorials, but a book placing Python learning within the context of programming the Raspberry Pi is always going to have an advantage: building quickly towards your own projects on the Pi is a great motivator. Nixon's book makes the link between basic Python learning and our favourite small board computer, even in the basics – such as treatment of numerical variables to best fit GPIO values.

Nixon excuses his use of Python 2.7: "this has the widest library support and is still the default Python version on many operating systems." We suggest it's time to drop Python 2 for newcomers.

Nevertheless, the bulk of early chapters are a good Python introduction without distorting the lessons to be overly Pi-focused, giving a good grounding in control flow and data structures – procedural with a hint of functional flavour.

Object orientation is then introduced as a concept in a chapter also covering threads and locks. The peculiar areas of focus continue with a look at packaging in Python, but then the book turns to GPIO and the Camera Module. Data parsing and interfaces round out a useful introductory book, which will give confident learners enough immersion in Python to move onto their own projects.

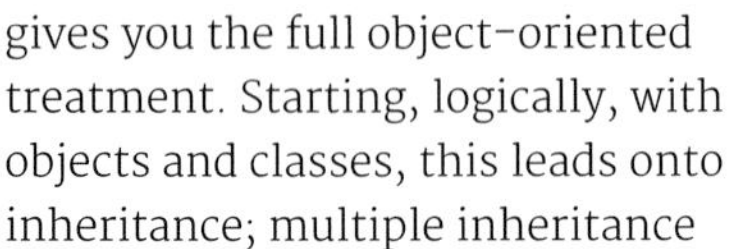

PYTHON 3 OBJECT-ORIENTED PROGRAMMING

Author: Dusty Phillips
Publisher: Packt
Price: £31.99
ISBN: 978-1784398781
bit.ly/1LinBQP

A decade ago, Python was an overlooked scripting language and object-oriented programming (OOP) was introduced via Java (kitchen sink attached), Smalltalk (in academia at least – and subsequently powering Scratch 1.x), or even C++ (ouch). Luckily for learners of today, Python is widely accepted, and as a multi-paradigm language with strong OOP leanings it makes an ideal introduction to OOP. Phillips's book builds on basic Python knowledge you may have picked up with simple procedural scripts for the Pi, for example, and gives you the full object-oriented treatment. Starting, logically, with objects and classes, this leads onto inheritance; multiple inheritance is discussed (take that, Java) and then the first case study. Each chapter is rounded off with a useful case study and practically oriented exercises, often generating further thoughts on the topic to be carried to the reader's own work.

From attribute accessibility to design patterns, Phillips gives the essence of OOP in the context of Python's way of doing things – along the way stretching best practice a little, as some places aren't a comfortable fit for regular expressions – but he keeps pushing the reader to consider each bit of knowledge in the context of their own code, making for a very interactive book.

MAKE: THE BEST OF, VOLUME 2

Author: The Editors of Make
Publisher: Maker Media
Price: £19.99
ISBN: 978-1680450323
oreil.ly/1hpWhbr

Want to be inspired? Pick a project from the contents page and start reading. We'd recommend something from Chapter 6: Music and Audio, which includes Cigar Box Guitars, a Laser Harp, and a Solar Xylophone. Having been inspired, you may find the slightly macho introductory section on building and equipping your workshop easier going, and be more forgiving of the jargon-laden text.

Inspiration can be found on almost every page, as this is a distillation of eight years of *Make* magazine since the first *Best Of* book was published. Projects are grouped by chapters such as Robots and Drones, Microcontrollers and Microcomputers, and Fun and Games. That middle one includes many interesting Arduino projects including sound synthesis, as well as turning a Pi into a Tor proxy for anonymous browsing, or an FM transmitter.

Projects range from the mundane but useful (audio amplifiers, lost screw finder), through difficult to classify (a Geiger counter), to pure fun (amazing light-up shoes). One of the most compelling, which few can read without feeling the urge to build, is The Most Useless Machine: flick the switch, and an arm reaches out from a door and turns the switch back off. That's all it does. Strangely compelling, eh?

SCRATCH FOR KIDS

Author: Derek Breen
Publisher: Wiley
Price: £21.99
ISBN: 978-1119014874
bit.ly/1FSU6Jm

Delete the cat. That's Breen's first instruction. Scratch is for everyone, not just younger children who like cute cats. But Breen has written a book that will get young and old quickly coding and learning – creating a *Flappy Bird* clone in the first chapter, such is the power of Scratch.

The introduction, very much in the spirit of Italo Calvino's *If On A Winter's Night A Traveller* – but with stronger overt humour – draws you straight in, and you'll only put the book down long enough to switch on your computer and open Scratch. The author's humour and personality bring the tutorials to life, but the useful level of detail ensures that the lessons stay with the reader much longer.

Split into three sections – Designer, Animator, Game Developer – *Scratch for Kids* is very strong on graphics, with the vector and collage chapters being a great end to the first section. The Animation section builds into a great way to teach visually oriented children how to code. Attention to detail, good graphics and great writing characterise a game section that takes four classic arcade games and once more sneaks in learning by osmosis. Unreservedly recommended for kids of all ages – including grown-up ones!

ESSENTIAL READING: DATA

Data – big or otherwise – is a growing concern for coders in any language

Clean Data

Author: Megan Squire
Publisher: Packt
Price: £29.99
ISBN: 978-1785284014
bit.ly/1FWlLJh

Practical strategies to quickly and easily bridge the gap between the data we want and the data we have.

Python Data Science for Dummies

Author: John Paul Mueller & Luca Massaron
Publisher: Wiley
Price: £21.99
ISBN: 978-1118844182
bit.ly/1VEcYO1

A comprehensive introduction to practical data science using Python. Good for Python learners without being patronising.

Learning Haskell Data Analysis

Author: James Church
Publisher: Packt
Price: £22.99
ISBN: 978-1784394707
bit.ly/1RtmVxc

Haskell-based intro to dealing with data that doesn't neglect its mathematical nature. Practical and educational.

Derivatives Analytics with Python: Data Analysis, Models, Simulation, Calibration and Hedging

Author: Yves Hilpisch
Publisher: Wiley
Price: £60.00
ISBN: 978-1119037996
bit.ly/1HzDGSG

Growing use in the financial community has given us some useful tools for data analysis in Python.

Learning JavaScript Data Structures and Algorithms

Author: Loiane Groner
Publisher: Packt
Price: £27.99
ISBN: 978-1783554874
bit.ly/1MYzqzd

Beginner-friendly introduction to data structures and algorithms, using JavaScript. Comprehensive, approachable, excellent.

RASPBERRY PI BESTSELLERS

A PACKT AUTUMN

Autumn started with more than a dozen Pi-relevant titles from Packt. These three are flying off the shelves...

RASPBERRY PI LED BLUEPRINTS

Author: Agus Kurniawan
Publisher: Packt
Price: £19.99
ISBN: 978-1782175759
magpi.cc/1SNflZy

Never underestimate the power of switching on a light by code to attract children to coding. Kurniawan's book harnesses this magic to introduce a range of GPIO and I²C programming techniques.

RASPBERRY PI ANDROID PROJECTS

Authors: Gökhan Kurt
Publisher: Packt
Price: £22.99
ISBN: 978-1785887024
magpi.cc/1SNfQbu

A short but handy roundup of many ways that your Android device can be used with a Pi 2, from remote desktop and sensors, through surveillance cameras and media centres, to collecting automotive data.

PYTHON GAME PROGRAMMING BY EXAMPLE

Authors: Joseph Howse & Alejandro Rodas de Paz
Publisher: Packt
Price: £25.99
ISBN: 978-1785281532
magpi.cc/1SNfVfd

Classic games, useful libraries, and essential algorithms: Rodas and Howse build your knowledge through well-chosen combinations of all three, then add computer vision with OpenCV as the icing on the cake.

FLUENT PYTHON

Author: Luciano Ramalho
Publisher: O'Reilly
Price: £33.50
ISBN: 978-1491946008
oreil.ly/1FAcbtb

There are now a few books to answer that 'where do I go next with Python?' question, but Fluent Python makes a persuasive case for a place on your bookshelf or SSD. Ramalho delivers all of the good things about Python that you may miss when coming from another language, as Python has many features that are unique or only found in a few languages. All this without straying far from the core language and standard library.

From the power of slicing operators on lists, through duck typing on the Vector Space Model, to unlocking some of the powerful but poorly documented features in Python, like coroutines, every chapter contains something to make you a better programmer. Some will impress straight away, while others make subtle improvements to your future code.

Fluent Python is split into six sections, books-within-the-book. The first gives essential insights into the data model, the rest can be read in any order as desired; it covers topics such as collections (sequences, mapping, sets), functions as first class objects, building classes, generators, concurrency, and much more. The REPL is used throughout for hands-on learning, and there are many glimpses into the workings of the very welcoming Python community. Destined to be another O'Reilly classic.

PYTHON PARALLEL PROGRAMMING COOKBOOK

Author: Giancarlo Zaccone
Publisher: Packt
Price: £31.99
ISBN: 978-1785289583
magpi.cc/1SNgPYZ

A cookbook but also a tutorial, teaching parallel programming with the *aid* of Python as much as parallel programming with Python. Python 3 is used in all but the GPU programming chapter, which mostly uses Nvidia's CUDA – not relevant on the Pi – but it also covers PyOpenCL.

The introductory chapter delves into Von Neumann architecture and shared memory schemes to build a picture of the parallel programmer's operating environment, then tackles Python's biggest problem for concurrent programmers, the Global Interpreter Lock (GIL). Starting with the threading package for traditional multi-threading, Zaccone goes from how to do it to how it works in each example, building through semaphores, conditions, and queues.

He moves onto process-based parallelism, with a useful exploration of collective communication; asynchronous programming, including Python 3.2's concurrent.futures module, Asyncio to manage events and coroutines, task manipulation, and the Future class; the Celery framework to handle distribution across machines, and other useful libraries. Occasional idiosyncrasies in English usage - not the author's first language - could have been tidied up, but technical content is spot on and worth the rare need to re-read a sentence for clarity. A good introduction and useful reference on parallel programming.

ELECTRONICS WORKSHOP

Author: Stan Gibilisco
Publisher: Tab Electronics
Price: £18.99
ISBN: 978-0071843805
magpi.cc/1SNgXrF

Stan Gibilisco has been writing on, and tinkering with, electronics for a long time, so this short reference and introduction benefits from distilling decades of experience, showing a clarity of approach that indicates a writer and tinkerer with plenty to pass on to newcomers. The opening chapter on 'Setting up Shop' is a pleasingly minimalist alternative to the 'we assume you have a giant spare room and lots of money' approach of some other maker introductions.

Although ideal for newcomers – and it can be read linearly – there's plenty of useful reference and tips worth dipping into for those who've been soldering since the NE555 was a hot new chip. Remaining chapters are organised by topic in the expected manner: Resistors, Capacitors, Inductors, Transformers, Diodes, Transistors, ICs and Digital Basics, More Components and Techniques, followed by useful appendices and further reading.

What really makes the book stand out, in addition to the clear explanations, is the experiments at the end of each chapter, which combine practical use of components and tools with demonstrating various bits of electronic theory which would be quite dry and dusty if taught only as theory. For example, in testing a JFET, you gain understanding of where electrons should and should not flow.

LEARN GAME PROGRAMMING WITH RUBY

Author: Mark Sobkowicz
Publisher: Pragmatic
Price: £15.99
ISBN: 978-1680500738
oreil.ly/1OlpRON

From the contents, introduction and content of Sobkowicz's otherwise useful introduction to 2D game programming, you'd think the GNU/Linux platform didn't exist. Windows and Mac OS X get a chapter each, but Raspbian's Linux relatives don't even make a footnote in an appendix. Fortunately, you can find full instructions on installing the Gosu library used in the book on Raspbian (or Ubuntu, et al) at **github.com/gosu** – we used rbenv to install Gosu on Ruby 2.1.2. That done, turn to chapter three, because Ruby Game Programming still has plenty to offer on the Pi. This isn't a book about Gosu, or even solely about Ruby, but about the various techniques used in programming 2D games, which encompass a wide range of gameplay and perspective. And Python's expressive and slightly less buttoned-up cousin Ruby makes a good language for introducing them: it's concise and easy to read.

Introducing sprites, interaction, platform gaming and sideways scrolling, Sobkowicz is an able guide to all the components and has written a book suitable for early-stage coders of all ages. Niggles about leaving Linux users out in the cold aside, this is a practical and enjoyable introduction to game programming.

ESSENTIAL READING: COMPSCI ESSENTIALS

Recent academic tomes to boost your brain power, with Python for CompSci learning.

Introduction to Computing Using Python

Author: Ljubomir Perkovic
Publisher: Wiley
Price: £159.99, or £29.16 for e-book
ISBN: 978-1118890943
magpi.cc/1SNieiu

Welcome update to the breadth-first computer science introductory textbook, with a strong focus on OOP.

Discovering Computer Science

Author: Jessen Havill
Publisher: Chapman and Hall/CRC
Price: £57.99
ISBN: 978-1482254143
magpi.cc/1SNijTe

Computational thinking as "a powerful mode of inquiry and a vehicle of discovery, in a wide variety of disciplines."

Doing Math with Python

Author: Amit Saha
Publisher: No Starch
Price: £19.99
ISBN: 978-1593276409
magpi.cc/2dXgete

Pre-computer science; catch up on high-school mathematics, and have fun with Python along the way.

Computational Physics

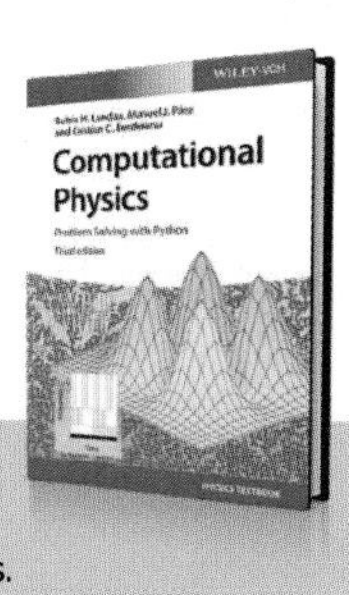

Author: Rubin H Landau, Manuel J Páez & Cristian C Bordeianu
Publisher: Wiley
Price: £75.00
ISBN: 978-3527413157
magpi.cc/1SNiw95

Pythonic reworking of a classic that's essential for any physics student. Useful maths and programming for all scientists.

Making Music with Computers

Author: Andrew R Brown & Bill Manaris
Publisher: Chapman and Hall/CRC
Price: £31.99
ISBN: 978-1439867914
magpi.cc/1SNizl7

Computer science introduction for a non-traditional audience, using music creation with Python in a Jython environment.

RASPBERRY PI BESTSELLERS ERLANG

17 years after the source was opened, it's time you embraced the robust, functional language which shines at concurrency

LEARN YOU SOME ERLANG FOR GREAT GOOD!

Author: Fred Hébert
Publisher: No Starch
Price: £33.50
ISBN: 978-1593274351
magpi.cc/1NuXisx

Accessible introduction full of real-world examples, with an honest look at the good and not so good of using Erlang. Comprehensive, and a good introduction to functional programming.

PROGRAMMING ERLANG

Authors: Joe Armstrong
Publisher: Pragmatic
Price: £27.99
ISBN: 978-1937785536
magpi.cc/1NuXoAm

From one of Erlang's creators, containing real insights into the thought process of programming in Erlang. The 2nd edition contains much for beginners, but finishes with an open-ended problem, 'Sherlock's Last Case'.

PROGRAMMING ELIXIR

Authors: Dave Thomas
Publisher: Pragmatic
Price: £23.99
ISBN: 978-1937785581
magpi.cc/1NuXzM4

Elixir runs on the Erlang VM, and the underlying Erlang/OTP architecture, but with an extendable, Ruby-like syntax that's quick and powerful in use. Full review in *MagPi* #33.

CLOJURE FOR THE BRAVE AND TRUE

Author: Daniel Higginbotham
Publisher: No Starch
Price: £23.50
ISBN: 978-1593275914
magpi.cc/1NuXHeC

Books with humour can be hit-or-miss affairs, but Higginbotham's introduction to the powerful JVM Lisp is such a good language tutorial that even those who usually prefer a drier approach will be bowled along.

Early on, readers are introduced to Emacs as REPL and editor: downloading the book's Emacs configuration package will actually give you one of the best starts in using Emacs; you'll soon be appreciating Emacs features like the kill ring, and discovering why it remains a top choice for editing and interacting with Lisp family languages after 40 years. After setting up your tools comes a crash course in Clojure fundamentals, with comparisons with how you would do similar things in languages like Ruby along the way, to highlight key differences such as immutable data.

"Clojure is so elegant that it's difficult to tell anyone anything about it without somehow improving them," writes Alan Dipert in the introduction. Improvement here involves fun examples – particularly if your idea of fun is violence towards hobbits – that can make the learning less onerous than some contrived 'real world' examples. Every topic is introduced in the best order for growing real understanding of Clojure, in a journey that will change the way you code.

GIT FOR TEAMS

Author: Emma Jane Hogbin Westby
Publisher: O'Reilly
Price: £33.50
ISBN: 978-1491911181
magpi.cc/224fsew

"You can do more with Git than just build software," says Hogbin Westby of this people-first approach to version control. *Git for Teams* combines a practical look at best practices in Git usage with a look at the 'why' of Git – where it fits into workflow, and even how to build the right team for a project – and concludes with a useful section on Git hosting.

The chapter 'Workflows that work' covers the neglected essentials of documenting your process – something often left until after your project has got into a confusing mess. The practical chapters start with 'Teams of One', giving an excellent introduction to Git use, then the 'Rrrrgh!' chapter – rollbacks, reverts, resets, and rebasing – shows the best way to make amendments without losing code or having a negative impact on the workflow of team members. Reviews and bug-fixing get a chapter each, and the poorly named blame command receives a fair examination.

The section on various Git hosting services may help you find the right public or private repository. This book is a most useful single guide for those needing the technical and social side of managing a project, whether in traditional employment, an IoT startup, or an open source project.

PROGRAMMING THE RASPBERRY PI

Author: Simon Monk
Publisher: Tab Electronics
Price: £9.89
ISBN: 978-1259587405
magpi.cc/224fOlh

This could be the perfect introductory programming book to give to someone who's just got a Raspberry Pi for Christmas. With no wasted words, Monk introduces the Pi and its operating system, then teaches both Python and using Python with the Pi, in a direct and easily absorbed text that harks back to the best beginner guides of the 8-bit era.

Skip the first two dozen pages if you are not new to the Pi, and dive into Python with an introduction that – through well-chosen examples, such as a dice rolling simulation – will have you learning conditionals, control flow, and comparison operators before you know it. Next, Hangman introduces functions, as well as strings, lists, and dictionaries. OOP is touched on with a temperature converter, then file handling and GUI programming (with Tkinter) through building on the earlier code examples. The Pygame chapter makes use of many of the techniques learned, then moves on to refactoring.

The same concise style is used to cover the Pi hardware for the rest of the book: GPIO pins, breadboard prototyping, connecting an Arduino, then a range of sample projects culminating in a Raspberry Pi robot. Unreservedly recommended for confident beginners of all ages.

FUNDAMENTALS OF WEARABLE COMPUTERS AND AUGMENTED REALITY

Author: Woodrow Barfield
Publisher: CRC Press
Price: £95.00
ISBN: 978-1482243505
magpi.cc/224g3wG

As computers get small enough to mount on the cover of a magazine, and as sensors get better, wearable computing – data where you need it – is within reach of all. From Google Glass to Google Cardboard, ubiquitous computing is getting nearer and cheaper. Augmented reality is used across many industries, and children solder together wearable computers at MakeFests. If you're a maker or programmer involved in an AR project, this collection of essays will broaden your appreciation of the field considerably. Barfield presents 25 academic papers, over 700 pages, split over four sections: Introduction (with some shorter, more philosophical, overviews of the topic); The Technology (mostly displays and haptics, but also tracking); Augmented Reality (with some fascinating and varied cases); and Wearables. The last section particularly highlights integration into textiles and clothing, as well as presenting useful research on haptic rendering.

This is a collection of academic papers: extensive references are given, and the language is academic, though mostly quite approachable. The research crosses many disciplines, and non-mathematical readers will only be given pause by a couple of chapters. An expensive purchase, but perhaps a worthwhile one for the local makerspace library, particularly if you have an augmented reality project in development.

ESSENTIAL READING: NEW YEAR RESOLUTIONS

Kick start your resolution to learn something new, or even boost your IT career!

Resolution: Invent that Pi add-on!

Fritzing for Inventors

Author: Simon Monk
Publisher: Tab Electronics
Price: £21.99
ISBN: 978-0071844635
magpi.cc/224guXY

Develop, prototype, test, produce, and fund an electronics project. Full of useful tips.

Resolution: Get arty!

The SparkFun Guide to Processing

Author: Derek Runberg
Publisher: No Starch
Price: £19.99
ISBN: 978-1593276126
magpi.cc/224gyHd

Lovingly produced guide to art and code with Processing, which now runs on the Raspberry Pi.

Resolution: Get a new job!

Cracking the Coding Interview

Author: Gayle Laakmann McDowell
Publisher: Career Cup
Price: £25.36
ISBN: 978-0984782857
magpi.cc/224gPd8

Start the New Year with a confident crack at a major coding job interview, with McDowell's peerless guide.

Resolution: Machine learning!

Python Machine Learning

Author: Sebastian Raschka
Publisher: Packt
Price: £28.99
ISBN: 978-1783555130
magpi.cc/224gXJw

Process, learn from, and draw actionable insights out of the otherwise impenetrable walls of big data.

Resolution: Functional programming!

fp101

Author: Delft University
Publisher: EdX – Online MOOC
Price: Free – Online MOOC
ISBN: N/A
magpi.cc/224h3Rp

Get to grips with the what, why, and how of functional programming while seamlessly absorbing Haskell, then apply in the real world.

READ US ANYWHERE

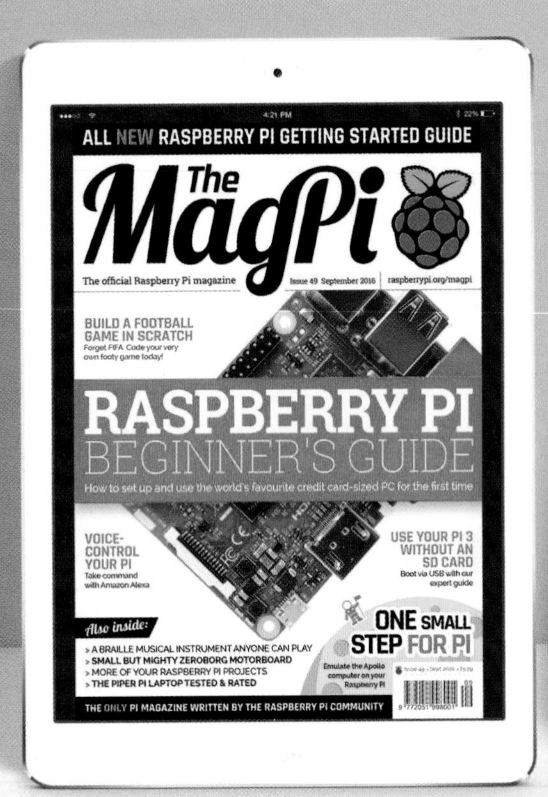

FREE: DOWNLOAD ALL 30 ORIGINAL ISSUES

Available now
for smartphones & tablets

Subscribe from
£2.29 or $2.99
rolling subscription

Download it today - it's free!

- Get all 30 legacy issues free
- Instant downloads every month
- Fast rendering performance
- Live links & interactivity